C000231487

Say I do

When two gorgeous hunks propose marriage. Faith and Meg are determined to discover whether the men they'd always dreamed of are asking out of love—or duty…

Join favourite authors Karen Rose Smith and Sara Orwig in these classic stories from Silhouette's Special Edition and Desire series.

We're proud to present

SILHOUETTE SPOTLIGHT

a second chance to enjoy two bestselling novels by favourite authors every month— they're back by popular demand!

February 2005
Say 'I do'
featuring
The Sheriff's Proposal by Karen Rose Smith
The Cowboy's Seductive Proposal by Sara Orwig

March 2005
And Mum Makes Three
featuring
Molly Darling by Laurie Paige
His Daughter's Laughter by Janis Reams Hudson

April 2005
An Office Affair
featuring
The Bride Means Business by Anne Marie Winston
Badge of Honour by Justine Davis

Say 'I do'

Karen Rose Smith
Sara Orwig

*Silhouette and Colophon are registered trademarks of
Harlequin Books S.A., used under licence.*

*First published in Great Britain 2005
Silhouette Books, Eton House, 18-24 Paradise Road,
Richmond, Surrey TW9 1SR*

SAY 'I DO' © Harlequin Books S.A. 2005

The publisher acknowledges the copyright holders of the
individual works as follows:

The Sheriff's Proposal © Karen Rose Smith 1996
The Cowboy's Seductive Proposal © Sara Orwig 1999

ISBN 0 373 60224 3

64-0205

*Printed and bound in Spain
by Litografia Rosés S.A., Barcelona*

The Sheriff's Proposal

KAREN ROSE SMITH

KAREN ROSE SMITH

Karen is a former teacher and home decorator. Now
spinning stories and creating characters keeps her
busy. But she also loves listening to music, shopping
and sharing with friends as well as spending time with
her son and her husband. Married for thirty years, she
and her husband have always called Pennsylvania
home. Karen Rose likes to hear from readers. They
can write to her at: PO Box 1545, Hanover, PA 17331,
USA or visit her website at www.karenrosesmith.com

To my husband, Steve.
Happy twenty-fifth anniversary.
I love you.

Chapter One

Sheriff Logan MacDonald's office phone rang making his heart ache and pound at the same time. At the Willow Valley sheriff's office, a phone call could mean a life-and-death situation or, more likely, a few cows had escaped their fencing and blocked a county road. A call could also bring Logan news of his son.

But now after four months, when he answered a call or page, he tried to keep his heart from racing and his hopes from rising. Still, an insistent voice inside him whispered, *This could be the one. Maybe it's news of Travis.*

He snatched up the receiver.

"Doc Jacobs, Logan. I'm on my way over to Lily and Ned Carlson's. They found a migrant couple in their barn. The woman's having a baby, and they don't want the rescue squad. But I might need some backup."

Logan's heart rate slowed, and his hopes hit the ground. Then Doc Jacobs's words sunk in. The rescue squad in Willow Valley, Virginia, took care of the small town and the surrounding rural area. The closest hospital was a half hour away in Lynchburg. "I'm leaving now."

Logan snapped down the receiver and tried to push thoughts of his sixteen-year-old runaway son out of his head.

Although it was midmorning, the steamy, end-of-August heat blasted him as he hurried to his car. The temperature would probably hit a hundred by three o'clock. He could have sent one of his six deputies to the Carlsons' place, but he preferred taking some time out from his administrative duties and getting into the thick of things himself.

The inside of the sheriff's cruiser was as hot as blazes. He flipped on the air conditioner full blast, letting the panel air hit him in the face. He tried to forget that his hopes had been crushed yet another time, that he still didn't know whether his son was alive or dead. Four months. Four long months to agonize over every mistake he'd made as a parent.

Logan brushed his black hair from his brow as the cool air fought the intense heat, and he switched on the siren. The stores on Main Street flashed by, then the corner grocery. A few teenagers stood out front, reminding Logan that school would be starting in a week. And Travis…

Travis. Logan's chest tightened.

He had moved his family to Willow Valley five years ago in large part *because* of Travis. Logan had wanted more time with his son in a wholesome country environment, rather than on the streets of a big

city. His career as a cop had always added tension to
a marriage that had been troubled from the start. Even
Shelley had agreed that moving might help—that a
job as deputy sheriff in Willow Valley and the surrounding county could make a difference in their
lives. But their son had hated leaving the familiar—
his school, his friends.

And Shelley? She'd never had any intention of
starting over. Once they were settled in Willow
Valley, Logan had figured they'd all have a chance
at a fresh start. But he'd figured wrong. For his marriage. For Travis.

The farmland surrounding Willow Valley zipped
by as Logan sped toward the Carlsons' farm west of
town. The green pastures, the cedars, the trees in
abundance, usually filled him with a sense of peace.
Even now he felt it, although his surroundings blurred
as he pushed down the accelerator.

Logan drove down the lane to the Carlsons' barn
and parked on a patch of gravel beside Doc Jacobs's
station wagon. He didn't recognize the blue compact
beside it, though he guessed it might belong to the
Carlsons' niece. He'd never met her, but he'd heard
she was in town for a visit. As small towns go, anything happening in Willow Valley was everybody's
business, and rumors, as well as accurate information,
traveled faster than the rescue squad with its siren
blaring.

He rushed to the open barn door and stepped inside.
The smell of hay and old wood wound about Logan.
But when he heard a woman's moans, he forgot about
his surroundings and hurried to the far corner. Although he'd learned CPR and emergency-aid training
as a police officer, he'd never delivered a baby. He'd

been out on patrol when Travis was born. But if Doc needed help, he'd do whatever he could.

The tableau Logan found was one he wouldn't forget for a long time. The woman in labor held on to her husband's hand. A second woman kneeling beside her spoke to them both in a low voice. Her fluent Spanish was melodic and soothing, a calm in the midst of a strange situation. She looked vaguely familiar. The observer and investigator in Logan noticed every detail—from the slight tilt of her nose, the silkiness of the brown hair swinging along her cheekbones, to her eyes, which were a rich chocolate color that deepened as she suddenly realized someone else was in their midst. Her gaze slid over his uniform. Logan's body responded to her figure in denim cutoffs and blue-and-white-checked cotton blouse. He almost smiled. That hadn't happened in a very long time.

Again she spoke to the woman lying on a blanket, patted her hand and explained something in Spanish. But it wasn't her talent with the language that mesmerized Logan. It was her tone of voice, her smile. She was so kind, so compassionate. Then her gaze rested on Logan's again for a moment. As it did, the place inside of him that hurt so badly suddenly felt a glimmer of sunshine.

"How can I help?" he asked, his voice husky. He cleared his throat.

Doc Jacobs looked up from his position at the woman's feet. "We're letting nature take its course. Hold her shoulders for her, Meg, or tell Manuel. This last push ought to do it. Come on now, Carmen. Give it all you've got."

As Carmen moaned and another contraction

gripped her, the young woman beside her translated what the doctor had said. Logan had a limited working knowledge of Spanish, and he could catch a phrase here and there as Manuel held his wife, and Meg coached and soothed.

Logan forgot his purpose, that he was the law-and-order keeper in Willow Valley. Rather, he got caught up in the drama before him. It brought back so many memories, both good and bad. He'd never forget the day Travis was born, the sense of pride, the overwhelming wave of protectiveness and responsibility that had washed over him the first time he'd held his son in his arms. He'd never regretted his decision to marry Shelley when he'd found out she was pregnant. He did regret the interests they'd never shared, the conversations they'd never had, the barrier that had grown between them until Shelley had felt deception was her only option. Most of all, he regretted the night of their worst argument—the night she'd rushed out of the house and...

Carmen's face contorted in pain, and she squeezed Meg's hand. Her husband spoke to her, and Logan heard, *"Te quiero tanto."* "I love you very much." His throat constricted.

Logan absorbed all of it—the love between the couple, the soft, caring voice of the woman acting as interpreter and coach, the tears in her eyes as they all heard the first cry. And then it was over, yet in most ways it had just begun.

The doctor suctioned the baby's mouth, wrapped him in a towel and laid him on his mother's stomach. Manuel kissed Carmen, and they gazed at their child.

Doc said, "Meg, why don't you get some fresh air?"

"I'm okay, Doc."

"Yes, I know you are, but I'm not going to need you again until after I clean up the baby," replied Doc Jacobs, who tended to act as if he were everyone's father. "I'll call you if Carmen and Manuel want you. Now, scoot. Go get Lily. I know she'll want to help, too."

Logan waited for the woman who could speak Spanish as fluently as she spoke English and walked with her to the door. Close to her in the hay-baked heat of the barn, he smelled the faint scent of roses. Perfume? Shampoo? Whatever it was, along with her lovely smile and gentle voice, it packed a wallop.

He let her precede him outside. His shirt stuck to his back, but except for the swath of pink on her cheeks, she didn't look as if she'd just helped deliver a baby.

He extended his hand to a lady whose smile could make him believe the sun would come up tomorrow. "I'm Logan MacDonald."

Meg had heard a little about the sheriff over the past few years from her aunt and uncle. Not much, just that he was a widower and he ran his jurisdiction with an iron hand. Yet he was well liked by the constituents who'd gotten to know him as a deputy and had elected him sheriff because of his reputation and career in law enforcement. She'd been aware of his presence as soon as he'd walked into the barn. Her experiences had led her to be acutely aware of her surroundings, the tiniest inflections and mannerisms. All were elements of communication.

What Logan MacDonald had come upon in the barn had affected him deeply. She could tell from his expression, the huskiness in his voice.

The birth had affected her, too. Though early, this baby had been no accident. Manuel and Carmen didn't have much, but they already had a nurturing love for this child, the kind of love Meg had only felt from Aunt Lily and Uncle Ned.

As Meg placed her hand in Logan MacDonald's, she was aware that his physique in his uniform spoke of authority; the open top two buttons of his dark brown shirt told her he was impatient with the heat. He was sleek and muscled—tall with black hair and green eyes that seemed to be searching hers for something. He looked almost fierce in his concentration.

"Meg Dawson," she returned as he gripped her hand. The touch of his skin against hers made her that much more conscious of the intensity in his green eyes. She felt warm and more than a little bothered.

Releasing her hand, he snapped his fingers. "That's it. Now I recognize you. Margaret Elizabeth Dawson—the interpreter. Your picture was on the front page of most newspapers in the country not so long ago. I didn't realize you were Lily and Ned's niece."

She'd shied away from the *Willow Valley Courier* and their attempts to persuade her to do an interview after the initial wire-service story ran. She'd wanted to recover and forget.

But Logan remembered the details. "You were taken hostage in Costa Rica with a diplomat and wounded when your kidnapper started shooting. Finally you talked him into letting you and Pomada go in exchange for a plane. He didn't even get off the runway before the officials nabbed him. You should have been given a medal!"

She could feel her face turning pink. She hadn't even blushed when the president of the United States himself had shaken her hand. Of course, she might have still been in shock then. Part of her still was. "We got out alive. I didn't care about a medal," she said softly.

Her heart rate increased as Logan studied her. Standing in the shade of the barn, she noticed the strands of silver along his temples, the slight beard shadow that she guessed would grow darker as the day progressed, the male scent of him that tightened her stomach in an exciting way. She willed her pulse to slow. She didn't feel strong enough yet to get involved with anyone, let alone with a man like Logan, who exuded authority, intensity and a quality that told her he was hurting right now for some reason. She'd seen it on his face before Carmen's baby had arrived. She could see it now as she looked into his eyes.

"Did you come to Willow Valley to hibernate?" he asked with a perception that rattled her.

There were so many reasons she'd come back. But she simply answered, "I feel safe here."

Before Logan could respond, Doc Jacobs emerged from the barn. "Meg, ask Lily and Ned if they can put Manuel and Carmen up for a few days."

Meg looked concerned. "Do you think Manuel will agree?"

"For Carmen's sake, I hope so. We'll work on him. Logan, any word on Travis?"

The same pain Meg had glimpsed on Logan's face earlier shadowed his features again. "No."

"Your P.I. have any new leads?"

"No. Nothing. But I have to believe he's still out there somewhere."

Doc Jacobs grasped Logan's arm. "I know you do.

And this whole town's praying.'' He ducked back into the barn.

Meg knew she had to talk to her aunt and uncle, yet her focus was still on Logan and the tortured look on his face. But she didn't feel she could ask any questions.

The next moment, Logan seemed to compose himself, only the creases on his forehead hinting something more important was on his mind. ''So, tell me what happened here today.''

Suddenly fatigue settled over Meg, fatigue that told her she was healing but wasn't yet healed. She leaned against the rough wood of the barn. ''Manuel and Carmen are migrants. Legal ones. They were on their way to Pennsylvania for the apple harvest. Manuel's brother is already there.''

''I can guess the rest. They didn't expect Carmen to deliver until they arrived in Pennsylvania.''

Meg nodded. ''When Carmen's labor pain became intense last night, Manuel knew he had to stop. He thought he could deliver the baby himself, but he got scared and, when we found them in the barn, he let us call Doc.''

''Why wouldn't Manuel and Carmen stay here a few days?'' Logan asked, studying her carefully.

''Because Manuel is proud and won't take handouts. He insists he'll pay Doc.''

''Doc'll cut his fee in half.''

''Probably. But although Manuel doesn't speak English fluently, he does understand it fairly well and knows the score. Convincing him to stay could be a problem. These two are stubborn. Manuel parked his truck on Black Rock Road last night, and he carried

Carmen across the fields to the barn so no one would hear them.''

Logan looked away, to the willow tree not far from the house with its graceful branches silent and still in the August heat. After a pause, he said, ''Manuel has to do what's best for his wife and child.''

Something in Logan's voice told her he'd had to make that decision. ''I hope he will. He loves Carmen very much. I can feel the bond between the two of them. It's the same kind my aunt and uncle have.''

Logan faced her again. ''How long are *you* going to stay in Willow Valley?''

She was more comfortable talking about Manuel than herself. ''I'm not sure. I've already been here a month. But it's really hit me this time that my aunt and uncle are getting older. I think I'd like to stay until Thanksgiving, anyway.'' The explanation was reasonable, but she knew her decision to stay was more complicated than that.

Disconcerted by the sheriff's probing green eyes, Meg pushed away from the barn. ''I'd better talk to Aunt Lily. It was nice meeting you, Sheriff MacDonald.'' She started toward the backyard.

''Meg?'' His deep voice vibrated through her.

She turned. ''Yes?''

''My name's Logan.''

With the hint of a smile, she nodded and headed toward the house.

Logan watched Margaret Elizabeth Dawson disappear. But he still felt the impact of her searching brown eyes. He could have gone back to the office, but he told himself he had to make sure the situation here was under control. In Willow Valley, helping sometimes became more important than enforcing. He liked that.

A half hour later, he and Doc Jacobs carried an old door from the basement of the farmhouse to the barn.

Meg sat on the floor next to Carmen and Manuel, speaking in Spanish. Manuel looked agitated. All three stopped talking when he and Doc came closer.

Huffing and puffing, Doc helped Logan lower the door down to the straw-covered floor beside Carmen and her baby. "I'm getting too old for this," he grumbled.

"More like you should take the advice you give to your patients," Logan suggested blandly.

"I suppose you mean about trimming down and getting exercise. You're only forty, Logan. When you hit sixty, then you come tell me how easy it is to do that."

Logan caught Meg looking at him as if wondering what kind of physique was hidden under his clothes. Her appraisal sent a surge of desire through him. This time he almost welcomed it. He couldn't help but say to her in a low aside, "I jog."

Her cheeks pinkened. She avoided Logan's gaze and looked at Doc. "Lily says Manuel and his family are welcome to stay until Carmen feels well enough to travel, but Manuel won't agree."

"We go north," Manuel said in explanation.

Doc glared at the young Hispanic and said slowly, "Lily and Ned are good people. If they invited you to stay, they want you here. You must think of your wife and child."

Meg put her hand on Manuel's arm. "Carmen and the baby need a few days to get stronger. Do this for them."

His almost black eyes searched Meg's face, then his wife's. In halting English, he said, "We stay tonight." Then he lapsed into Spanish. *"Sólo esta noche."*

Doc nodded. "We'll start with that. Tomorrow's another day." He pointed to the door. "Manuel, you and Logan can carry Carmen to the house using that as a stretcher."

Meg asked Manuel, *"Lo entendió?"*

"Sí."

As Manuel helped Carmen and the baby get situated on the door, Meg slipped a folded towel under the mother's head. When she did, the edge of her sleeve caught on the corner of the door, pulling it above her shoulder. Logan saw nasty red lines, healing but not completely healed. He remembered she'd been shot in the shoulder. He wondered just how serious the injury had been.

His gaze found hers. She quickly pulled the sleeve down, then fiddled with the towel swaddling the baby.

Logan and Manuel carefully and slowly carried Carmen to one of the guest bedrooms. Lily seemed to be everywhere, her smile warm, her manner gentle, making sure the new mother was comfortable. With a broad grin, Ned carried in a cradle. "I made this for Meg when she was born." He winked at her. "I guess you don't remember."

She smiled fondly at the balding man. "I remember putting my dolls in it for their naps."

Lily flicked back a stray strand of hair that had escaped her bun. "I'll get it ready. We found a few baby blankets and kimonos in the attic. I threw them in the washer. We'll be all ready for this little one in no time. Now, how about all of you come down to the kitchen and we'll get some lunch.''

Manuel looked worried. ''No trouble.''

Lily planted her hands on her hips. ''Meg, tell him we have to eat. A few more mouths are not a problem.''

In Spanish, Meg explained her aunt's philosophy. Manuel didn't look convinced. Doc Jacobs motioned everyone out of the room. ''C'mon folks. Let's let mother and baby get some rest. Meg, after lunch I want to go over a few points with you about nursing. You can explain it to Carmen.''

Logan watched as Meg said a few last words to the young mother. Then she followed him into the hall.

Standing close to her, he blocked her from going down the steps. ''How serious was the injury to your shoulder?''

''It looks worse than it was.''

''How bad?'' he pressed.

Her back straightened, and she lifted her chin. ''Does the sheriff want to know?''

''No. The man wants to know.'' He wanted to know too badly for his own good. Something about Meg Dawson drew him. Maybe it had to do with them watching a new life enter the world.

Tension hummed between them for a moment— man-woman tension…and awareness.

Finally she let out a pent-up breath. ''I finished with formal physical therapy in Lynchburg last week, but still do exercises every morning and night. I'll recover completely.''

The vulnerability in her eyes told him she might recover physically, but he wondered about the emotional toll the incident had taken. He knew about emotional tolls. First there had been Shelley's accident, then his son's change in behavior...now his disappearance.

Logan's job sometimes drew crisis situations like a magnet. But he was used to investigative work or breaking up a brawl in a local tavern. Personal crises were a different matter. He suddenly realized the last thing he ought to do was get involved in Meg Dawson's.

He moved away from her and waited for her to start down the stairs. "I have to get back to the office."

She looked over her shoulder. "You're not staying for lunch?"

It was just a polite question. He didn't hear interest in her voice. Thank goodness. "No. Duty calls."

At the bottom of the steps, she waited for him. "Thanks for your help with Carmen and Manuel."

"No thanks necessary." She was standing close enough to touch, close enough that he could see golden lights in her eyes, close enough that he had to leave now. He stepped away from Meg toward the door. Then he left, unsettled, without saying goodbye. Because if he did, he might decide to stay for lunch, and he wasn't looking for another complication in his life.

Chapter Two

After supper that evening, Meg weeded the flower garden by the front porch. As Lily peered over her shoulder, the older woman said, "I want to plant yellow and orange tulips this year and put pink ones out back."

"They'll look pretty in the spring with the daffodils," Meg responded, her mind on Logan MacDonald, not the flower garden.

Ned pushed himself back and forth on the porch swing, his head covered by a straw hat. "I should go see if Manuel is still tinkering with his truck. Maybe I can learn something."

"Carmen and the baby are napping," Lily replied. "I checked them before I came out."

Meg had looked in on them, too. She'd stood for a long time watching mother and baby, an unfamiliar longing deep inside her.

Suddenly a yellow-striped kitten scampered out from behind a yew and brushed against Meg's leg. She smiled at Leo, a stray she'd found and befriended soon after she'd returned to Willow Valley.

Ned stood and came to the edge of the porch. "A reporter called from the *Willow Valley Courier*. He wanted to do an interview with Manuel and Carmen, but they didn't want to talk to him. They're very private. I told him to call Logan for the details."

Meg glanced at her uncle. "I'm hoping we can convince Manuel to stay for a week or so."

"It's a shame Logan couldn't stay for lunch." Lily cast a quick look at her husband.

"He's a fine man," Ned remarked as if on cue.

"Fine" wasn't quite the way Meg would characterize Logan. Strong. Decisive. Intuitive. "Who's Travis? I heard Doc ask Logan if he'd heard anything about him."

Lily tidied a few strands of hair that always came loose from the chignon at her nape. "Travis is Logan's son. Logan moved his family here about five years ago. From what he's said and I've heard, Travis never liked Willow Valley. Coming from Philadelphia, I guess that was natural. Logan wanted to give him somewhere wholesome to grow up. But Travis wanted none of it."

"So he ran away?"

Lily exchanged a look with her husband. "I think there's more to it than that."

Ned added what he knew. "About a year after they moved, Logan's wife was in an accident and died. It was tough on the boy. Afterward Travis gave Logan quite a few headaches—coming home late, drinking, grades slipping. Logan was at his wit's end and tried to get the boy help. But Travis wouldn't go to the appointments with the counselor. One day about four months ago, he just up and ran off. He's only sixteen, and Logan's worried sick.''

"The police are still looking," Lily explained, "and for the first two months, Logan searched for the boy himself as far as Richmond.''

Meg sat back on her heels, forgetting about the weeds. "Doc mentioned a private investigator.''

Ned grunted. "Logan's trying everything he can to find Travis.''

Her heart aching, Meg said, "Logan must be in unbearable pain. Not knowing where his son is, imagining the worst. How does he go on?''

"He's a strong man," Ned answered.

"A good man," Lily added.

Ned pushed his hat back on his head. "Rumor has it Logan's marriage was rocky before Shelley died. But Logan never talks about it.''

Meg couldn't forget the look in Logan's green eyes when Doc had asked for news of Travis.

"Are you going to see Logan again?" Her aunt's tone was filled with eager interest.

"What?" Meg asked dropping her gardening trowel.

"Honey, I can read you like a book. You don't ask idle questions.''

"Aunt Lily…''

Her aunt laughed. "It would be good for you to get out, go to dinner, date a man.''

"You know dating is the furthest thing from my mind.''

Lily's smile faded. "I'm worried about you, child.

You're not the same person you were before that terrible man shot you."

Most of the time Meg tried not to think about it. She just wanted to get over it. The problem wasn't the shooting. It was the terror, the panic and the trapped feeling that still gripped her sometimes. But she hadn't had a nightmare in over a week. That was progress. "I'm fine, Aunt Lily. You and Uncle Ned and Willow Valley are all I need."

"For now," her aunt pronounced.

Petting Leo, who'd curled in a ball by her knee, Meg decided she wasn't going to ask what her aunt meant. She didn't want to know.

The following morning, Logan drove to the Carlsons' farm. He was curious to see how Manuel and Carmen were faring. He wished he could do something for the young couple, but he knew Manuel wouldn't accept charity.

He was halfway down the lane when he saw Manuel packing the back of his truck. As he drove closer, he saw Meg standing by the open passenger door. She was gesturing to Manuel and speaking fast while Lily and Ned looked on. Logan could guess what was happening.

He parked on the gravel patch beside the blue compact. Climbing out of his car, he heard Meg speaking to Carmen. All he caught were the words *quédese,* "stay," and *unos pocos días,* "a few days." Carmen spoke quickly and gestured to her husband. As Logan approached, he could see the tears in the young woman's eyes.

Stopping beside Meg, he denied the sudden surge

of adrenaline rushing through him. "They're leaving," he said, summing up the situation.

"Yes, and they shouldn't. I've talked to Manuel till I'm blue. But he won't listen."

"Has Carmen tried?"

"She says he's the head of the family—he makes the final decision. But, Logan, just look at her! She needs rest and care…at least for a few days. Doc wants to make sure Tomás—that's what they named him—is nursing adequately. But Manuel insists he can't take advantage of our hospitality."

The baby in Carmen's arms wriggled and cried. Carmen looked as if she were close to tears herself.

Meg spoke to her in Spanish. Carmen let her take Tomás. As the baby squirmed, Meg positioned him on her shoulder as naturally as any mother and patted the infant's back. She looked so…beautiful, standing there like that.

Giving himself a mental shake, Logan said, "I suppose Doc is afraid if they leave, Carmen won't seek out proper care if she needs it."

"That, too. But I can't convince Manuel to stay." Meg gently rubbed her chin against the baby's downy black hair.

Logan was gripped by an emotion so strong he knew he had to get away from this woman. "I'll talk to him."

Meg took a quick glance at Logan's broad back as he went to the truck. He'd taken her by surprise when he arrived. She'd never expected he'd come back and check on Carmen and Manuel. Yet maybe with the birth of Tomás, he'd felt involved in their lives, too. It proved one thing about him—he was a caring man. She could never see Todd caring about this young couple, whether they stayed or left. Why hadn't she seen his selfish streak sooner? Why hadn't she recognized his self-absorption? His story, his career, his needs, always came first. Actually it was an old pattern, one she'd learned with her parents. But finally, at age twenty-nine, she'd realized in time that her needs mattered, too.

Logan called, "Ned, come here a minute."

Meg could hear the low rumble of the men's voices but couldn't tell what they were saying as they walked toward the barn. When they reemerged, they were all smiling. Manuel came over to Meg and Carmen. "We stay. A little while. If I have work." He helped his wife from the cab of the truck.

Carmen squeezed Meg's hand. *"Gracias."*

Meg shook her head. *"No hicenada especial."*

Carmen gazed at Logan. *"Gracias."*

He smiled. *"De nada."*

Meg handed Tomás to the young Mexican woman. Manuel put his arm around her shoulders and guided her back to the house. Lily and Ned followed.

Closing the door of the cab, Meg turned to Logan. "What did you say to him?"

"It was what Ned said. I reminded him of all the machinery that needs a good overhauling and the back field that has to be mowed before winter. Manuel is going to take care of that and, in return for the work, he'll accept room and board for his family."

Meg clasped Logan's arm. "What a wonderful idea!" His skin was hot under hers, the hairs on his forearm rough against her fingers. His green eyes darkened, and her heart raced. She removed her hand.

"Not wonderful. Just expedient. The trading of goods and services. I'm not so sure we shouldn't do it more often." Logan glanced at his watch. "Did you have breakfast?"

She shook her head.

"I'm not officially on duty for a half hour or so. How about going to the bakery with me for a doughnut and a cup of coffee?" When she hesitated, he added, "I get tired of my own company sometimes. I thought maybe we could just…talk. But if you're too busy—"

"No, I'm not too busy. A cup of coffee sounds good. Aunt Lily makes me herbal tea. Even after all these years, I just can't get used to it."

Logan laughed, a deep, masculine sound that warmed Meg through and through. "She tries to serve it to me when I visit."

"You visit? You haven't since I've been here."

"Yes, well, circumstances the last few months have changed my habits."

Meg saw the pain again. "Aunt Lily told me about your son. I'm sorry."

He shook his head. "Sorrow, blame, regrets. None of it matters except finding Travis. But I don't go on wild-goose chases anymore, driving into the dead of night, speeding down a highway, hoping when I get wherever the road takes me I'll find him. Now I spend my time printing more pictures and flyers, studying the computer data bases, keeping in touch with contacts on other police forces and my private investigator…and working. Working to forget."

Although Meg had always enjoyed her work, she knew about working to forget. She wanted to clasp Logan's arm again, to say she understood, but touching him was dangerous. Doubting he needed her understanding, she nodded toward the house. "I'll make sure Carmen is settled again and meet you at the bakery on Elm. Then you don't have to drive back out here.''

The bakery bell tinkled as Meg pulled open the door. Logan sat at one of the five black wrought-iron tables for two. She'd had second thoughts about meeting him, and thirds. Why had she accepted the offer? Because she liked Logan MacDonald, besides feeling attracted to him. If talking could ease his pain concerning his son, she'd listen.

A mug of coffee waited at the empty place across from him, along with two doughnuts and a muffin. Meg couldn't suppress a smile as she sat down. ''Do I look underfed?''

His gaze brushed over her quickly. ''No. You look just right.''

She felt the heat creep up her cheeks again. No other man had ever made her blush. She chose the cranberry muffin and pushed the other pastries toward him. ''Aunt Lily tries to feed me constantly. She always has.''

''She mentioned a few times that you lived with them when you were a teenager.''

Meg had accepted Logan's invitation expecting to talk about him, not about herself. But he was obviously fishing for her background. Picking up her coffee, she took a sip before she said, ''My parents are anthropologists. For my first twelve years, I traveled with them most of the time—mainly in Central and South America, but I also spent time with my aunt and uncle. At twelve, I decided I'd rather stay in Willow Valley than globe-trot.''

He gazed at her a few moments as if he was trying

to see what she wasn't saying. She wasn't even sure herself about all the emotions that surfaced when she thought about those years, when she thought about her parents not wanting her. Even though she'd had her aunt and uncle, she'd still felt abandoned.

Logan added cream to his coffee. He offered one to Meg, and she shook her head. "A purist," he teased.

"What's the point of caffeine if you dilute it?"

He grinned. "On my fourth cup, I find it more palatable. I have a pot sitting in my office all the time." Leaning back in his chair, he broke off half of the doughnut and ate it. "So, at twelve you didn't want to globe-trot, but for your adult life, you have."

"I didn't go into this profession to travel. That just goes along with it sometimes."

He leaned forward again, his hand almost brushing hers as he rested it on the table. "Why did you choose to be an interpreter?"

Instead of touching his large hand, as she wanted to do out of curiosity to see what would happen, she toyed with the paper around her muffin. "Because I wanted to help people understand each other. I had a talent for languages because of my upbringing. I was always amazed by the difference in the way people treat each other when they can understand each other. There's less fear, less anxiety, less suspicion."

He pulled his hand back and wrapped his fingers around his mug. "How many languages can you speak?" His knee briefly touched hers under the table, but he moved his away.

"Four fluently, not counting dialects." She sipped again at her coffee.

"You're uncomfortable talking about yourself, aren't you?"

"I didn't expect to have coffee with you and talk about me."

He smiled. "Why not?"

"Because I thought you might want to talk about Travis."

He went silent and his jaw tensed. If she'd ever seen a man in pain, that man was Logan. She waited.

His voice deeper, his words terse, he responded, "I think about him day and night. Believe me, I don't want to talk about the thoughts that are running through my head. And you don't want to know what they are."

They sat at a stalemate, Meg wondering if Logan kept all his feelings bottled up, not just those about Travis. She understood his need to keep a lid on his emotions. She did the same thing.

Logan's pager beeped, breaking the tension. "Excuse me, I have to make a call."

Meg watched Logan as he went to the phone behind the counter. The calls for him must be a constant source of hope, but disappointment, too. His face remained neutral as he dialed a number. As he began talking, there was a slight change in his stance, and he rubbed the back of his neck. He wasn't getting news of his son—not good news anyway.

When he came back to the table, he said, "I have to cut this short. Cal needs me at the office."

She stood. "I need to get back, too." All of a sudden, Meg knew that getting involved with Logan would be more complicated than being involved with a photojournalist who always considered his career more important than their relationship. She didn't need involvement; she needed peace. As they walked to the door and she said goodbye, she knew the less she saw of Logan the more peaceful she'd feel.

A few days later, Meg picked up the *Willow Valley Courier*. When she saw her own picture on page one, the same picture that had run in newspapers across the country five weeks ago, memories overwhelmed her. By the time she'd finished the article, the numbness had worn off and she was furious.

Logan's comments to the reporter about Manuel and Carmen were strictly factual. But he had included her in the mix. Inadvertently or not, he'd dragged her into their drama. He might be sheriff, but she had a right to her privacy just as Manuel and Carmen did. She sat and fumed for a few minutes, then suddenly decided to tell him how she felt.

Meg drove to the sheriff's department and turned off the ignition before she changed her mind. When she pulled open the door to the office and stepped inside, she saw Cal Martin, one of Logan's deputies, sitting at the front desk.

In a crisp tone, she said, "I'm here to see Sheriff MacDonald."

Cal looked her over. "And your name?"

"Meg Dawson."

Cal's gaze flashed with recognition. He pointed to the closed office in the back. "Just knock on his door."

She could feel Cal's eyes on her back as she crossed the room. Seeing Logan sitting at a massive, scarred wooden desk, she rapped sharply on the glass-paneled door.

He looked up and rose from his chair, opening the

door in one quick motion. She'd stood face-to-face with him before, but today his shoulders seemed broader, his legs longer. She should have done this by phone.

"What's the matter, Meg?"

No doubt her color was high. She hadn't bothered to run a brush through her hair, and her old cutoffs and short, sleeveless knit top didn't add to a sense of self-confidence. Boy, she really hadn't thought this through.

She slapped the paper on his desk and her purse on top of it. "That's what's wrong. Why did you mention me and Costa Rica?"

Logan's brows arched. "Everything I told the reporter is a matter of public record. Doc Jacobs delivered Manuel and Carmen's baby boy in Lily and Ned's barn. You acted as interpreter. The reporter was the one who remembered you'd made news before. I just confirmed it."

"Why did you have to mention me at all?"

Her voice had risen with her question. Cal was looking at her and Logan.

Logan firmly clasped her arm and tugged her away from the door so he could close it. "What's going on, Meg?"

Feeling embarrassed for making herself a spectacle, she stepped away from him. "Carmen and Manuel turned down the interview. I certainly wouldn't have agreed to one. This…this—" she waved to the picture "—was unexpected. That's all."

Logan's gaze probed hers until she looked away. She took a few deep breaths, then pushed her hair behind her ear, staring at her picture in the paper, the picture of her and Ramón Pomada standing at the car on the airport runway after the kidnapper had run to the plane. She involuntarily clutched her shoulder, remembering the way it had hurt. She remembered...

Logan was close again. "Meg," he said gently, "what are you thinking?"

"I, uh, I guess I shouldn't have bothered you. I should have realized even old news is still news in Willow Valley."

Logan rested his hands on her shoulders. "Have you talked to anyone about what you went through?"

She looked over his shoulder, trying to deny the emotions swelling inside her. "Just the debriefer." Her breaths were coming quicker.

"You weren't allowed to give interviews, were you?"

Her chest tightened, and the air in the room suddenly got thinner. "The governments involved thought it would be better if I didn't. They just gave the facts."

"So why did the rehash of the story bother you now?"

His gentle voice stirred her emotions into chaos, making her feel too vulnerable. "The picture," she murmured as she felt tears prick at her eyes. Now she really felt foolish. She ducked her head and stared straight into Logan's chest. She could see each breath he took, could feel the warmth of his hands on her shoulders...and wished she was anyplace else but here.

He tipped her chin up. "It's okay to let it out. If you haven't yet, you're going to have to soon or it will eat at you."

"But I..." She couldn't stop the tears.

He pulled her against his chest. "It's okay," he murmured. "It's okay."

Logan couldn't help but wrap his arms around Meg. Her reaction seemed to have surprised her more than him. He suspected she wasn't used to leaning on anyone. From what she'd said about her childhood, she'd learned at an early age to depend on herself. When he'd invited her to have coffee with him, he'd acted on impulse. He'd found himself thinking about her often, wanting to know more about her, weighing the pros and cons of seeing her again.

Right now she was a woman who needed a shoulder…his shoulder. With his arms around her, her hands pressed against his chest, he wished she could just let go of her ordeal and its effects, but it wasn't that easy. Nothing ever was. He could feel her quick breaths, feel the tension as she resisted his support.

The scent of roses teased Logan, Meg's curves against him felt too right and holding her aroused him. The warmth between them became heat. Her top was a thin barrier as his thumb slipped from the material to her bare skin. His desire grew stronger, and he closed his eyes. Bittersweet pleasure. His life was a mess. She'd go back to her job after Thanksgiving. Even if he wanted just a—

Meg abruptly pulled away, avoided his gaze and reached for her purse. She took out a tissue, blew her nose, then faced him. "I'm sorry."

"There's nothing to be sorry about."

She looked at the file cabinet behind him. "I'm not like this. I don't cry. I don't overreact."

"Do you want to talk about it?"

"I don't even know what to talk about."

"Maybe how terrifying it is to be held hostage?"

She shook her head. "I just want to forget it."

"I've been in the middle of gang wars and drug deals. I understand, Meg, I really do."

She took a deep breath, and he wanted to pull her into his arms again. "Have dinner with me tomorrow night."

"Dinner?" She looked surprised he'd asked.

He'd surprised himself. "Yeah. I'll cook something at my place. And if you want to talk about Costa Rica, you can."

She gave him a weak smile. "And if I don't want to talk about it?"

He could think of something else he'd much rather do than talk, starting with kissing and ending with...
"If you don't want to talk, you don't have to talk."

She moved closer to the door, but it also brought her closer to him again. "Lily might need my help if Carmen and Manuel are still here."

He thought about stepping away from her, but didn't. "I think she and Ned can handle one evening by themselves. Don't you?"

When Meg slowly nodded, her shiny hair barely brushed her shoulders. It was as natural and free as she was. He wanted to touch her hair, to touch her. Leaning forward, he felt led by a force greater than them both.

She gazed into his eyes and he couldn't help but slip his hand along her neck under her hair and lower his head.

Meg waited for Logan's kiss, thought about it, was eager for it. He'd felt so strong and sturdy and safe as she'd let him hold her. But now, as she gazed into his eyes, she knew he wasn't safe. There was passion there, and yearning and needs only a woman could fulfill for a man. If he kissed her, they'd tap the need—in both of them.

But Logan didn't kiss her. Instead, he removed his hand from under her hair, the touch of his fingers as they slid along her neck leaving a burning heat she wouldn't soon forget. When he raised his head and dropped his hand, she felt a loss of something she suspected would curl her toes.

A slip of a smile turned up one corner of his mouth. With a nod, he gestured to the outer office. Cal stared directly at the two of them through the glass pane.

Logan's tone was wry. "This isn't the most private place in Willow Valley."

She backed away from Logan and picked up her purse on the desk. "Sometimes I wonder if *any* place is private in Willow Valley."

He studied her carefully for a moment. "We'll have privacy tomorrow night."

Flustered, her emotions swirling, not only from what had almost happened with Logan but from the confusion the picture in the paper had stirred up, she moved toward the door. "All right. Can I bring anything?"

He shook his head. "Just yourself."

If she was making a mistake, she'd find out tomorrow night.

Chapter Three

Standing at the door to Logan's house Saturday evening, Meg took a deep breath. The air was getting cooler. September had arrived, and with it the promise of fall. She shifted the bottle of wine to her left arm and rang the doorbell.

A few moments later, Logan opened the door to the brick bi-level. She'd never seen him dressed in anything but his uniform before. He wore a simple white polo shirt, black shorts and Docksides without socks. His thighs were muscled, his legs long, his arms bronzed by the sun. Black hair curled at the V where his two buttons were unfastened. He was sexy and virile, and she was suddenly very nervous.

She handed him the bottle of wine. ''I couldn't come empty-handed.'' His green eyes swept over her, from the gold barrette in her hair, over her emerald culotte dress to her white sandals. When his gaze lingered a moment on her lips, she felt shivers slide up her spine.

Taking the bottle from her, he smiled. "This will be just right. I've barbecued chicken on the grill. I thought we could eat on the deck." Logan motioned her inside. "Come on in."

She followed him up a few stairs to the living room. "Do you have a family room downstairs?"

"I use it for storage. I'm a little short on family right now."

The pain on his face hurt her. He looked as if he were far away somewhere, and she suspected he was thinking about his son. "I'm sorry, Logan. That was thoughtless of me."

When he met her gaze, the pain was still there but controlled now. "You couldn't be thoughtless if you tried."

"You just met me."

"Maybe so. But in my business, I have to read people in an instant sometimes. My life has depended on it."

"Willow Valley must seem tame compared to what you came from."

"It's different. But that's what I wanted when I moved my family here."

Despite how Logan had reacted at the bakery when she'd mentioned Travis, she wouldn't let his son be a taboo subject between them. "Aunt Lily told me Travis wasn't happy here."

"He wasn't. He had his mind set before we came." Logan's curt tone told her he still preferred not to discuss his son.

Meg examined the living room. A gray sofa, streaked with abstract shapes of navy, sat across from an ebony entertainment center. A gray easy chair complemented the sofa. A ladder-backed rocker, two end tables with gray ceramic lights and a coffee table completed the room. But the place still didn't look lived-in.

She crossed to the entertainment center and picked up a framed picture on one of the shelves. A teenage boy stood by the trunk of a maple tree, staring absently across the yard. "Travis?"

Logan nodded.

"He's a handsome young man." He looked a lot like his father.

Logan crossed the room and stood beside her. "He's an unhappy young man."

Meg thought about her own upbringing. "Raising children is complicated."

The silence between them lasted a few moments. Finally Logan said, "You're determined to make me talk about him, aren't you?"

"You need to talk about him, about more than his disappearance."

When Logan raised his hand, she knew he was going to touch her. His fingers on her cheek gave her a thrill of pleasure she'd never known.

His voice was husky when he asked, "How did you get so smart?"

"It doesn't have anything to do with being smart. The heart and the head don't always speak the same language."

He smiled. "I guess the trick is getting them to understand each other."

She nodded and, when his fingers slipped away, she wished he was touching her again. She took the picture with her to the sofa. "Tell me about him."

Logan sat beside her, his knee barely brushing hers. "He's sixteen, thinks he's the smartest kid in the world and is more rebellious and stubborn than any teenager I've ever known."

"He's a junior?"

"Yes. At least he would be if he came home."

"What does he like to do?"

Logan looked at a loss for a moment. "Besides getting in trouble, I don't really know. We haven't had an amicable conversation in a long time."

Logan's expression was full of regret for all that had been. "The last time we talked, he called me his jailor. If he wasn't home by curfew, I'd go out and find him. I think he hated me."

"Logan."

"That's the truth, Meg. And now I can't sleep at night wishing I'd handled everything differently. If I could just find Travis, I'd tell him I don't care if he wears three earrings or torn jeans or shaves his head. I'll even make his curfew an hour later. I just want him home."

Meg reached out and covered Logan's hand. "Doc said the whole town is praying. *Is* there anything else anyone can do?"

He sandwiched her hand between his and gently rubbed his thumb over the tops of her fingers. "No, there's nothing anyone can do except pray."

She stared into his eyes, feeling his pain, feeling his need, drawn to him in an elemental way. Finally Logan cleared his throat and released her hand. "I have the chicken wrapped in foil on the grill. We'd better get to it, or it'll be too dry to eat."

Supper. That's why she was here.

Logan had already set the redwood table. A light

breeze stirred the paper napkins under the silverware. Steps led from the deck down to a long yard separated by a spirea hedge from the next-door neighbor's property.

"Is there anything I can do to help?"

"There's a salad in the refrigerator."

Besides the salad, Logan's refrigerator was practically empty. Two bottles of beer, two cans of soda, a hunk of Swiss cheese, the remainder of a head of lettuce and a package of carrots sat on the top shelf. Other than that, his cupboard was bare.

Meg carried the teak salad bowl outside. Logan had just placed the chicken on a platter and unwrapped the foil from two baked potatoes. As she slid onto the bench, he straddled the one on the other side and gave her a quick grin. "I forgot to buy butter at the store. But I have salt and pepper. I don't cook often."

"You don't spend much time here, do you?"

He swung his other leg under the table and raised his head. "No. Is it so obvious?"

"Nothing out of place in the living room, a spotless kitchen. Sure signs."

"I spend most of my time in my office. When I'm hungry, I run up to Gibson's Grocery."

"Chips and cookies?"

"Uh-oh. The lady is on to me."

She smiled. "Quick and filling. I do the same thing when I'm on the run. I get tired of cucumber sandwiches at receptions and hotel food."

"Where's your home base?"

"An apartment in Chevy Chase."

"Are you looking forward to getting back?"

When she was traveling, she did. Her apartment was sunny, comfortable and close to anything she needed. "I'm enjoying my time with Lily and Ned. D.C. and foreign embassies seem a world away."

Logan delved into world affairs with Meg as they ate. He was a stimulating conversationalist, quick to catch her train of thought, a good listener. Her stomach would jump whenever he smiled. His deep voice, lower when he disagreed with her, carried a timbre of authority, yet he listened when she explained her views. They both veered away from personal subjects. That moment in the living room had been too fraught with emotion, too tempting, too dangerous, to explore further, at least right now.

The sun slipped behind the clouds, streaking them and the sky with orange, pink and purple. The passage of time seemed inconsequential as shadows vanished into dusk and fireflies blinked under the maples in the yard.

Suddenly Logan stopped in midsentence. "We forgot the wine. Some host I turned out to be. I set it on the counter, so it's not even chilled."

"Perfect with ice cubes," she teased.

"You *are* kidding."

"Nope."

"All right. I'll be right back."

She called after him, "Just half a glass."

Climbing from the bench, she straightened her belt and wandered to the railing, folding her arms on the weathered wood.

It wasn't long before Meg felt Logan at the back door, watching her. But she didn't turn around. Whenever their gazes connected, the tumult inside her was too unsettling for her to analyze. Out of the corner of her eye, she could see the glow of the kitchen light. The door opened and shut, and she found herself holding her breath, which was silly.

At least, she thought it was silly until Logan stood beside her and offered her a glass of wine. When he handed her the juice glass, she realized the trembling inside her extended to her fingers. She took a sip and set the glass on the balustrade.

He did the same. "We didn't talk about Costa Rica and what happened to you there." His voice was low, and in the shadows he seemed almost larger than life.

"It's not necessary, Logan. I'm fine."

"That's a generic word that doesn't describe or explain anything. You're not a generic lady."

Logan made her feel feminine and special. As she was growing up, tagging along with her parents, she'd often felt she was a bother. She'd thought she'd put all that behind her—the feelings of loneliness and isolation. Costa Rica had stirred them up, and being cared for and loved by Lily and Ned hadn't eased them but had brought even more confusion to the surface. And now Logan, making her feel she was special...

"Meg?"

Even in the darkness, her eyes sought his. Connected to him for the moment, she felt the impact of her loneliness, more loneliness than she'd ever felt before.

Logan stroked her hair away from her cheek, and she trembled. When he bent his head, she knew she wanted his kiss and needed his kiss. But panic rose within her. In an instant, she realized she was as afraid of involvement with Logan as she was of returning to her profession.

Afraid? Of doing the work she loved? Why?

The questions alarmed her almost as much as the thought of drowning in Logan's embrace. She pulled away from him, confused and afraid, but not sure of what.

"I have to go, Logan." Her voice was firm although her insides were quivering like jelly. *Always keep an outwardly calm appearance. Always hide personal feelings. Always smile and act gracious.* She'd learned to hide her feelings from her parents, and her profession reinforced her inner rules. Often she had to hide her thoughts while she conveyed someone else's words. But she didn't want to think about it now; she just wanted to escape.

Logan didn't mention the almost-kiss. But he did confront her. "What's wrong?"

"Nothing's wrong. It's getting late, and Lily and Ned will worry."

"You're a big girl, Meg."

She summoned up a smile. "Lily forgets that."

"You don't have to run off just because we were getting a little too intense."

Intense. Yes, and turned-on, too. Ignoring his statement, she plowed on as if he were a foreign diplomat and she were his interpreter. "Thank you so much for dinner. I enjoyed it."

Logan frowned. "I did, too. Maybe we can do it again sometime."

Not until she straightened out her thoughts. Not until she knew what was scaring her so. She nodded and went to the door. "I can let myself out. Really, Logan, I had a lovely time."

She reached for the door, and he didn't move. Maybe he realized if he came toward her, she'd run even faster.

"Tell Lily and Ned I'll stop by soon," Logan said in a low voice, reminding her she couldn't run from him forever. "I want to see Manuel, Carmen and the baby again before they leave."

Opening the door, she stepped into the kitchen. "I will. Thanks again for supper."

Meg let the door shut behind her. Logan didn't follow her, and she told herself she was glad. But when she reached her car and turned on the ignition, she wondered how different the night might have been if he had.

The morning was clear, the sky blue, the air carrying the lingering fragrance of the last days of summer. Meg had decided to walk to Willow Valley high school Monday morning for her appointment with the principal instead of driving. She needed the time alone to think.

After she'd left Logan's apartment Saturday night, she'd returned to Lily and Ned's and sat on the porch in the old wooden swing. For the first time in a long time, she'd remembered the conversation she'd overheard when she was twelve. The conversation that had changed her life.

"Meg was an accident that never should have happened," her mother said to her father. "But everything has worked out. She's only held us back a few times. If she decides to stay with Lily while we go to Calcutta, that's her choice. She's old enough to make it."

At that moment Meg had realized she *was* old enough to make a choice and decide what was best for her. She would stay with her aunt and uncle permanently while her parents traveled, and accept the love her Aunt Lily and Uncle Ned could offer—because her parents apparently had none to give.

Swinging and staring at the moon last night long after midnight, she understood why she was afraid to get involved with Logan. When she was a child and her parents left her at her aunt and uncle's while they traveled, she'd learned that attachment hurt. Loving her parents, wanting their love in return, she'd discovered abandonment hurt even worse. Nurtured by Lily and Ned, she'd missed them when she traveled with her parents. But staying at Lily and Ned's, she'd longed to be with her parents. The situation was confusing for a child. At twelve she'd tried to end the confusion by staying in Willow Valley.

When she was an adult, her relationship with Todd had just reinforced the fact that attachment led to hurt. She'd made friends in D.C. But they were social friends, not friends in whom she'd confide. She'd never confided in Todd, either, not about her deepest feelings and dreams. Yet she'd let Logan see a vulnerable side of her she usually kept hidden. She could still feel his arms around her, the brush of his fingers against her cheek. Her attraction to Logan had taken her by surprise. Yet she could cope with that. After all, she didn't have to be around him. She didn't want to get involved, so she'd simply stay away. The solution to that problem was easy.

But her career and her fear of returning to D.C. were another matter. She loved her work. It was important and necessary. Yet she was scared that she'd be put in a situation again where her interpretation skills could be a matter of life and death. She was afraid of the responsibility, afraid of getting hurt again, but most of all, afraid of making a mistake.

She could have cost everyone involved their lives. It was her fault that their kidnapper had started shooting. Thank God she was the only one who'd gotten hurt. But what about the next time? What if...?

Meg hurried across the parking lot of the high school, trying to chase her thoughts away. Entertaining doubts would only give them more power. She swung open the door to the building and headed for the office. The lobby had a familiar wax-and-chalk smell, and she smiled. During her time in high school, living with her aunt and uncle, she'd finally experienced a sense of belonging and stability that had been missing from her first twelve years.

When Meg opened the door to the office and stepped inside, the secretary smiled at her. "Can I help you?"

"I have an appointment with Michael Holden at eleven-thirty."

The door to the principal's office stood open. Meg heard two masculine voices. In fact, if she wasn't mistaken...

Michael stood in the doorway and motioned to her to come into his office. He was six feet tall and in his late thirties. He'd accepted the position as principal of Willow Valley high school the year before. Lily had introduced Meg to the man after church services one Sunday. Meg didn't know much about him—just that his blue eyes twinkled when he smiled and his voice was gentle yet strong enough to persuade recalcitrant teenagers to listen to him. He'd written to her, asking her to consider participating in an assembly for the students. She'd made this appointment with him to discuss it.

Except she hadn't expected to see Logan MacDonald standing in the principal's office. In his uniform, he always seemed to be taller, broader, a force she couldn't ignore.

Logan stared directly at her, as if he were trying to see something inside. "I had a meeting with Michael this morning. He's organized a local parents' group that will go to work as soon as a child is lost or missing."

The Sheriff was making it clear his presence here had nothing to do with her. Without waiting for a response from her, he said to Michael, "I'll call you after I've spoken with my P.I. again. Meg, I'll see you soon."

His tone was cool and polite, reserved in a way it hadn't been before. But she knew it was better for both of them if they limited contact. After all, she'd be going back to D.C. eventually. She focused her attention on Michael Holden and the program she wanted to present to his students.

Logan left the school, fully intending to drive back to his office. But once in his car, he didn't put the key in the ignition. All he could think about was Meg Dawson—the way they'd connected, the way she'd left his house so abruptly, the way she'd stood in Michael Holden's office, a wall surrounding her. Something had spooked her. And damn if he wasn't going to find out exactly what it was.

He examined the visitors' parking places and didn't see a blue compact car. It was possible Meg had walked to the school. Ned and Lily's place was about a mile away. Logan checked his watch every five minutes. Finally the sun blazing in his windshield urged him to get out of his car.

Twenty minutes later, Meg pushed open the door of the lobby and stepped outside. The sun shone on her brown hair, making blond strands glow. The gold buttons on her red sailor blouse gleamed. Her red skirt molded to her legs as a warm breeze blew.

Logan slid behind the wheel, shut his door and started the car. He moved on instinct rather than logic. Before Meg stepped off the curb, he'd driven in front of the entrance, reached across and opened the passenger door.

Her expression showed her surprise. "What are you still doing here?"

"I decided to take my lunch break and give you a ride home. You don't have your car, do you?"

"No, but..."

He appraised her, from her silky brown hair to her sandals. "And you certainly don't need the exercise, so hop in."

"Logan, I don't need a chauffeur."

"Of course you don't. And I don't want to be one. Hop in anyway. We need to talk."

"Logan, really..."

"Miss Dawson, we're soon going to cause a scene if you don't get in. Because I'm not leaving without you."

She looked thoroughly frustrated with him as she slid inside, then slammed the door.

It was clear that whatever talking he wanted to do, he'd have to initiate. He pulled his car out onto the two-lane road and headed towards Lily and Ned's. "Tell me what happened Saturday night."

"Nothing happened."

"I don't see you as a woman who hides behind denial. You're too intelligent for that."

Meg stared out the windshield. "I've solved my own problems for a very long time. I'm not about to depend on someone else to do it now."

"So there *is* a problem."

"Let it go, Logan. Life's like a puzzle. You just have to figure out how to fill in the pieces so they fit."

He glanced at her profile. "Your philosophy?"

"Uncle Ned's."

Meg was making it very clear she wanted him to butt out of her life. And he should. Their roads wound in different directions.

After he cruised down the lane to the farm, he got out of the car quickly and went around to Meg's side. She'd already opened the door. When she climbed out, she stood beside him looking nervous.

He was feeling a bit jittery himself, unsettled by the inner turmoil he felt whenever he was close to her. "I understand if you don't want someone to problem-solve for you. But if you need to talk, I can listen."

When she looked up at him, he wanted to kiss her. But he knew he'd scare her away. So instead, he gently tapped the tip of her nose. "You know where to find me."

It was hard for him to leave her there, to drive away without another word. He'd give her some time. If she didn't come to him, he'd be back to find out why she was afraid of him...of them together.

The terror. She could still feel terror. She was cold...so cold. Despite the heat. Despite the perspiration. She interpreted their kidnapper automatically. But her teeth were chattering, she hadn't slept

*for three days and she was scared…scared she'd say
or do something wrong. Think something wrong and
put it into words.*

*The terrorist rattled off his demands. She conveyed
what he wanted to the official on the phone. Suddenly
their kidnapper shouted and waved his gun. Pomada
yelled. Meg didn't know what she'd said wrong. But
she moved toward the man, hoping to reassure him—*

He shot.

*The searing pain brought her to her knees. No one
helped her. She knew Pomada was afraid he'd get
shot, too. She reached out anyway. No one reached
back. Her ears rang, and dots floated in front of her
eyes, turning everything to gray. She couldn't pass
out…she couldn't…she couldn't….*

Meg awoke, drenched in sweat, the terror as real
as it had been that day weeks ago. When would the
nightmares stop? When would she forget?

Sunday afternoon, Meg drove to Logan's house,
not sure she was doing the right thing. But maybe
Logan *was* the one person who could help her. Maybe
he'd understand her fear of going back to work. She
needed someone else's perspective. Logan himself
had said he'd experienced traumatic situations. How
did he make himself do it again? How did he persuade
himself to take the same risks or face the same challenges when he'd narrowly escaped injury before?

Meg rang Logan's doorbell, not wanting him to
solve her problem but hoping he'd share his experience. When he didn't answer the door, she rang the
bell again and reminded herself she was here to talk
about her work, not to satisfy her curiosity about her
attraction to him.

Both the sheriff's car and Logan's sedan sat in the driveway. The garage door was open, so he had to be around. She descended the porch steps and followed the path around the side of the house. A low buzzing became louder as she rounded the corner. Logan was using a hedge trimmer on the spirea. His bare back, tanned and muscled, gleamed with sweat in the bright sun.

Because of the buzz of the trimmer, he couldn't hear her as she walked toward him. She stared at the strong column of his neck, his hair damp and wavy on his nape, his straight spine, his denim cutoffs riding low on his hips. The sparks inside Meg flicked against her warning to herself, threatening to ignite with a matching response from Logan.

Suddenly he turned around.

She stopped and took a deep breath. But that didn't help because she inhaled sun and male, potent enough to make her head spin.

Logan's stare was intense, then he smiled. "I wasn't expecting company."

Her gaze went straight to his chest—a broad chest covered by black hair. A mat of it whorled around his dark male nipples then arrowed down the center, disappearing under the snap of his shorts. Meg felt herself getting hotter the longer she stared. "I, uh, thought I'd ask about your perspective."

"On…?"

"What happened to me in Costa Rica. There's something you don't know."

He came closer. Her fingers tingled, and she realized she wanted to touch him. There was no point denying it.

"Why don't you sit on the deck while I shower? Then we can talk."

Meg went up the stairs to the deck and settled in a lawn chair while Logan wound up the cord to the hedge trimmer. He climbed the steps and opened the door, his gaze lingering on her. "I'll just be a few minutes."

She heard the underlying message. He didn't want her to run away. As he went inside, she closed her eyes. She'd never been afraid of life or the challenges it presented. But right now she felt like running far away and hiding. She made herself sit still and wait.

Not ten minutes later, Logan opened the screen door. "Iced tea or soda?"

"Iced tea."

He gave her a smile that made her knees wobble although she was sitting.

She heard the ring of the phone in the kitchen and Logan's deep rumble as he answered it. A few seconds later, he came outside, his expression grim. "That was a hospital in Richmond. Travis was mugged."

Chapter Four

Logan's expression reflected a mixture of dismay, relief and worry.

Meg couldn't keep herself from going to him. "How is Travis? Are his injuries serious?"

Logan raked his fingers through his hair and shook his head. "Cuts and bruised ribs. A black eye. They kept him overnight for observation. He only gave them my number now because his doctor threatened him with the juvenile authorities if he didn't. They wouldn't release him on his own."

Meg knew the drive to Richmond would take about three hours. She could imagine Logan's concern, recriminations and hope as he drove. "Would you like me to go along?"

His green eyes gentled, then darkened with the same intensity that had been there right before she'd evaded his kiss. "I'd like that."

An hour later, Meg sat beside Logan as he drove and wondered if she should have offered to come along. She'd called Lily so her aunt wouldn't worry. But Logan had been silent ever since they'd gotten into the car. Meg felt as if she was intruding.

Suddenly he glanced at her. "I'm sorry I'm such lousy company."

"I understand."

He grunted. "No, I'm afraid you don't. You'll probably wish you'd stayed in Willow Valley. Travis can be..." Logan sighed.

"Are you afraid he won't want to come home with you?"

Logan adjusted his sun visor with a snap. "I *know* he won't want to come home."

"Even after what he's probably been through?"

"I told you he hates me, Meg. And maybe he has good reason."

"Logan!"

"He's never said it, but he thinks his mother's accident was my fault. And I'm not so sure it wasn't. We had a serious argument. Travis came home just as she raced out of the house. An hour later, she was dead."

Meg didn't know what to say to ease Logan's pain and guilt. "Have you talked to him about it?"

"Since that night, he's pulled away. Now I'm not sure all the talking in the world will help."

Meg could feel Logan's torment. He wanted to love his son, but he thought his son no longer loved him. Meg knew what it felt like not to have love returned. Love was more than saying words. It was a bond that transcended arguments and misunderstandings.

But not abandonment.

As long as Logan kept trying to communicate with his son, trying to reach him, that bond would live. Somehow she had to explain that to Logan. "I didn't know how to talk to my parents. They were so far above me."

He glanced at her. "What do you mean?"

"Their concerns were lofty. They cared about the history of civilization and their research, not about what I'd learned about basket weaving from a native girl my own age, or about the friendship we developed. They met my physical needs—they made sure I was safe. But a child needs more than that."

"I couldn't even keep Travis safe."

Meg could imagine the feelings of responsibility as a parent—the immensity of protecting a child, guiding him on the right path. "Maybe if you talk to him about why he ran away…"

"If I know Travis, he won't be in a talking mood."

"There's always tomorrow."

"If I can chain him down," Logan muttered.

A few minutes later, he switched on the tape player, and classical music filled the car. But as they drove closer to Richmond, the tension increased. Meg wanted to reassure Logan in some way, but didn't know how. She was much too aware of his foot going from the brake to the accelerator, his large hands on the steering wheel, the curling black hair on his forearm and wrist, his tan skin. He drew her gaze again and again. Whenever she peeked at his profile, her stomach fluttered. His rich black hair was cut close to the nape. The lines around his eyes hinted at his forty years, but his strong cheekbones and his determined jaw gave his face vitality and power that wouldn't diminish with age.

He'd shaved when he'd showered. Meg could smell spice, not strong, just part of his scent. Yes, she was too aware of everything about Logan MacDonald. She had been since the first moment she'd felt his presence in her aunt and uncle's barn.

Logan followed signs to the hospital in Richmond. After he parked, he came around to the passenger side and opened Meg's door. She stepped out, and he gave her a wry smile.

They entered the hospital, and Logan halted in the lobby. "The doctor gave me Travis's room number. Would you like to wait here?"

Meg preferred activity to inactivity. "I'd rather come along if you don't mind."

"I don't mind. But I don't know what Travis's attitude will be."

She smiled, hoping to ease Logan's tension. "I'm not afraid of sticky situations. I get involved in them often."

He smiled back. "I guess you do. I keep forgetting you're a professional woman who's been around the world a few times."

"Forget?"

His gaze caressed her face. She could feel it and knew he wanted to touch her. "When I'm with you, I only think about the here and now."

She knew what he meant. It was scary. With Logan, she felt different. Yesterday and tomorrow seemed faraway. The feeling wasn't only scary; it was also dangerous.

If she turned the conversation back to Travis, she could ignore the tugging she felt toward Logan. "What floor is Travis on?"

Logan's eyes remained the same deep green. He

knew exactly what she was doing. "Five." When he broke eye contact and nodded toward the elevators, she walked ahead of him, knowing if he touched her, the tugging would become stronger.

They found Travis's room easily. Logan paused outside the door, his jaw set, his forehead creased with concern. Then he strode in, as if he belonged in the hospital, as if he belonged in his son's room.

Travis was dressed, sitting in a chair by the window flipping through a magazine. The sleeve of his shirt sported a long tear, and the denim of his jeans hung in strips over his knees. His school jacket lay across the back of the chair. The right side of his face was swollen, and his right eye was as black and blue as it could be. Meg saw Logan take a deep breath and realized how difficult it was for him to see his son in this condition.

The teenager looked up when he heard footsteps. Meg glimpsed fear in his eyes, relief and, an instant later, defiance.

Logan stood before his son. "How are you?"

"Just fine, Dad. Can't you tell?"

Logan frowned. "I can tell you've gotten yourself into a mess of trouble. Are you ready to come home?"

Travis grunted. "I don't have any choice." He looked over at Meg. "Who's she?"

"This is Meg Dawson."

Coming closer to Travis Meg extended her hand. "Hi."

Travis scowled at his father. "Seems like you've been busy while I've been gone."

"Travis…" The anger in Logan's tone was evident.

Meg dropped her hand. "Have *you* been busy, Travis?"

The sixteen-year-old looked at her curiously, then dropped his gaze. "Yeah. I sure have. Enough to know I want to be on my own."

"That's impossible until you're eighteen," Logan snapped. "You don't even have a job."

"Maybe I'll get one. Maybe as soon as I get some money, I'll leave again."

Logan looked as if he wanted to shake some sense into his son. "You try it, and I'll be more of a warden than I've ever been."

"You mean you'll lock me in my room? You might as well."

Meg saw the distress Logan was trying to hide. She saw him try to make himself relax, and she knew his next words were a real effort. "Do you know how worried I've been?"

Travis's expression didn't change, and he didn't respond. Instead, he said, "You have to sign release forms out at the desk before we can go."

Logan tried to hide his pain. "All right. I won't be long."

Travis watched Logan leave, closed the magazine and stared out the window.

"I only met your dad a short time ago, Travis, but I know he *has* been worried."

The teenager looked at her then, as if assessing her. Meg let him study her. Finally he asked, "So how did you meet Dad? Did he stop you for speeding or something?"

She knew he was goading her on purpose. Instead of becoming combative, she asked, "Do you know Ned and Lily Carlson?"

Travis nodded.

"They're my aunt and uncle. I lived with them on and off when I was growing up. I'm back for a visit."

Travis grimaced. "Why would you want to visit Willow Valley? There's nothing there."

"My aunt and uncle are there, and I love them."

"It's a one-horse town."

"Were you any happier in Richmond?" she asked softly.

His tone turned defensive. "I was on the streets. If I had my own place, it would be a lot better than Willow Valley."

Her questions for him came from a deep place inside her. She'd never known a real home, and she wondered why he was so anxious to run away from his. "Would it? Or would you get tired of it the same way you got tired of Willow Valley?"

He took his jacket from the back of the chair. "I never liked Willow Valley. It wasn't my choice to move there."

"Did you give it a chance?" she asked quietly.

He remained silent and slung his jacket over his arm.

"Sometimes it's not the place that matters but the people there or the work."

He studied her curiously. "So what do you do?"

"I'm an interpreter."

She'd apparently piqued his interest. "Where do you usually live?"

"Washington, D.C."

Travis's eyes widened, and he looked impressed.

Logan came back into the room. "Everything's set. Are you ready?"

"As ready as I'm going to be," Travis mumbled.

Logan frowned and waited for Travis to stand. The teenager held his ribs. Logan moved forward, then stopped. The expression on Travis's face told him to stay clear.

If Meg thought the trip *to* Richmond was tense, the trip home couldn't be described. Logan asked his son questions about where he'd been, what he'd been doing, and Travis sullenly mumbled a few monosyllables. The muscle working in his jaw, his hands taking a stranglehold on the wheel, Logan gave up and drove.

An hour from Willow Valley, they passed a few fast-food restaurants. At a red light, Logan asked his son, "Are you hungry?"

"Maybe."

"Yes or no, Travis." Meg could tell Logan was at the end of his patience.

"Go ahead and stop. I don't care where."

Logan pulled into the next fast-food restaurant.

The silence at the table was deafening as Travis devoured two deluxe burgers and a large order of fries. After a slurp of his milk shake, he checked out Meg again. "Do you travel much with what you do?"

"Quite a bit. I have albums full of pictures. In fact, I'm going to be giving workshops at your high school on some of the places I've seen."

"Yeah?" There was a gleam of interest in his eyes, the same green as Logan's.

"Your principal and I have been discussing the best way to do it. Probably through social-studies classes. What do you think I can do so I don't bore everyone?"

Travis shrugged. "Dunno."

Logan frowned.

Meg didn't give up. "What would make it interesting for you?"

The teenager thought for a while. "Not just a slide show. But talking about something neat that happened each place."

Travis had a point. She didn't want to do a travelogue or a lecture. Getting the kids involved would work the best. "I'll have to think about that. If you come up with any ideas, let me know."

His expression was doubtful.

"I mean it."

Travis settled back in his seat with his milk shake.

Logan leaned forward as if physical closeness would bridge the distance between him and his son. "We'll have to go see Mr. Holden and find out what you have to make up from the end of last year. Maybe you could do some independent study and join the rest of your class."

"I'm not sure I want to go back to school."

"You don't have any choice."

"I'm sixteen. I can quit."

"No, you can't. I'll personally escort you every morning if I have to," Logan said with a sternness Meg had never heard from him.

Travis slammed his cup on the table. "Nothing changes, does it? You expect me to do what *you* want."

"I expect you to do what's best for your future. And you will."

"I'll say. Maybe I'll take off again."

Logan stared directly into his son's eyes. "Think about it, Travis, and so help me I'll put you in a military academy so fast your head will spin."

"You'd have to catch me first."

"Do you want me to put a personal bodyguard on you so I know where you are every minute?"

"You wouldn't dare!"

"Try me." Logan's voice was deep with authority and intent.

The two males stared at each other, silently engaged in war. Meg took a deep breath. If someone didn't intercede, they'd do irreparable harm to their relationship.

Laying her hand lightly on Logan's arm, she said to Travis, "You know where Lily and Ned live, don't you?"

Travis blinked and turned toward her. She'd given him an excuse to break eye contact with his father first. "Yeah, I know."

"Stop by sometime, and I'll show you the latest pictures I had developed. If you don't like Willow Valley, you'll probably want to travel some day."

"Some day soon."

She felt Logan's arm tense under her hand. "It's good to have an idea of where you'd like to go, what kind of work is available in those countries—if you're planning to leave the States."

"I'd like to backpack through Spain," he said as if he'd given it lots of thought.

"Do you speak Spanish?"

"I've had two years."

"The best way to learn is to live among the people," she advised.

Logan tried to remain calm, realizing he'd better stay out of the conversation if he wanted to hear what his son had to say. He never knew Travis wanted to backpack through Spain. What else didn't he know? What would Travis let him discover? Nothing had changed between them. It tore Logan up to look at his son. The bruised face, eye, his gaunt cheeks. He'd lost about ten pounds. All Logan wanted to do was to keep his son in Willow Valley until he was mature enough to make his own decisions. He'd do it with a gentle hand or an iron hand. Whatever it took.

In the parking lot, Travis slammed the car door as he settled in the back seat. Logan opened Meg's door. Her elbow brushed his arm as she slid in, and his pulse sped up.

Meg.

She shouldn't be distracting him now. All of his thoughts should center on Travis—what he'd put himself through, what could be done to keep him from running again. But Logan was stumped when it came to his son. And maybe he was letting Meg distract him because her presence was welcome. She was optimistic, insightful and so damn pretty his body tightened every time he looked at her or smelled her perfume or saw her smile.

As he drove the last stretch toward Willow Valley, he wished he knew what to say to Travis. He wished he knew what to say to Meg to tell her how much he appreciated her company today, how much he appreciated her attempts to reach his son. Trouble was, he wasn't sure anyone could get through to Travis.

Back in Willow Valley, Logan pulled into his driveway and pressed the garage-door opener. As soon as the car stopped, Travis got out and disappeared through the garage. A light went on in the house.

Logan leaned his head against the headrest for a moment, letting his emotions settle, trying to tell himself tomorrow would be a better day.

Meg touched his arm. Her fingers were light as if she was hesitant to disturb him. "Is there anything I can do to help?"

He managed a weak smile. "Not unless you have a ton of patience in your pocket you can lend me."

"I wish I did."

He turned his head toward her, surprised by the tenderness he felt for Meg already. She pulled back her hand, and he was sorry she did. He liked her touch. He liked everything about her.

She unsnapped her seat belt, and Logan did the same. By the time he walked around to her side, she'd climbed out and closed the car door. They walked slowly side by side to her car.

He opened the door for her. "Thank you for coming along today."

"I wasn't much help."

The stars seemed to be reflected in Meg's eyes. "You were more help than you know. At least Travis talked to you."

"It's not all your fault," she said softly with so much conviction he almost believed her.

"I've done so many things the wrong way."

"Even parents who do everything right have problems with their children."

"Don't try to ease my conscience, Meg. The move and Shelley's death were hard on him. I should have listened to him more."

"You still can."

"If he'll give me the chance. When we're separated, I have hopes. When we're together..." Logan rubbed the back of his neck. "But he's home. Right now that's what matters. I talked to his doctor at the hospital. He said Travis needs to take it easy for a few days, but he should be fine.''

Meg tilted her head up and smiled. "He's safe tonight."

"Thank God. And thank you. I appreciate your support."

Their gazes locked. They seemed to lean toward each other at the same moment. Logan needed to thank her with more than words. Just a thank-you. That was all. A simple thank-you.

But the instant his lips touched Meg's, he knew nothing would be simple with her. Her caring, her kindness, the quiver in her body when his heat met hers told him they were dangerous together. She was understanding and softness, loveliness and intelligence—a woman who could bring richness to his life.

He pushed his tongue between her lips, hungry for her, yearning for something he couldn't name. He thought she might resist. Maybe he even hoped she'd pull away so he wouldn't have to decide between fair and right, restraint or abandon. But she didn't pull away. She let him taste her, and she tasted him.

This kiss wasn't a thank-you. It was passion as complex as his life. His body surged toward hers. He shuddered as their hips met and he felt her breasts against his chest. The scent of her was as intoxicating as her taste. His fingers closed over tendrils of her hair, sliding into its silkiness. He heard her moan and he caressed her back, stopping at her waist, rocking his hips against hers.

Part of him waited for a protest. Shelley had been a practical lover. She'd taken and given what was necessary, nothing more. But Meg didn't protest. Her hands moved from his shoulders to his neck. She stroked his jaw, and his passion burned even stronger with her touch. He ached to lay her down on the grass and—

Travis was home. Logan had to find out what his son needed and give it to him. He wasn't free to start a relationship with anyone—not when Travis was so unsettled, not when Logan wasn't sure of his abilities as a father, let alone a husband. Shelley's decision to continue to use birth-control pills without telling him had left him wondering what kind of husband he'd been. How many nights when sleep was beyond his grasp had he analyzed their marriage, analyzed his career, his actions, his words, looking for the answer to what he'd done wrong?

He'd married Shelley because it had been the right thing to do. He'd moved his family to Willow Valley so Travis could grow up in the right atmosphere— without danger lurking on every corner. And now…

Travis wanted to run, and Logan couldn't seem to fit the pieces back together again. What business did he have kissing Meg Dawson as if he'd never kiss again? What business did he have involving her in his life when involvement would only bring them both chaos?

She had a life in Washington, D.C. Willow Valley was only a stopping-over point for her. It wasn't home.

As much as his blood raged with the desire to kiss more deeply, touch more intimately, make love with her until confusion was only a memory, he knew better. He was stronger than his desire, more reasonable than a drive that could only cause them both a pack of trouble. He had enough of that already.

He pulled away and opened his eyes. He'd been

lost in Meg, lost, for a few minutes, to the reality around him. She opened her eyes, too. He saw the passion still lingering, her surprise that the kiss was over and vulnerability he had no right to see.

But she was quick—quicker than he was. Dropping her hands to her sides, she took a deep breath, then said, "It's been an emotional day, and we're both tired."

As if that explained it all. Could she dismiss the kiss so easily? Could he? He had no choice. "I have to go to Travis."

She nodded. "I know."

Worried about Travis all day, he'd forgotten why Meg had come to him in the first place. "Earlier today, you said you wanted my perspective on Costa Rica. We never got to it."

She shrugged. "I'll work it out."

He clasped her shoulder. "You don't have to work it out alone."

"I always work out my problems alone."

The frustration of the day and the potency of their kiss made him swear. "Dammit, Meg. You don't have to. You gave me moral support today. Can't you see I'd like to do the same for you?"

She took a step back. "You don't owe me anything. And I don't need moral support. Just forget I mentioned Costa Rica."

Maybe she was acting defensive and remote because the kiss had shaken her, too. "The same way I should forget about that kiss?" he pressed.

She didn't hesitate. "Yes."

He touched the back of his hand to her cheek. "You're still flushed. I don't think you can forget it so easily."

Her voice trembled slightly as she asked, "Can you?"

He shook his head. "No. But like you, I'm going to try. If you decide you do need moral support, call me. I'll be glad to listen."

As she stepped away, he knew she wouldn't call. That kiss had changed everything between them. That kiss had pulled them closer together, yet pushed them further away. When she got into her car, he found he was angry at himself, angry with her, but most of all angry at fate. Timing was everything. And the timing for him and Meg was all wrong.

Chapter Five

Pulling a chocolate cake out of the oven Wednesday afternoon, Meg took an appreciative whiff as she set it on a cooling rack. Her uncle loved chocolate cake, and Lily baked one once a week. But today her aunt had complained about feeling tired. Meg had convinced her to nap while *she* baked the cake. Carmen and the baby were sitting in the backyard under the shade of a maple, watching her husband mow the plot of grass on the side of the house.

When Meg looked out the kitchen window, she caught a glimpse of her uncle as he disappeared inside the garage. She couldn't help but smile. Just this morning, he'd patted her head as if she were twelve and told her to enjoy her day. He and her aunt took pleasure from such small things, like their vegetable garden, taking walks by the stream, sitting together on the front porch, talking with Carmen and Manuel. Meg sighed. It was a life she might never know.

The doorbell interrupted her reverie. She placed the pot holders on the counter and went to the living room. To her surprise, Travis stood at the door, looking unsure. He wore jeans, an oversize T-shirt and a baseball cap. His face was flushed, and he looked hot.

"Hi, Travis. It's good to see you." She opened the wooden screen door.

He stuffed his hands into his pockets. "You said to stop by sometime if I wanted to look at your pictures."

"Sure. Come on in."

He looked agitated as he removed his hands from his pockets and shifted on his worn sneakers. "I didn't know if you meant it. I mean, if you're busy or something…"

"I'm not busy. The photographs are right over there on the coffee table. Would you like some lemonade?"

"Yeah. That'd be great. I walked over, and it's kinda hot."

She gestured to the sofa. "Make yourself comfortable. I'll be right back."

Meg poured two glasses of lemonade and glanced at the cake. Crossing to the archway, she asked, "Would you like a piece of chocolate cake? It's still warm, and I didn't ice it yet.…"

"I don't care about icing. But…" As he trailed off, his gaze was probing. "Why are you being so nice to me? Because you're after my dad?"

So that was the real reason for this visit. Meg picked up the lemonade and went to the couch. She set one glass on the coffee table for him and took the other with her to the rocker across from it. "I told you I've only known your dad for a short while."

Travis sat on the edge of the sofa. "That's all it takes."

Meg couldn't lie to Travis. She certainly wasn't "after" Logan, but she couldn't deny the attraction between them that Travis probably sensed. "I admire your dad. We were thrown into an unusual situation together. Did he tell you about Manuel and Carmen?"

Travis shook his head. "He only lectures me. He doesn't talk to me."

Briefly Meg told Travis about the birth of the baby.

The teenager still seemed wary. "But you came with him to get me."

"For moral support."

"Dad doesn't need moral support," Travis argued. "He's a rock." Travis sounded almost sorry, as if he wished Logan weren't so strong.

"He was worried about you, relieved he knew where you were, but concerned about your injuries."

The boy stared at the stack of photographs. "Yeah, so concerned he's making me go to school tomorrow."

It was obvious Travis needed someone to talk to, someone who wouldn't either judge or dismiss him. "You feel you need more time? Are your ribs still bothering you?"

He flushed. "No. It's just…it's going to be hard seeing everyone after being gone. But dad told me if I get decent grades this year, he'll buy me a used car next summer. He called it a contract, and if I screw up I don't get the car. I know it's a bribe to get me to do what he wants."

"What do *you* want?"

Travis met her gaze directly with the same honesty she'd found in Logan. "I don't know. I feel trapped here."

Somehow she wanted to help him see his options so he could start living life instead of running away from it. "Can you look at getting your diploma as the key to freedom?"

He looked puzzled for a moment. "You really believe that?"

"Yes. Without it, you *will* be trapped. With it, new worlds will open up to you, and you can choose whichever one you want. You mentioned backpacking in Spain. Did you ever consider becoming an exchange student for a semester?"

"No. I never even thought I could."

Smiling, she suggested casually, "I bet if you ask Mr. Holden, he'll find information for you. But it would depend on your grades whether you're eligible or not."

Travis picked up his glass and took some long swallows. Then he set it down with a click. "So, if you're not after my dad, why do you care? I'm nothing to you."

"I guess because I relate to how you feel. I know it makes a difference if you have a goal, if you're heading toward something rather than running away from something, whether it be your parents or a small town or a life you don't want."

Travis turned his lemonade glass around on the table and stared at the top photograph on the stack, a shot of the Jefferson Memorial. "So, what was *your* goal? If you like it here, why don't you stay?"

Meg had thought about that ever since she'd graduated from college. "Because I traveled so much as a child, I had a talent for languages. I knew what it was like to stand face-to-face with someone in a strange place and not be able to communicate even simple things. I wanted to help people understand each other. That was more important to me than anything else.''

"So if I want to get out of Willow Valley, I should find the fastest way out. If that's a diploma, then that should be my goal."

"That's one way of looking at it. But you don't have to hate where you are while you're accomplishing your goal. Don't you think you can have some fun at the same time?"

He flipped off the baseball cap. "With Dad breathing down my neck?"

"Why do you think he does that?"

Travis ran the bill of the cap through his fingers. After some hesitation, he blurted out, "Because he feels responsible for me."

"I think it's more than that. He loves you."

"Like you said, you haven't known him very long."

"I get thrown into situations with people, and I'm pretty good at seeing what's below the surface. Your dad loves you and wants to protect you. He wants what's best for you. Do you ever try to talk about all this with him?"

Travis snapped his cap down on the sofa beside him. "He doesn't want to listen to what I have to say."

Forgetting she'd ever been thirsty, Meg sat forward in her chair and set her lemonade glass on the coffee table. "Travis, try to talk to him, tell him what you want, what you feel. It will help you both."

Travis shook his head. "It'll just stir up trouble. I know it."

She couldn't give up that easily, and she didn't want Travis to give up that easily. "Will you think about it?"

He shrugged. "Maybe." After a pause, he said, "You never really answered me about you and dad."

"I'm going back to Washington soon, Travis. So nothing can happen with me and your dad."

He didn't look quite satisfied with her answer. She wasn't satisfied herself, but she didn't know what else to tell him. Closing the topic for now, she asked, "Do you still want that cake?"

He looked at the stack of photographs on the table, then he looked back at her. "Sure. Chocolate's my favorite."

Meg went to the kitchen. She didn't mind talking about Travis's feelings, but she didn't want to analyze hers too closely. Cake and pictures would distract them both.

Since Travis had walked to Ned and Lily's, Meg asked if he'd like a ride home. He accepted, the conversation between them flowing smoothly about the places she'd been. She couldn't tell him about her work since much of it was classified, but she could tell him about the sights she'd seen.

He was enthralled.

When Meg pulled up in front of Logan's house, both the sheriff's car and the sedan were parked in the driveway. "It looks as if your dad's here now."

"Yeah. I wonder why. Unless he came home to check up on me."

Meg heard the anger in Travis's voice. Before they

could get out of the car, Logan stepped out onto the porch and strode toward them. When Travis opened his door, Logan demanded, "Where were you? I called and you weren't here."

"Don't worry. If I take off again, I'll leave a note," Travis said sarcastically.

Logan rubbed his hand across his forehead. "Travis, it would help if you'd try to work with me on this."

"If you mean telling you minute by minute where I'll be, forget it. For four months, I took care of myself. I can do it now, too."

"You took such good care of yourself I had to pick you up at a hospital!"

Travis climbed out and slammed the door, then took off for the house without another look at Logan.

"Travis, I'm not finished talking to you...."

Travis ignored his father and went inside.

Logan came around to Meg's open window. "Where did you find him?"

"I didn't find him anywhere. He came to see me—to look at the photographs I mentioned. Logan, he's sixteen. He wants to be treated like an adult, not a child."

Anger creased Logan's brow and was evident in his words. "When he starts behaving like an adult, I'll treat him like one."

She remembered everything Travis had said, the sense that he wanted to get closer to his father but didn't know how. "You'll lose him if you keep this up."

Logan tightened his hands into fists, his body rigid. "I didn't ask for your advice."

"No, you didn't. But I'm telling you what I see.

Like any boy Travis's age, he wants his father's approval. But for some reason, he doesn't think he can get it.''

''You see Travis twice and you think you know him. I've spent sixteen years with him.''

''Do *you* know him?'' she asked softly.

Logan's face was etched with pain. ''Thanks, Meg. I really need another guilt trip. He's wild and out of control, and nothing I say or do settles him down. He doesn't want to spend time with me. Can't you see that? Adults and their authority are taboo right now. Especially mine.''

Meg had chosen a different route to rebel against her parents. She'd never felt she could earn their love. But instead of acting out to get their attention, she'd decided to go toward the love she knew she *could* get. She'd decided to live with Lily and Ned. And she'd thrown herself into her life's mission—helping people understand each other.

Travis was acting out. Something was definitely bothering him. For some reason, there was a wall between Logan and his son. Because of guilt, hurt, something else?

Silence fell between Meg and Logan, and distance grew though neither of them moved.

Logan finally said, his voice cold, ''Maybe you should stay out of this.''

Hurt stabbed deep, and she responded automatically, ''Maybe I should.'' When she turned the key in the ignition, Logan stepped away from the car. He was granite-still, his expression hard. Nothing she could say would change his attitude; more than being angry with her, he was angry with himself because he couldn't find a solution. For that, he'd have to look into his heart.

Meg pulled away from the curb. Although she was tempted to look into her rearview mirror, she kept her gaze straight ahead. She was just a bystander. She didn't have a good reason to get involved. And she'd better remember that.

The next evening, Meg rocked Tomás on the front porch, a yearning in her heart as she did. He was so adorable with his black hair and beautiful dark eyes. He waved his arms, and she took one tiny fist in her hand. Already he'd grown.

She always felt excited when Carmen let her hold Tomás. Meg indulged herself a moment, fantasizing. A picture of Logan appeared in her mind. She tried to block out his face. She was thinking about motherhood, not about him.

Tires on the gravel lane made her look up. Logan's car. Had she conjured him up? Sure, and she could make everything right between him and Travis, too, she thought wryly. She wished she could stop thinking about Logan and his son. No one could do anything about their relationship but them. If she knew what was good for her, she'd stay out of it. Logan had said as much.

She thought about hiding out in her room. She thought about leaving.

As Logan walked toward the front porch, he remembered his last conversation with Meg. He'd caught a glimpse of her as he'd driven down the lane. Still, he wasn't prepared for her sitting on the swing like a beautiful madonna, holding Tomás in her arms. A need inside him, so basic it hurt, urged him closer to her while self-preservation shouted he should get back in his car and drive away as fast as he could.

But he wanted to say goodbye to Manuel and Carmen.

Meg looked up as he approached, her expression wary. No wonder. His attitude yesterday had been anything but pleasant. Not knowing where to start, he just said, "Lily invited me to supper."

"I see."

The invitation was obviously a surprise to Meg. It was also obvious that she was going to let him carry the ball. "She said Manuel and Carmen are leaving in the morning."

Meg looked at the baby, not at him. "Manuel feels he has to keep his commitment to his brother."

Logan nodded, feeling awkward at best, like a heel at the worst. "Doc has given them the okay to travel?"

"Yes, Carmen is getting her energy back, and the baby is gaining weight beautifully."

"And you're giving her a respite?"

Meg glanced up from the bundle in her arms. "Carmen wanted to help with supper, and I couldn't resist."

Couldn't resist. So unlike Shelley. Shelley had disliked all the aspects of taking care of an infant. She'd been much more comfortable as Travis had gotten older. Logan watched as Meg gently caressed the baby's cheek. So natural. The half smile on her lips hinted at her pleasure in simply holding the child.

Silence wrapped around them until Logan knew he had to bring what was bothering them both out into the open. "I'm sorry I took my frustration out on you yesterday."

"Frustration? It sounded more like anger. But you had a right. Your personal life is none of my business."

He'd expected her to just accept his apology and they'd go on from there. But not Meg. She was an all-or-nothing type of person. "I was angry at Travis."

She smoothed the baby's light blanket. "For visiting me?"

As soon as Meg's car had pulled away, he'd realized where the anger originated. "No. For scaring me again. All I could think about was him hitchhiking to God-knows-where."

Touching the front of her sandals to the porch floor, she swung slowly back and forth. "You're going to have to trust him."

"You've got to be kidding!"

"He feels your anger and your disapproval, and he's trying to get away from both."

"Look, I already know he ran away because of me...."

She stopped swinging and met his gaze squarely. "You don't know for sure why he ran away. Stop blaming yourself and look at the situation for what it is. He doesn't know how to get your attention, so he's doing it any way he can." Meg snapped her lips shut. Then she murmured, "I told myself I wasn't going to do that. You don't want me to be involved."

Logan climbed up the three wooden steps and sat beside her on the swing. "No, I didn't think I did. But it's obvious I'm not getting anywhere with Travis."

"He told me you made a deal with him."

Logan could smell baby powder and Meg's perfume. The combination was unsettling and damnably arousing. "You disapprove."

"I didn't say that."

"You don't have to."

"He has to motivate himself, Logan. He has to want a future as much as you want a future for him."

Just as Meg had caressed the baby's face, he couldn't keep himself from caressing hers. "You're a wise lady."

After a moment, she responded in a husky voice, "All those years I traveled with my parents, I felt as if there was some invisible wall between us. I tried to break it down. I tried being the best I could be. I studied hard. I tried to give them whatever they wanted. If they wanted me to be quiet, I occupied myself. If they wanted me to make friends in a new place, learn a new language, I did. Whatever they wanted. But I could never please them. At least, that's the way I saw it because I never felt their love."

Logan could see the hurt and sadness in Meg's eyes. He wanted to take her in his arms and erase all of it.

"Logan, I'm only telling you this so that you'll realize Travis might have some of those same feelings."

He pulled his hand away from her. "I didn't desert him or abandon him!"

"No, you didn't. And I know you love him. But he doesn't know that."

Logan stared straight ahead, into the fields and peace that had brought him here. "He can't quit school. Getting him a car will give him a reason to at least finish this year."

"What are you going to offer him his senior year?"

Logan couldn't get angry with Meg when she was only asking what he'd asked himself. "I'm hoping by then we'll straighten everything out."

Meg tilted her head and gave him a look that said she thought he was hoping for the impossible.

He rubbed the back of his neck. "Usually I'm a realist. But with Travis…" He shook his head. "Tell me something. I'd imagine you have to stay optimistic each time you go into a new situation. How do you do it? How do you keep past prejudices, past difficulties, from bogging you down?"

"How do you know I do?"

"Because you love what you do. You couldn't keep doing it if you didn't have hope that what you were doing would solve problems and help."

"I think you've gotten to know me a little too well."

Putting his finger under her chin, he turned her face toward his and realized exactly why he was here—despite logic and reason and timing. "I'd like to get to know you better."

Her eyes sparkled for a moment, and then he saw the sadness. "This isn't a good time for either of us."

"Time doesn't have anything to do with this."

"I'll be leaving after Thanksgiving."

"That's over two months away."

"Logan, I don't want to get hurt again."

"Again?"

She ducked her head and fidgeted with the baby's blanket. "It's not important."

"Everything about you is important."

Meg kept her head bowed, but Logan wasn't going to let her evade him this time. He had been angry yesterday…with himself, with Travis, with her. With her because her opinion of him counted, and he didn't want it to. But he respected her. And what she'd said yesterday had stung—a little too much. He'd thought about it last night. He'd thought about changing his tactics with Travis. He'd thought about Meg. And he knew he wanted to kiss her again. Now.

When he slipped his hand under her hair, she gazed up at him. He saw the same desire, the same need. He brushed her lips lightly, teasing them both. As his tongue slid between her lips, he heard her catch her breath. He was about to take advantage of her yielding when the screen door opened.

"Uh, supper's ready, you two. Unless you'd rather stay out here…"

Logan lifted his head and caught the sly smile on Lily's face. He felt like smiling himself—for the first time in a long time.

Logan watched from the barn door as Meg and Carmen strapped the infant seat into the truck. Manuel checked the oil as Ned looked on. The couple planned to leave in the early hours of the morning. He ducked into the barn to look for rope. Manuel could use it to tie down whatever they put in the bed of the truck. Lily, Ned and Meg had given the couple the cradle for the baby plus a few other things.

The late sun's rays danced through the open door, and the heat of the day lingered in the hay stacked along one wall. Logan found the rope coiled on a hook above buckets, a pitchfork and a broom. He heard footsteps but didn't turn.

"Did you find it?"

Aware of Meg the way he'd never been aware of another woman, Logan knew she was there before she spoke. During dinner, he'd caught her watching him as often as she'd caught him watching her. Her soft footsteps on the hay and old wood created an expectancy in him.

"Right over here."

She seemed to bring the sunlight inside with her. She definitely brought warmth. Her yellow T-shirt lay gently over her breasts, the material gathering at her slim waist. Her jeans weren't tight, but snug enough to hint at the curves underneath.

She stopped a foot from him and looked around the barn. "When I'm in D.C., I miss the smell of hay and barn timber. I miss the meadows and streams and woods to walk in. There's a peace here I haven't found anywhere else."

"That's why I wanted to move here. But I'm not going back. You are."

She stooped to the bales of hay and picked up a handful. "I fill up when I'm here. When I'm in D.C. or traveling, the work makes me forget about the necessity of time alone in the country."

"We haven't talked about Costa Rica."

"I told you...."

He took the hay from her hand and let it flutter to the floor. "I know what you told me. But whenever you talk about going back to work, I see fear and confusion in your eyes, not anticipation."

"I don't want to talk about it."

"Why?"

"Because...because already I feel some kind of connection with you."

A connection that was gaining strength any time they were together. "And you don't want to make it any stronger."

She shook her head.

"Because you were hurt once?" he asked gently.

"It's more complicated than that."

Her wide eyes spoke the messages he felt inside. Neither of them was putting them into words. "Then let's do something very simple. Something we both want."

Meg's warmth and light came with her as he drew her closer. She came willingly as if she knew he needed both unconditionally, with no restrictions.

He didn't even remember his arms surrounding her. But he knew the first moment his lips touched hers, everything in him came alive. When they'd returned from Richmond and he'd kissed her, he'd blamed the intensity on overreaction after an exhausting day. But this kiss had nothing to do with overreaction or fatigue. And there was nothing simple about it or the desire and needs that came with it.

Sex had ceased being a need for him. After Shelley's death, he'd found the energy necessary to find a satisfactory partner was better spent elsewhere. He'd denied physical needs before—often during his marriage. But now he couldn't deny yearnings that were more potent than any he'd ever experienced.

When Meg parted her lips, he took full advantage of her yielding, pulling her tighter against him and sweeping her mouth with his tongue. Her sweetness, her softness, made his heart pound. He longed for more—her delicate hands on his body, her satin skin against his, her heat surrounding him. Just the thought stoked the fire already primed to burn out of control.

He pulled her T-shirt out of her jeans, and she didn't protest. As his hand skimmed up her back, he felt her shiver of response. Her tongue danced with his until he knew she wanted him as much as he wanted her. He unhooked her bra, longing to touch more of her, longing to touch her intimately.

Her hands stroked the muscles of his back and restlessly moved to his backside. Logan felt ready to explode. He didn't need Meg's language skills to interpret what was happening between them. Their bodies cried out for each other, and they both understood. Meg's soft moans and his groan of excruciatingly sweet arousal didn't need any interpretation.

He slipped his hand between them, even though that meant unwanted space between their bodies. But their tongues continued to mate as if to make up for the deprivation. When his fingertips touched her breast, she made a noise in her throat, a sound of approval and encouragement. She was so soft, so responsive, so wonderfully a woman. His thumb found her nipple, and the feel of it gave him so much pleasure, he forgot to breathe.

But air didn't matter, and the shadows dimming the barn didn't matter; only he and Meg and the pleasure they could give each other mattered. When he took her nipple between his thumb and forefinger, she yanked his shirt from his jeans and nestled her fingers in the hair on his chest. Nothing had ever felt so right.

The slam of the tailgate of Manuel's truck shattered the fall of night, the momentum of their passion.

Meg went still, then abruptly pulled away as if everything about Logan burned her. She stumbled. Shaking himself loose from the haze of desire, he realized he didn't want her to regret any part of what had happened. He enfolded her in his arms and, even when she tried to pull away, he held tight.

But she wouldn't let him keep her there. She

stepped away, murmuring, "Someone might come in."

He didn't argue with her. "Meg, don't be embarrassed."

She hooked her bra and, as best she could, tucked her T-shirt in her jeans. "I'm not embarrassed, I'm sorry. We'll only get hurt, Logan. You know it and I know it."

All he knew was that *not* kissing her, touching her and talking to her hurt. "So you can just dismiss whatever's happening?"

"No, of course I can't. But I should know better than to let it go too far."

"It's already gone too far."

Her gaze met his. "What do you want, Logan?"

"You."

She blushed. "Sex."

"For a talented interpreter, you've got that wrong. And I think you know it." He tucked his shirt into his jeans. "You think about it, Meg. And you ask yourself the question if all *you* wanted just then was sex." Angry because she wasn't facing up to what was happening between them, he took the rope from the hook on the wall and headed for the door. If he stayed, he'd take her in his arms again.

Until she was sure that was what she wanted, too, he'd have to keep his distance. Or one of them *would* get hurt.

Chapter Six

Gibson's Grocery had stood on the corner of Main and First Avenue ever since Meg could remember. It had seen few changes. Green siding now covered the weatherboard for maintenance reasons, and the refrigerated cases in the back of the grocery had been modernized. Olan Gibson had lengthened his store hours to nine in the evening, as well as afternoons on Sundays, and his brown hair had thinned, turning salt-and-pepper. But the twinkle in his eyes and the quirk of his smile remained the same, constants in a changing world.

Lily needed a few groceries and preferred shopping at Gibson's rather than at the sparkling but sterile supermarket in the strip shopping center on the west end of town, where new housing developments had overtaken the landscape for the past five years. Meg stood beside her aunt as she reached into the produce case for a head of lettuce.

Meg picked up a bag of carrots and, when she put them in the cart, she noticed the pallor on her aunt's face. "Aunt Lily, what's wrong?"

"Nothing, dear. Just some indigestion."

"You had indigestion earlier this week. Maybe you should call Doc Jacobs."

"I'll think about it. I wonder where Ned disappeared to. He said something about the hardware store but...speak of the devil." Lily nodded to the door. "Look who he has with him."

Ned clapped Logan on the back and said to the women, "This man said he was coming in for a fresh turkey sub. I thought maybe we could all get one and go over to the park. We can pick up the groceries later."

Lily and Ned exchanged a look that told Meg better than words that the two were matchmaking. She even wondered if this little trip had been planned. She couldn't think about Logan, definitely not look at him, without remembering their last kiss. When he'd left the barn, she'd composed herself as best she could and gone outside. Not long afterward, Logan had shaken Manuel's hand, said goodbye to Carmen and the baby and left...without another look at her, without another word just for her.

"Yes, why don't we do that?" Lily agreed, and went to the deli case. "Four turkey subs, Olan," she said to the grocer behind the case. "And four of those bottles of juice."

Neither Meg nor Logan protested. Logan's gaze met hers as he held the door for her. She felt the fire from the kiss all over again.

With school back in session, only a few people strolled through the park. No one else sat at the weatherworn picnic tables sequestered under a canopy of maples and elms. Lily acted as hostess, spreading napkins for place mats. She and Ned kept up a constant run of conversation as the four of them ate, though Meg did notice that her aunt barely touched her sandwich. Logan commented on the warm weather and the chances of the high-school football team this season. Meg contributed what she knew about Manuel and Carmen's departure, confirming that the couple had promised to stop back in Willow Valley when they drove through to Florida. She didn't admit how much she missed them, how much she missed rocking Tomás in her arms.

She couldn't finish her sub. She wasn't hungry to begin with. Logan didn't have any trouble with his. But after he'd finished, he said, "I have to get back to the office."

Lily and Ned exchanged another one of those looks. "Stay a few more minutes until Meg finishes and keep her company. Ned and I will go get the groceries."

And before either Logan or Meg could comment, the older couple walked away from them.

"They're not very subtle," Meg said with a grimace.

"I thought about calling you," Logan informed her with his usual honesty. But his frown told her he'd thought better of it.

"I've been thinking about you, too," she admitted. Between worrying about Logan and going back to D.C., she hadn't thought of much else.

"But not enough to call."

"I didn't know what to say." She felt her cheeks grow hot, remembering the barn, remembering her response to him.

"So you think if you ignore me I'll go away? Just as your fears of going back to work will go away?"

His words stabbed her, but when her gaze confronted his, she knew he didn't intend to be mean. His expression softened, and he came around to her side of the table. Instead of sitting beside her, he sat on the table, his long legs propped on the bench. "Talk to me, Meg."

"I thought you had to go back to work."

He brushed his hand along her cheek, then slowly ran his thumb along her bottom lip. She closed her eyes and willed the trembling to stop.

"Is that what you want?"

The timbre of his voice urged her to open her eyes and look at him. "No. But I'm not sure I can trust my decisions right now."

"What are you doubting? What's bothering you?"

"I am afraid to go back to my job. I'm afraid I'll make another mistake."

"What mistake did you make?"

"It's my fault the terrorist went off the deep end and started shooting. It's my fault. I said the wrong thing. What if I do it again?"

"Meg…"

"It could happen. Anything could happen. What if I freeze? What if the words won't come? What if I'm the only one who can speak the language, and the full responsibility of everyone's safety rests on me?"

"You'll do your best."

"And what if my best isn't good enough? What if instead of me getting hurt, someone loses their life?"

"You can't live your life in fear of making a mistake!"

Anger bubbled up. "That's logical and easy to say, but I can't feel that way." Logan's leg brushed her arm, and the anger faded away. Is this how he'd felt when she'd offered him advice?

"So what are you going to do?"

She shook her head. "I don't know. I'm supposed to go to D.C. to a fund-raiser in a few weeks. Maybe once I'm back there, I'll feel differently."

"And what about us?"

She frowned. "We're almost as complicated."

He chucked her gently under the chin. "Oh, you think so? Is being friends so complicated?"

His large body next to her, his scent all around her, his face leaning toward hers with its character and determination and kindness, made her ask bemusedly, "Friends?" Suddenly the reality of their kiss and the definition of the word clashed. Leaning just a tad away, she tried to tease, "Friends who kiss?"

He held her chin in his palm, and the heat from his hand traveled through her whole body. "Friends who kiss and learn about each other and let whatever happens happen."

She withdrew from his touch, protecting herself. "I don't live like that."

"You don't have friends?"

"I don't jump without a parachute."

"What kind of a man do you think I am, Meg?"

"I don't know. I don't know if you go to bars on weekends and pick up women. I don't know if sex means more to you than the moment."

"Don't you?"

She was building walls, maybe trying to shock him

into going away. She was scared to death to get close to him—scared because of the last time she'd fallen in love, scared because she didn't live in Willow Valley and he did.

"I'm not ready to jump into anything, either," he said. "Lord knows, I've got enough to handle right now with Travis. But I like being around you. And I *really* like kissing you." His eyes twinkled as his crooked smile melted her.

She returned his smile. "I think you've had a lot of training in learning how to convince and charm."

"You think I'm charming?"

His smile was so sexy, his expression so ingenuous, she laughed.

He cradled her head and drew her toward him. His kiss was easy, no demands, no promises. But there was excitement and a sense of adventure that left her breathless.

Logan pulled away. "I'll walk you to Gibson's."

She felt as if she were traveling to a foreign country, one where she'd never been before. When she looked up at Logan, she didn't see the uncertainty she felt, and she wondered just how well she knew him.

Michael Holden closed the folder on his desk. "It sounds good, Meg. The letters to the parents went out last week. Parents aren't as involved with teenagers as they are with elementary-aged children, so you might only get four or five per class. And these days, with both parents working, it's tough for them to *be* involved."

"I'm hoping the students will get a peek of other cultures and widen their perspective."

"Well, something you said sparked Travis Mac-

Donald. He was always a good student without much effort. Now he's putting forth some effort. He's interested in the student-exchange program.''

''I'm glad he's looking into it. You know, I could use some help with the technical aspects of the presentation on Friday, setting up the slide projector and that type of thing. Do you think he'd be interested?''

Michael checked the schedule of classes on the board on the wall. ''He's at lunch. Why don't you go to the cafeteria and ask him? He usually sits with his friends at the table nearest the back exit.''

''I think I'll do that.''

''You're trying to get him more involved, aren't you?''

''He needs roots, something to hold on to.''

''Can I ask you something personal?''

She cocked her head.

''Are you and Logan seeing each other?''

And how was she supposed to answer that? She hadn't heard from Logan since he'd walked her to Gibson's a few days ago. ''Not formally.''

He studied her for a moment. ''If some night you decide you'd like to go to dinner, give me a call.''

Michael Holden was a nice man and very good-looking to boot. But she didn't feel the pull toward him she felt toward Logan.

He must have seen her answer on her face. ''Think about it.''

She smiled. ''I will.''

After Meg left Michael's office, she headed for the cafeteria. She entered the large, noisy room, remembering lunches in high school, the rowdiness, the chattering, the food fights that occasionally broke out as teenagers let off steam. The boys at Travis's table shoveled in food and talked around their forks.

One of them whistled as Meg walked toward the table. Her navy slacks and oxford shirt were nothing to snag attention. She ignored the blonde with the leering smile and addressed Travis. "Can I talk to you for a few minutes?"

"Woo-eee, Travis. Who's the babe?" the blonde asked, his elbow jabbing Travis.

Travis scrambled from the bench. "Stuff it, Kyle." He walked with Meg over to the corner of the room. Digging his hands into his pockets, he asked, "Is there a problem?"

"No. Not at all. I wondered if you'd like to help me set up the equipment for my presentation on Friday."

"What equipment?"

"The slide projector mainly. I have enough to keep my mind on without worrying about the order of slides and running the projector. Would you like to help?"

Travis glanced over at the table where his friends sat.

"If you don't want to, Mr. Holden can get someone else. I understand if you're worried about what your friends might think."

"I don't care what they think. Besides...since I took off and managed to come back alive, they think I'm cool."

She smiled. "You *are* cool but not because you ran away and survived."

"Oh, yeah. Real cool."

"Don't sell yourself short, Travis."

He shifted on his sneakers, uncomfortable with her praise. "I'll help you."

"Can you come in early? I'm going to set up in study hall C."

"What time?"

"Is eight o'clock too early?"

"Nope."

"How are you and your dad getting along?"

"We're not."

Meg decided maybe what these two males needed was a referee. But she wasn't sure if she wanted to volunteer for the job.

Friday evening, Lily handed Meg a stack of dishes to load into the dishwasher. "Word has it your presentation at the high school went very well."

Meg shook her head and smiled. "Word" had probably been spread by one parent who had talked to so-and-so, who had talked to so-and-so. "The kids seemed to enjoy it. At first they thought I was going to lecture and they could sleep. But when I made it clear I wanted their comments and questions, they weren't shy."

"How'd it go with Travis?"

Meg had told her aunt she'd asked him to assist her. "He was a big help. I think his reputation went up a notch because the other students thought he 'knew' me."

"You counted on that, didn't you?"

"I'd hoped. Now, if I'd have bombed, I don't know what would have happened to Travis's reputation."

The only discordant note had been the tension between Travis and Logan. Travis had ignored his father from the moment Logan had entered the study hall, and he'd pretended to be too busy to talk afterward. Logan had simply nodded to Meg and left after the period was over.

A warm breeze fluttered the leaves of the philodendron sitting on the kitchen window's ledge. Meg looked up and saw her uncle attempting to climb onto the garage roof. "Oh, my gosh."

"What's the matter? Did you— Ned! Good Lord. He's going to break his neck."

Meg hurried out the back door, her aunt close behind her.

When they reached the garage, Meg took hold of the ladder to steady it. "Uncle Ned, this really isn't a good idea."

"Ned, you get down here this instant. You're too old to be up there," Lily called.

"'Old' has nothing to do with it. I need to fix the shingles before winter. If I don't do it, I'll have to pay someone to do it. That's foolish."

"What's foolish is you being up on that ladder," Lily argued. "You should have had Manuel do it."

"I didn't realize how bad it was until after he left."

"What am I going to do if you break your neck?" Lily asked.

"I'm not going to break my neck." The ladder wobbled as Ned found his footing on the roof. "Stop distracting me, and I'll be just fine."

"Ned, I think these women are worried about you. Maybe we could work out another deal."

Still gripping the ladder, Meg glanced over her shoulder, though she'd know that deep baritone anywhere.

Lily edged closer to Logan and murmured, "You

get him down from there, and I'll bake you apple dumplings every week for a month."

Logan chuckled. "Now, that's a bribe I can't refuse."

His gaze found Meg's. There was no laughter in his eyes, but a depth and intensity that took her breath away. She gripped the ladder harder.

Logan called to her uncle, "You told me you'd show me how to refinish that old chest I bought. What if I nail on the shingles in repayment?"

"Some of the wood might be rotted."

"You buy the plywood, I'll make the repairs."

"Did these women call you before they came running out here?" Ned asked with a ferocious scowl.

"We most certainly did not," Lily protested.

Ned rubbed his hand over his forehead and peered down at Logan. "All right. Seems as though these two will have a conniption if I don't agree. But I'll help you sand that chest, too. I'm not going to just stand by and watch. And I supervise the roof."

Logan crossed to Meg. His hand brushed hers as he said, "I'll hold it for him."

She stepped aside, her hand tingling, her whole being vibrating because Logan was so close.

"Sounds good to me, Ned," Logan agreed.

"Now come down," Lily demanded.

Ned turned around and found the first step on the ladder. As he descended, he grumbled, "If it was up to you, I'd sit on the porch rocking all day. That's no life."

Logan waited until the older man was safely on the ground before he moved away.

Ned wagged his finger at his wife. "Now, don't

you scold. I was perfectly safe. These legs are as sturdy as ever.''

''But your balance isn't.''

''Lily, you worry too much.''

Logan cleared his throat. ''Do you mind if I go up and see what we need?''

''Offhand, I'd say two boxes of shingles. See what you think.''

''I'll hold the ladder,'' Meg said.

Logan didn't argue with her but started climbing up.

Ned put his arm around his wife's shoulders. ''Come on, darlin'. They don't need us watching.''

As her aunt and uncle walked back to the house, Meg watched Logan climb the ladder. His jeans pulled snug with each step. She smiled at the great view. As if he'd read her thoughts, he glanced at her over his shoulder. Caught looking, she felt a flush creep up her cheeks.

''I could hold the ladder while you climb up,'' he teased, eyeing her tan twill slacks and red blouse.

''No, thanks. Roofs aren't my specialty.''

After a smile that made her want to follow him up the ladder, he climbed to the top and stood on the slightly slanted roof. He walked from side to side, bending to examine the shingles. Surefooted and balanced, he looked as comfortable on the roof as he did on the ground, and Meg couldn't take her eyes from him.

His shoulders were broad against the blue sky. His hands, as he ran them over the shingles, were deft and sure. He liked to touch. She could tell. The sensation of his hand on her face lasted long after the moment. Was that because of him? Or her?

It didn't much matter. His touch made her want more of it. No man had ever caused that reaction in her. She'd gone through life believing she didn't need a close relationship with a man. And after her experience with Todd, she'd been sure of it. Was she simply afraid? Was she afraid she couldn't please a man any more than she could please her parents? Was she afraid of an abandonment that would hurt even worse than her parents leaving her in Willow Valley?

Why hadn't she asked herself these questions before? The answer to that came swiftly. Because Logan was different than other men she'd met. The way she felt around him was different. His effect on her was different. Maybe because when they'd delivered Manuel and Carmen's baby, her barriers had been down. Logan knew how to face life honestly. Had his no-games attitude reached a place inside of her that was tired of surface conversation, diplomacy and politeness?

The questions rang in her head with no definite answers.

Suddenly Logan beckoned to her. "Come on up and sit on the edge with me. The view is great."

"You *are* kidding."

He smiled. "C'mon. I'll make sure you don't fall off. I'll even steady the ladder."

An adventurous imp inside her—which didn't mind airplanes but wasn't too crazy about walking across bridges—pushed her to go to the foot of the ladder. When she put her foot on the first rung, she thought she might be crazy. But when she looked up at Logan and saw the twinkle in his eyes, she didn't care. She wanted to sit up there beside him.

When she climbed to the top, he took her hand and

didn't let go until she sat on the roof. The landscape spread before them like a peaceful pastoral painting, rich in color and texture and mood. The day's sun spread its rays across the sky, leaving streaks of orange and brilliant pink. Lavender led into blue as heaven and earth met at the horizon.

Logan took in a deep breath. His thigh brushed hers, and she felt as if they were alone in a different world.

"Sitting up here, I wonder how problems get so big." His voice was deep and husky and washed over Meg, filling her with his sadness.

"Maybe you and Travis should come up here and sit on the roof."

His gaze caught hers. "I was thinking about you and what you do."

"Were you?"

"I think Travis and I have come to a stalemate."

"Only if neither of you tries to move again."

"He doesn't want me around, Meg. He picks an argument every time we're together, as if he wants to drive me further away. I came to your presentation at school so he'd see I care about him. He made it clear he didn't want me there."

"It would help if you could see his point of view."

"Do you think I haven't tried?"

"I don't know."

Logan's jaw tensed, and his expression grew hard. "Well, I do know."

Meg had to say something she knew might make Logan angry, might make him less eager to be around her or talk with her. But she felt it needed to be said. "I think something is holding you away from Travis."

Logan was silent. And there was an anger in the silence that shook Meg's heart and the peace of the countryside.

In a fluid motion, Logan stood. He climbed onto the ladder and pinned her with a look that said she'd gone too far. "I'll hold the ladder for you as you come down."

"Logan…"

"Enough, Meg."

The words were terse, and Meg had the distinct feeling Logan wanted to say more but was refraining. Maybe that was the problem. He refrained too much. Maybe if he got it all out… But as he made his way to the ground, she didn't know if she dare suggest it. She didn't want to sever their bond of friendship, if she hadn't already. She should have kept quiet. She should have minded her own business. She shouldn't care as much as she already did.

She'd expected Logan to be striding away when she neared the last rung. But he continued to hold the ladder. His face was hard, etched with the anger she'd heard in his voice and sensed with her heart. If she didn't care, she could leave more unsaid.

She didn't know if she was pleading for herself as a young girl or Travis when she said, "He needs you, Logan. Don't turn your back on him. Show him you love him. Show him his words and actions hurt you. Don't just stoically accept—"

Logan's eyes darkened as he reached for her. She never thought to be afraid…not of Logan. When his mouth crushed hers, she fleetingly wondered if this was his way of shutting her up. It certainly was effective. Rational thought fled as his tongue parted her lips and thrust inside. The thrusts were rhythmic and deliberately arousing, and she could envision them mating in the same primal way. Logan was rigid and hard as he pressed against her. Was he trying to shock her?

She tore away, more affected than she wanted to admit. Holding on to the ladder instead of Logan, she almost felt hurt, almost felt... "You can't use me to soothe feelings you don't want to talk about. You can't use me to—"

"I wasn't using you for anything," he snapped. "I was trying to show you nothing is as simple as it seems. Not between me and Travis and not between me and you. Don't you get it yet, Meg? You can't fix everything with a few right words."

"No, you can't. You need to explore the feelings behind the words. Why can't you talk to Travis? Why can't you reach out to him? Why...?"

"Stop it, Meg. Don't you see that I don't have the answers? Solutions aren't as easy as adding a column of numbers."

"Have you honestly looked for the solution?"

A crow cawed. The quiet, which before had been restful, was now abrasive. Logan broke it. "If you have to ask that, then we really don't know each other at all, and maybe that kiss and the passion behind it is all that will ever be between us. I don't think this conversation is about me and Travis at all. I think it's your way of pushing me away, making me too uncomfortable to want to stay around. You don't have to push me away, Meg. If you don't want me here, all you have to do is say it."

She couldn't tell him to go, yet she couldn't ask him to stay. He was right. Nothing was simple anymore. "I don't know what to say."

"Neither do I, so maybe we'd better leave it at that. Tell Ned I'll be over tomorrow morning to work on the roof."

As Logan waited, she wanted to ask him to think about what she'd said and tell him she'd think about what he'd said. But she couldn't, and maybe that was another way of pushing him away.

Logan just arched his brows and cocked his head expectantly.

All she could manage was "I'll tell him to expect you."

Logan frowned and nodded, then walked to his car. Right before he opened his door, he gazed at her again.

Meg felt as if he could see right through her. She turned and walked to the house. Dealing with Logan had become as dangerous as being kidnapped by a terrorist. She had to figure out why.

Chapter Seven

The stones crunched under Meg's feet as she jogged back to the house. Breathing fast but feeling better than she had after tossing and turning all night, she slowed her jog to a walk, absorbing the sunshine, letting the heat beat through her, trying to forget about her confrontation with Logan last night. Jogging always gave her a sense of well-being—muscles working, blood flowing, adrenaline rushing. Logan's face appeared unbidden in front of her eyes. Yep, the adrenaline rushing. She remembered too well the thrill of it when Logan had kissed her...and touched her....

Lily had heard her roaming in the middle of the night when she'd finally gone to the kitchen for some milk, hoping it would make her sleepy. Her aunt had asked what was wrong. Meg had simply said, "I have too much time on my hands during the day, so I'm not sleepy at night.''

Lily hadn't bought it. She'd smiled and said, ''Maybe you have too much time on your hands at night.''

Meg's shock must have shown.

Her aunt's smile had spread into a grin, and she'd said gently, ''I always sleep better when your uncle is holding me.'' Then she'd disappeared down the hall without another word.

Meg did long for someone to hold her. Not just someone—Logan. She wished she could get the man off her mind. She wished she could forget his words. *You don't have to push me away, Meg. If you don't want me here, all you have to do is say it.*

She pushed away so she wouldn't get hurt. It wasn't his conclusion that had kept her awake most of the night; the truth of it had nudged her until it echoed too loudly to drown out.

Though Meg tried to rush inside and hurry up the stairs before Lily could continue their middle-of-the-night conversation, she only managed three steps when her aunt's voice stopped her. ''You had a phone call. Some office in Lynchburg. I put the number by the phone in the kitchen. The woman said she'd be there until noon.''

Meg glanced at the clock on the mantel. Ten. Logan would probably be here soon, and she'd rather not be anywhere around…at least not until she figured out a few things. But the call shouldn't take long.

Lily stood at the sink, coring apples as Meg made the call.

A receptionist answered and put Meg through to Victoria Lee.

"Ms. Lee, this is Meg Dawson returning your call."

"Miss Dawson, it is a pleasure to speak with you."

Meg guessed the cultured voice testified to more than one language in the woman's upbringing. "I'm sorry I don't recognize your name. Have we met?"

"No, we have not. A friend of mine sent me the article that appeared in the *Willow Valley Courier*. I made some calls and discovered you were taking time off and living in Willow Valley. I have a position I'd like you to consider. I run the Lee adoption service here in Lynchburg. We are an international adoption agency and are looking for a liaison who is fluent in many languages and could communicate with the officials and personnel in the countries we deal with as well as with the couples who want to adopt."

"You're offering me a job?"

"I understand this is quite different from the work you are used to. But I'd like to set up an interview with you if possible so we can discuss it. Please give me the time to show you the value in the work we do. Would that be agreeable to you?"

The offer took Meg completely by surprise. "Can you give me some time to think about it?"

"I'd rather give you the time *after* you give me the opportunity to present my offer. We will need to fill the position by February and have started our search early to find someone with the qualifications we desire. Can you come in Wednesday morning so we can discuss it?"

Meg had to smile at Victoria Lee's persistence. "All right, I can come in on Wednesday. What's your address?"

After Meg wrote down the address of the agency

and directions and ended the call, Lily studied her and asked, "Something to keep you busy?"

Meg told her aunt about Victoria Lee's job offer.

"What do you think?" Lily asked.

"I don't know. I've always loved my work."

"But something's keeping you from it."

Lily's perception shouldn't surprise Meg, but it did…often. "I've needed time to rest, to think."

"What's there to think about, honey? Unless you're thinking about not going back."

"Aunt Lily…"

Lily placed the apples on the cutting board, lined up in a row. "Would that be so terrible? Changing your mind about what you want to do?"

A loud meowing answered Lily before Meg could. Automatically Meg went to the screen door, opened it and picked up Leo. She cuddled the kitten in the crook of her arm. "It's not that simple. I have a life in Washington, an excellent reputation. I get paid well and I'm self-sufficient. I don't have to depend on anyone."

Lily dried her hands on a towel and pulled the flour canister toward her. "And why do you think changing your job would bother all that?"

Meg rubbed Leo's neck and heard him purr. "Maybe it wouldn't."

"Honey, there's nothing wrong with depending on someone. I know you're afraid to, I know Iris and Joe let you down over and over again. But that doesn't mean everyone will."

Meg went still. "This has nothing to do with Mother and Dad."

Her aunt faced her, concern and compassion in her

eyes. "I think it does. But that's something *you* have to think about."

Leo rubbed against Meg's hand. Reflexively, she cuddled and stroked him. "I'm going upstairs to change. And then I'm driving into town."

"Logan's coming."

"I know."

Lily didn't say a word, but Meg knew her aunt was thinking plenty. One tough decision at a time was enough.

"I really should get to work on the roof," Logan said as Lily set the apple dumpling in front of him.

"You need some nourishment before you start. You said you didn't have anything but coffee for breakfast."

He smiled at the woman who was so good at taking care of everyone. "That's the usual."

She shook her head. "You and Meg."

"Where is she?"

"Upstairs, taking a shower. She got an interesting call this morning. Some adoption agency offered her a job in Lynchburg."

He couldn't keep the question inside. "What did she say?"

"She's meeting with the woman on Wednesday."

Hope warming his heart, he dug into the apple dumpling. He shouldn't care what Meg decided. She was obviously running from more than him.

A few minutes later, Meg came hurrying into the kitchen, a kitten nestled in the crook of her arm. "Aunt Lily, I'm going to duck out now before…"

"Before I get here?" Logan asked, raising his head. His body responded to her appearance in coral cuffed shorts and a rib-knit T-shirt with a lace-up neckline. What he would like to do to that ribbon... If he knew what was good for him, he'd let her duck out and he'd get the roof started without distraction.

Lily interrupted the tense silence. "I have laundry to gather." With a knowing look at both of them, she headed for the stairs.

Meg's reluctance to be around Logan irritated him. "I told you before, if you want me to leave, all you have to do is say so."

Avoiding his gaze, she sat down in a chair across from him, the kitten on her lap. "I like you, Logan."

He leaned forward. "Then stop running away from me."

"I'm not running away from you any more than you're running away from Travis."

Anger erupted again, and he checked it. "Honest to God, Meg, don't you ever let up?"

"If we can't even talk about it..."

He pushed back his chair and stood. "Maybe that's the problem. You want to talk. I want to do something else." He couldn't keep the edge from his voice, or the tension of unfulfilled desire. "When you're ready to talk about that or, better yet, do something about it, I'll be on the roof."

The surprise on her face told him his bluntness had probably just ruined any chance he had. But his dreams were getting more vivid, his response to her more intense, every time he saw her. Maybe bluntness was what they both needed.

He left her sitting there, the kitten in her lap, her brown eyes wide and confused. He pulled in a deep breath and went into the backyard, looking forward to ripping off shingles.

* * *

Sweat dripped from Logan's brow as he straightened and stood on the garage roof. Impatiently he swiped the perspiration with his wristband. The sun beat down on him from its high-noon position. He needed something to drink. He also needed to have his head examined. If Meg had been skittish around him before, now she'd probably ignore him completely.

It had been years since he'd wanted a woman the way he wanted her. In fact, he couldn't ever remember a woman affecting him the way Meg did. He crossed to the ladder and climbed down. He needed a break from the sun and his thoughts. If he remembered correctly, a stream ran through Ned's property. Without bothering to grab his shirt, Logan headed toward the water.

As soon as he stepped into the tree line, he heard the slight breeze ruffling the leaves, the whistles of chickadees and the ripple of water over rocks. All he could think about was splashing his face in the cool water and letting the peace surround him.

The peace vanished when he stepped closer to the stream and saw Meg. Oblivious to everything around her, she waded on a large rock in the middle of the stream, dangling her hand in the water. He walked toward her because he couldn't walk away. Standing at the bank, he called her name.

She gazed up at him. Only about ten feet separated them, but he felt it was more like the width of the world. She gingerly stepped from rock to rock until she found her footing on the bank. "I come down here to think."

He asked what was foremost on his mind, guessing

it was foremost on hers. "Lily told me about your job offer. Are you considering staying here?"

She shook her head. "I can't."

"Why?"

"Because I wouldn't respect myself. I can't stay in Willow Valley because I'm afraid to go back."

"It's a damn good reason *not* to go back."

"I don't live my life that way. Just because I ignore a problem doesn't mean it will go away. I have to confront it to settle it."

Logan couldn't resist the vulnerability on her face, the honest way she faced life. He caressed her cheek, admiring Meg's strength and determination. Yet he wasn't sure either would bring her happiness. "Maybe we have to confront what's going on between us to settle it."

"We've done that."

Her breaths came faster, and he stroked her face again. "No, we haven't. We're resisting, pushing each other away so the sparks between us don't blaze out of control. Maybe we shouldn't be so afraid of the fire."

"Logan…"

He slipped his arm around her and bent closer. "Kiss me, Meg. As if you aren't afraid."

He thought she might back away. He thought what he'd said in the kitchen might make her angry. But she didn't look angry now. She looked as if she wanted to feel the fire as much as he did. His lips found hers, and the fire was the only thing that mattered.

Red-hot flames licked at him. As his tongue parted her lips, want and need rushed through him with such force and speed, he was hard and aching for satisfaction instantaneously. He'd always known runaway passion was dangerous. He'd never realized it would be so all consuming. Did Meg feel any of it? Could she deny it? Could she run from it?

Logan enclosed her tighter against him. She didn't protest; rather, she pressed her breasts against his chest and moaned in approval. He lifted her knit top and spread his fingers across her midriff. Her skin fascinated him. The satin softness of it. Everything about Meg fascinated him—her intelligence, her warmth, her genuine loveliness. He plunged his tongue deeper into her mouth—needing, searching, burning as he'd never burned before.

Meg had never played with fire. Caution had always guided most of her decisions. She collected information until her mind and heart united in deciding the best course for her. But now…here…caution floated away with the whistles of the chickadees. Logan's skin was hot, his chest hard, his scent intoxicating. And his touch created a longing inside her she couldn't begin to understand.

He pulled away and, when she protested, he came back to her again. His initial hunger transformed into teasing play, stoking her desire, making the longing become a living entity. He nibbled her bottom lip. She wanted more. He touched her bottom lip with his tongue. She wanted more. He slid his hands along the sides of her breasts, and she wanted so much more she couldn't comprehend the need.

Frustrated by her own need, not knowing what she wanted most—whether she wanted to touch him, or if she wanted him to touch her—she slid her hands up his chest, reveling in the texture of his skin, the curling hair between her fingers, the sheer masculine power of Logan. He groaned, and she kneaded his shoulders, loving the feel of him.

The tip of his tongue stroked against hers, then retreated. She chased him and found satisfaction in the deeper kiss. Logan knew what he was doing.

But did she?

She couldn't let fear keep her from living. But she couldn't let it keep her from working, either. If she didn't go back to her career, she'd feel like a quitter. She'd feel as if she failed. All her life, she'd felt as if she'd failed some test in her parents' eyes. She couldn't fail herself. She had to think about her future.

And Logan? She wanted to make love with him. The need was more than physical. But their situation was complicated enough.

And they were making it worse. She was making it worse by responding as if she was falling in love with him. Love. *No. She couldn't.*

She braced her hands on his chest and pushed away. His skin burned her, and she stuffed her hands in the pockets of her shorts to keep them safe...to keep her safe. Desire rippled through her until she almost lost her balance. But she spread her feet apart and closed her eyes, hoping the need would diminish, praying she was wrong about falling in love.

"Meg. Look at me." The authority in his voice vied with the huskiness of unfulfilled desire.

With a deep breath, she opened her eyes.

"What stopped you? What made the fear come back?"

"You. Me. What I have to do."

"You mean leaving Willow Valley."

"I mean going back to work."

He shook his head. "What drives you, Meg?" His gaze probed deep into her heart.

She reached inside for the reason she always confronted her fears. "It's not easy for a child to go to strange places, meet strange people and learn strange customs. But I did it over and over again. When I did, fear eventually subsided."

"Did your parents know you were afraid?"

"I hid it. I was afraid if they saw it, they wouldn't let me go with them."

"But you liked staying with Lily and Ned."

"Yes, but, Logan, they weren't my parents. I wanted to be with my parents. I wanted to make them proud."

His dark brows drew together. "So why did you choose to stay with Lily and Ned when you were older?"

Her voice softened. "Because by then, I knew Lily and Ned loved me. I'd figured out I could never earn my parents' love. I didn't stay because I was afraid to go. I stayed because I wanted to."

"So, if you're afraid of something, you feel you have to do it not to be afraid anymore?"

She nodded. "Yes."

He stood silent as the water rippled over the rocks and the leaves swished and the sun rose higher. "Are you afraid to make love with me?"

He'd caught her in a philosophical trap and he knew it. "That's not the same."

He grimaced. "Somehow I knew you'd say that." Walking to the edge of the bank, he gazed into the water.

Meg took a few more deep breaths wondering what would come next…wondering what *could* come next.

"I've been thinking about what you said...about something holding me back from Travis."

She approached him slowly.

"If it weren't for Travis, Shelley and I might never have gotten married." He stuffed his hands in his jeans as the water rippled and rays of sun danced like diamonds on the water. "We weren't right for each other. She hated me being a cop. When she got pregnant, she didn't want to get married. But I convinced her it was best. This was our child. I couldn't contemplate not bringing him into the world or giving him away. So I only saw one solution."

"What happened after Travis was born?"

"She resented me. The demands of an infant, a child. She was lenient with Travis. As he grew older, I had to counteract that. I believed he should have chores and be accountable for them—that kind of thing. We moved to Willow Valley because I thought it would help. I wouldn't be a 'cop' per se. Life would be slower paced." He shook his head. "I should have realized we'd never want the same things. But hindsight is always twenty-twenty."

Meg suspected there was more Logan wasn't telling her. "You've always loved your son."

He turned from the stream then and looked at her, the memories clouding his eyes. "Yes. But there was this tension between Shelley and me that seemed to grow each day. I didn't understand it until the night she died."

"What was it?"

The lines on his face deepened, and the muscle in his jaw worked. "It doesn't matter anymore. What matters is that Travis always saw me as the bad guy. I enforced discipline and rules. I made him take out the garbage. And too many nights, I wasn't there to be part of putting him to bed, taking him roller-skating, reading to him. I thought moving to Willow Valley would change that. But he was twelve by then.''

"Travis is a good kid, Logan."

"Maybe he is. But I'm not like you, Meg. I don't know how to nurture. Watching you with Manuel and Carmen's baby made me wonder how I ever thought I could be a good parent.''

She took a step closer to him. How she wanted to ease his pain. How she wanted to help him find a bond with his son. "You're being too hard on yourself.''

"No, I'm being realistic."

"It's never too late to learn or fix or start again. Not if two people are willing.''

"But Travis isn't willing."

"Logan…''

"I don't want to argue with you," he said evenly.

"What do you want?'' As soon as the question came out, she regretted it because she remembered their conversation in the kitchen.

Desire flashed in his eyes. Reaching out, he tenderly stroked her chin. "You know what I want.''

"Satisfying some physical need won't solve anything.''

"No, but we'd have a hell of a good time doing it.''

The blush crawled up her cheeks, but she didn't take her gaze from him. She couldn't deny the strength of the attraction between them. But she could keep a lid on hers, for both their sakes.

When she didn't respond to his comment, he asked, "Are you going back to the house?"

"In a little while."

"More wading?"

"It's peaceful here."

He nodded as if he understood.

About an hour later, Meg called to Logan from the back door. "Lunch."

He waved at her from the roof so she'd know he heard. She didn't go inside right away, but watched him from the doorway. He wondered what was going through her mind, if it was as arousing as what was going through his. She closed the door, and he walked to the ladder.

When he entered the kitchen, only Meg sat at the table sipping iced tea with the kitten sleeping in her lap. "Lily and Ned?" he asked.

"They've already eaten. Lily left a note saying she's resting and the sandwiches are in the refrigerator. I don't know what happened to Ned."

"I saw him heading to the side of the house with the pruning shears."

Meg waved to the plate of sandwiches on the table and the bowl of potato salad. "Help yourself."

Unfortunately she was talking about the food.

After washing his hands at the sink, he pulled out the chair across from her. Lifting the glass of iced tea, he drank half of it.

Meg refilled his glass from the pitcher.

The kitten meowed in disapproval as she woke him by changing position.

"What's your friend's name?"

"Leo. I thought he looked like a lion cub when I found him."

"You found him?"

"Out in the bushes one day, scared as could be. He was too little to have gotten here on his own. I think someone dropped him by the road, and he hid in the bushes."

"You care, Meg. Do you know what a valuable quality that is?"

She petted the kitten, soothing and caressing. "Whatever I know, I learned from Aunt Lily and Uncle Ned."

"Maybe. But I think some of it's innate. A magic touch that can't be bought or learned."

Raising her head, she fixed him with a probing stare. "You know what I think?"

He shifted on his chair. "I'm not sure I want to know."

"Well, I'll tell you anyway. You expect yourself to do everything right, best, the perfect way. Don't you think you're expecting too much?"

"I could ask you the same thing."

Scooping up the kitten, she stood and came around to him. "You talk about being realistic. Let's try it." Gently she set Leo in Logan's lap.

"What are you doing?"

She didn't answer.

The kitten padded from Logan's left thigh to his right, looked up and meowed.

"Now what?" Logan growled. "He'd rather be on your lap."

"I'm the interpreter, not you. He's saying he'd like you to pet him."

Logan frowned and lowered his hand to his lap.

Leo went to it and rubbed his head against Logan's thumb. When Logan gently rubbed the kitten's cheek, Leo licked his finger.

Logan chuckled. "What do you want? I'm sure Meg feeds you." He tore a tiny piece of cheese from the slice in his sandwich and held it on the pad of his thumb. Leo nibbled it into his mouth, then kept licking Logan's finger. When no more cheese was forthcoming, he rolled his head against Logan's palm.

"What do you feel, Logan?" Meg asked softly.

He felt protective of the small animal. The feeling came from the same source as his protective streak that ran deep for his son. Logan thought back to the night Travis was born. He remembered it as if it were yesterday. He'd offered his son his finger, and Travis had gripped it. The action might have been reflexive, but it had meant everything to Logan. He'd wanted to protect his son with a fierceness that remained through the years. But Travis had run away from him and his caring. It was obvious he'd failed not only as a husband, but as a father, too.

He lifted the kitten from his lap and held it out to Meg. "It doesn't matter."

She took Leo and cuddled him to her breast. "Yes, it does, Logan. You're a caring man."

"You haven't known me very long."

"I know enough."

And he knew if she kept looking at him like that, he'd kiss her again. "Before this conversation gets us both in trouble, I think we'd better eat lunch."

Shaking her head, she returned to her chair. "You and Travis are more alike than you know."

He didn't ask her what she meant, but picked up his sandwich.

Chapter Eight

Not knowing if her idea would cause trouble or make an important point, Meg rang Logan's doorbell late Sunday morning and shifted the wicker basket from her left hand to her right.

When Logan opened the door and saw her standing there, a slow smile spread across his face. "Are you inviting me on a picnic?"

"Not exactly. Can I come in?"

His smile faded, and he motioned her into the living room.

She slipped by him, her elbow brushing his stomach. Although he wore a T-shirt, she could vividly imagine his bare chest, the way his skin had felt under her hands, the texture of his hair. She was afraid too many impressions of Logan were burned into her mind forever. Pages of newspaper strayed across the couch as if Logan had been reading it when she'd rung the bell. The rest of the room was as orderly as she'd seen it before.

Carefully setting the wicker basket down in front of the coffee table, she knelt beside it. "I brought you a present."

"Some of Lily's apple dumplings?"

"Nope. Something a little more fun." She unlatched the basket, and before she could open the lid, Leo's head popped out. He took a look around and meowed.

Meg opened both sides of the basket. "I have a few more things in the car to bring in." Before Logan could recover from his surprise, she escaped out the door.

When she returned, Logan stood, hands on hips, watching the kitten as he meowed and rubbed against his sneaker. Logan's gaze found hers, and his scowl was fierce. "What do you think you're doing?"

"Giving you a gift, including supplies. Where do you want the litter box?" She set it on the floor, removing the sack of litter and the small cans of cat food.

"I don't want it anywhere. I don't want a cat."

"Why not?"

"Because I'm not here most of the time."

Leo clawed up Logan's jeans to his knee. He gently pulled the kitten away from the material and handed him to Meg. "Here. It found a good home with you."

She folded her arms and wouldn't accept the kitten. "He'll find a good life here with you." Ignoring the irritation emanating from Logan, she went to the kitchen. "Is it all right if I find a dish for water? I feed him one-third of a can three times a day." When

Logan didn't answer her, she opened a cupboard and found a dish on her own.

He strode into the kitchen after her, the kitten nestled in the crook of his arm. "What kind of point are you trying to make?"

"No point."

"You're a lousy liar."

She snapped the cupboard shut. "What point do you think I'm trying to make?"

"You think if I'm successful taking care of this cat, I won't feel so frustrated about Travis. The one has nothing to do with the other."

"Humor me. Try it for a week."

"I'm not here that much," he protested again.

"Cats are independent. They can occupy themselves. Give him some tinfoil balls, tie a string to the chair, he'll be happy. Oh, and don't forget to pet him. Between you and Travis, he'll get plenty of attention."

"Meg, read my lips. I don't want a cat."

Meg couldn't suppress her grin as she stood there watching Logan and Leo. Logan's combative stance and tone, as well as his annoyance, directly contradicted the picture of the kitten snuggled against his chest. "I knew he'd like you."

Logan swore, lifted Leo and set him on the floor.

Meg filled a saucer with water. "Should I put his dish by the table?" She didn't wait for him to answer, but set the saucer on the floor in an out-of-the-way spot by the wall. Leo came over to investigate. When she stood, Logan was right there, the intent to argue with her and win creasing his brow.

He hadn't shaved. Beard stubble darkened his jaw, and she longed to run her fingers along its outline.

His hair was rumpled as if he hadn't yet bothered to comb it or else he'd run his fingers through it many times. He looked rakish and altogether too sexy for her to stay in his house alone with him for very long.

"One week, Logan. Let Leo live here for a week before you make a decision."

He clasped her shoulders. "You are one exasperating woman."

Just the weight of his hands on her shoulders excited her, urged her to raise her lips to his for a kiss. But she knew better. Instead, she retorted, "And you are one very stubborn man. You really aren't even supposed to think about giving back a gift."

He slid his hands from her shoulders to her neck and rubbed his thumbs along her jaw. "*You* are a gift."

Her mouth went dry, her heart raced and everything inside her screamed for his kiss and his touch. "Don't be silly."

"What's silly is the two of us arguing about a cat when we could be doing something much more satisfying."

"Logan…"

"Tell me you don't want me to kiss you."

She could hardly catch her breath, but she managed to say, "I can't."

He tilted her chin up and stared deep into her eyes…into her heart. "I'm glad you came into my life. You've brought me light and smiles and passion I forgot I once had."

His low, murmured words aroused her as much as his hand on her face. She swayed toward him and his desire.

Every one of Logan's kisses was different. She

never knew what to expect. He didn't home in on her lips, but targeted the soft spot behind her ear. She wrapped her arms around his neck so she wouldn't fall.

She felt him smile against her neck, then he murmured, "You like that, don't you?"

"Yes."

He chuckled and kissed her there again. "I like a woman who knows her mind." He stroked down her back, cupped her bottom and brought her tight against him.

Not caring if she was acting wanton, she kissed his jaw and searched for his lips. Logan groaned deep in his throat when she found them. But he wouldn't let her kiss him. He pecked at her nose, softly kissed her cheek, drove her crazy with teasing nips that only made her want to kiss him more. Time stood still as she grabbed at his shoulders, aware of the bunched muscles under her hands, the passion stringing his body tighter and tighter. She could feel that same passion coiling inside her. With each heartbeat, she became more aware of her needs—to be treated, wanted and loved for herself, not for what she did or said or accomplished. Logan's desire for her opened a new world, more adventurous than traveling, more difficult than interpreting. It asked her to give more than her knowledge and talent. It asked her, no—demanded—that she give herself, all she was, maybe all she could be.

When Logan finally set his lips on hers and demanded to taste her, she accepted the demand because she wanted the satisfaction, too. Because when he tasted her, aroused her, consumed her, she could taste, arouse and consume him. Give and take. Equal to equal. Man to woman. Woman to man. She didn't have to worry about being good enough or pleasing him or responding too eagerly because Logan obviously understood her needs and answered them with his.

He slowed the darting of his tongue and hers, prolonging the strokes and prolonging the pleasure. Lost in the rocking of their bodies, the intensity of a kiss that was fast becoming too much to control, Meg heard a noise but didn't let it register. She didn't want anything to interfere; she didn't want...

A louder noise made Logan tear away. He swore under his breath, and Meg didn't understand until she heard someone say, "Not bad, Sheriff MacDonald. Do you give lessons?"

Meg vaguely recognized the voice. With Logan's arm still surrounding her, she opened her eyes. Travis stood in the living room with one of his friends, looking embarrassed and angry at the same time. He gave his friend a push. "Go back to my room. I'll be there in a minute."

Kyle didn't follow directions. "I'd rather stay here and watch."

The muscles in Logan's arm tightened, and so did his jaw. "You know you're not welcome here, Kyle."

"That was before Travis took off. I thought maybe you'd changed your mind."

Travis gave Kyle a "keep quiet" look and challenged his father. "He's my friend. I want him here."

"And I want you to stay out of trouble. If you're with him, you won't."

"I don't pick your friends. You don't get to pick mine."

Neither of the MacDonalds was about to back

down. Meg thought about intervening, but before she could, Leo darted into the living room and clawed his way onto the sofa.

Travis looked at the kitten. "What's that?"

Meg smiled and stepped away from Logan's arm. "That's your new housemate. Think you can take good care of him?"

Travis shrugged. "Yeah, I guess so." He turned back to Logan. "Look, Dad. Kyle and I can listen to a new CD here or we can go over to his place. It's your call."

Meg knew Logan hated being backed into a corner.

His voice was rough when he finally said, "All right. You can stay here. But I'm warning you both, stay on the straight and narrow or I'll come down on you so fast your heads will spin."

Kyle saluted Logan with a smile. "Yes, sir."

Travis gave his friend a vigorous shove. "Go. Before you get us both thrown in jail."

Logan watched the boys take off down the hall. "I don't trust Kyle. Not for a minute. I picked him up for shoplifting last year. Before Travis ran off, I caught the two of them drinking."

"Travis must see something he likes in Kyle."

Logan shook his head. "Kyle's dad left when he was ten. His mom's having a hard time making ends meet."

"Maybe Travis senses a loneliness in Kyle that he feels. Losing a parent is tough."

"I never thought of it that way."

Meg crossed to the couch. Now that she and Logan were alone again, she felt awkward about their kiss. "Do you think Kyle will spread around what he saw?"

Logan followed her. "Do you mind if he does?"

She petted Leo, who'd fallen asleep on the couch. "It won't affect me. I don't live here. You do."

"I don't give a damn about what anyone says. Why should I?"

"No, I guess you wouldn't. Things like that enhance a man's reputation."

He took her by the arm. "I don't have a reputation. Not for that. Between grieving, keeping Travis in line and working, I haven't had time for much else."

"There hasn't been anyone since Shelley?"

"No."

"Not even—?"

"Anything casual? I know better. What about you?"

She realized now how insulting the question sounded. Logan wasn't the type of man to take anything casually. "I'm sorry I asked. I…"

His voice was husky when he responded, "You can ask me anything you want. That doesn't mean I'll answer, but you can ask."

The two sides of Logan fascinated her. One side was hard and demanding; the other was compassionate and gentle. She'd guess the one protected the other. "I'd better go."

"So Leo and I can get to know each other better?"

She smiled and walked to the door. "Something like that." Opening the door, she shot over her shoulder, "One more thing, Leo likes to sleep with someone. So you might find him nestled at your feet in the morning."

Behind her, she heard Logan grumble, "That'll be the day." Thinking about being anywhere near Logan's bed tempted her to stay rather than leave. It was much safer to go back to Aunt Lily's and help her make lunch.

Meg sat on the porch with Lily and Ned on Tuesday evening. When the phone rang, she automatically hopped up, said, "I'll get it" and ran into the house so her aunt and uncle didn't have to jump up.

In the kitchen, she plucked the receiver from its cradle. "Hello."

"I have a bone to pick with you."

Logan's deep voice rolled through her like thunder at midnight. "And what would that be?"

"There's a furry little animal at my house who thinks he owns the place. He claws up the curtains like they're ladders made for him to get to the window."

"You'll have to teach him he can't do that."

"Which method do you propose I try? Lifting him off each time he does it and telling him no, distracting him or yelling? None of them work."

She muffled a giggle.

"I heard that," he scolded.

"You could fill a spray bottle with water and give him a little spritz each time. That should do it."

"You're serious."

"Very serious."

He sighed. "I suppose you also have a remedy for the scratch marks he makes on the furniture when he can't quite get where he wants to go."

"Logan, what are you doing to Leo? He was perfectly behaved when he lived here."

"I'll just bet he was. That's probably why you gave him away."

"Are you questioning my motives?" she teased, thinking he was protesting his dismay just a mite too forcefully.

"No, I'm just questioning what spell you cast over me to get me to agree to keeping him here."

"No spell. Honest."

Logan's voice lowered. "You know you never answered my question."

"Which question?"

"Is there someone special waiting for you in D.C.? Or anywhere else, for that matter?"

"No."

"Why not?"

"Because I tried it once and was very disappointed."

"Tell me."

"Logan…"

"Meg, I want to know. Someone as intelligent and pretty as you could have several special someones."

"He was a journalist. His career was more important than I was."

"According to you or according to him?"

The same anger she'd once felt resurfaced. "I was a convenience, not a partner. If a story broke while we were making love, he had his clothes on faster than he could say goodbye. And when he was out of sight, I was out of his mind. I deserve better."

"Yes, you do." After a long pause, Logan finally said, "I've never been kissed by a woman the way you kiss me. So I can't help but wish you'd be here longer than Thanksgiving."

His words scared her and excited her.

"Meg?" he asked.

"Yes?"

"I'll be over Saturday to finish the roof. Will you be there?"

"Where else would I be?"

"Avoiding me."

Making a decision, she said softly, "I won't avoid you."

"Good. I'll see you then."

When Meg hung up the phone, she smiled. She was looking forward to Saturday.

The following morning, Meg sat in Victoria Lee's office, which resembled professional offices that Meg had seen all over the world with its wood, quality fabrics and computer system. But Victoria Lee *was* her office. Her beautiful, long black hair, her poise, the culture in her voice impressed Meg. So did her forthrightness.

"We always need more help. We have two psychologists on staff who help parents and children in transition. We have two secretaries who set up appointments, take phone calls and try to keep up with the paperwork and copying."

"Does your liaison travel?"

"Now and then. But these days, most of the work is done by phone and fax. It's not a glamorous job. Most of it consists of red tape and bureaucracy. But you would meet with the parents and children, and I can assure you the work is rewarding."

"I imagine it is."

"But you are not ready to commit yourself."

"Miss Lee...."

"'Victoria,' please."

"Victoria, I like the work I do now. At least, I used to."

Victoria's eyes were filled with a wisdom beyond her thirty-some years. "But the experience you went through has given you doubts."

"Not doubts exactly. The point is I'm not going to know how I feel about going back until I'm back. Do you understand?"

She nodded. "Completely. I just don't want you to give me a definite no. I've checked into your background. I know your skills and your reputation. So I wondered if you would consider another option for the time being."

"Such as?"

"As I said, we always need help. How would you feel about putting in some time here, seeing how we work?"

"Could I volunteer?" Time was beginning to lie heavy on Meg's hands. Her energy level was increasing every day, and helping Lily around the house just wasn't enough.

"If you wish, though I'd feel as if we were taking advantage of you."

"No, you wouldn't be. It would give me something worthwhile to do with my time."

Victoria smiled. "That would be fine with me. Why don't you work out a schedule and call me. We'll go from there."

Meg felt good about this meeting, about Victoria Lee's agency, about her decision to help. Working would make her feel useful again.

Meg stood at the bottom of the ladder propped against the garage, a glass of lemonade in hand. Shading her eyes with her hand against the mid afternoon sun, she called up to Logan, "Would you like something cold to drink?"

Logan carefully made his way toward Meg and descended the ladder. His hair had been tossed by the breeze. He wore a shirt today, but he'd unfastened the buttons. The flaps lay on either side of his belt buckle. She couldn't keep her gaze from following the line of dark hair under the snap of his jeans.

"Would you like to touch it?"

His question held a sexy rasp that snapped her eyes to his. She felt the heat crawl into her cheeks and she felt like fanning herself.

"Sorry. I couldn't resist," he said, his smile sly.

He didn't look one bit sorry. "How's Leo?"

Logan tapped her nose. "You're changing the subject."

She tried to keep her expression bland, the idea of touching Logan a passing fancy. "Just checking to see if my little friend has a permanent home."

Logan took the glass of lemonade from her, lifted it to his lips and drank it. The strong muscles of his neck, the stubborn line of his jaw, drew her gaze as easily as the hair on his chest and his flat stomach. When he finished, he handed her the glass. "Your little friend is a pain in the butt. But I'm getting used to him. We have a deal. If he doesn't pounce on the morning paper while I'm trying to read it, I let him lick my cereal bowl."

Meg laughed. "And he understands this deal?"

Logan grinned. "Sure does."

"And where does he sleep?"

"Anywhere he wants. But if you mean at night, I've caught him curled up with Travis."

Meg's smile grew broader.

"Stop looking so smug or I'll have to kiss you, and that's not a good idea here in broad daylight. Considering what happened last time."

"Did Travis say anything?"

"No. But then, he doesn't say much. He goes to school, closets himself in his room in the evenings and stays out till curfew on weekends."

She could see Logan wanted more from his son but didn't know how to go about getting it.

"Speaking of curfews, how would you like to break a few and go dining and dancing with me tonight?" he suggested.

"Tonight?"

"Don't tell me you need more than an afternoon to get ready, because I won't believe it."

"What if I tell you I don't have a thing to wear?"

He arched his brows, and his jaw tensed. "You might as well tell me you'd rather not go."

"Logan, I'm not turning you down. I'm serious."

He stepped closer and pushed her hair behind her ear. "I want to take you dancing and hold you in my arms. For starters."

If she went tonight, she was agreeing to let him into her life. If she went tonight... "I could go shopping at Sally's Boutique this afternoon."

"Could?"

The hope in his voice as well as the desire in his eyes encouraged her to make the decision. "I will. What time should I be ready?"

"Seven?"

"Seven's fine. I'll see you then." She turned toward the house.

But Logan's voice stopped her. "Meg, I don't care what you wear."

One look into his eyes told her he'd prefer if she wore nothing at all. She hurried to the house, her cheeks hot, her hands trembling.

Meg had seen lots of men in suits, probably more than she could ever count. But Logan in a suit was a sight to behold. When she opened the door to him, he filled the doorway—broad shoulders in a charcoal jacket, long legs seemingly even longer in the pleated dress slacks. The steel gray shirt underneath looked like silk, and the gray, white and black tie was perfectly knotted. Despite the *GQ* look, he oozed the same sensual masculine appeal as when he wore his uniform or jeans.

Fingering her Aunt Lily's pearls in her ears, she opened the screen door.

Logan stepped inside. His green eyes glinted with golden sparks in the dim foyer light. "You might need a jacket...or something."

His gaze lingered on her bare shoulders. The black halter dress that she'd bought at Sally's with its wide cummerbund waist and straight skirt was a basic asset to her wardrobe. She could wear it out to dinner or to an embassy reception. Picking up a black fringed shawl folded over the banister, she asked, "Will this do?"

He took it from her and unfolded it. "Let me help you."

She turned her back to him.

Logan carefully laid it over her shoulders, then bent close to her ear. "I like your hair like this."

His breath at her cheek, his lips so close to her skin, escalated the anticipation inside her to an all-time high. She closed her eyes and tried to calm all the nerves that were rioting out of control.

He fingered a tendril of hair that had escaped the upswept hairdo. "You smell like Lily's rose garden after nightfall."

Before she did something impulsive like turning around and kissing him without caring what he thought about it, she took a deep breath.

He placed a teasing kiss on the nape of her neck and asked, "Are you ready?"

Hoping she wasn't acting like a teenager, knowing she might get hurt, she faced him and said, "I'm ready."

His slow, sexy smile didn't reassure her, but made her heart pound faster.

Logan drove to the Garden, the only choice for dining and dancing in Willow Valley. He had a vision of how he expected this night to end, although he hadn't worked out the practicalities. It was ironic that two adults couldn't find a place to spend time alone, but with Travis at home and Lily and Ned watching over Meg, they might have to rent a hotel room. The problem was he couldn't do that without everyone in Willow Valley gossiping about it.

Lily and Ned's barn was looking better and better.

He pulled into the parking lot of the restaurant and switched off the ignition. Meg's silence indicated her uncertainty about being with him. "Having second thoughts?"

She smiled. "No. Just a bit jittery for our first public appearance. You know people are going to talk."

"About two friends having a quiet dinner together?"

Meg's pretty brows arched.

He took her hand and stroked her knuckles. "I don't care about rumors or what people say."

"I was thinking about Travis and how he might feel."

Logan sighed and stared out the windshield. "Just for tonight, let's not discuss Travis, okay?" He turned and tried to see her expression in the shadows. "Let's just concentrate on us."

Meg reached over and laid her hand on his thigh. The simple overture revved him up until all he thought about was hauling her into his arms and kissing her until she begged him to bury himself in her. But he knew he had to take tonight slowly...if it killed him.

He picked up her hand and brought it to his lips. When he kissed her palm, he felt her tremble. This was going to be one very long, torturous dinner.

Logan learned several things about Meg while they ate. She didn't rush anything—not drinking her wine, not cutting her chicken *cordon bleu,* not chewing and savoring each bite. She was a careful person, but she knew how to enjoy herself, she knew how to relax, she knew how to drive him crazy from wanting her by simply being herself.

The table's breadth separated them, and he hated the distance. Yet the brush of his knee against hers, the answering expectation in her eyes, aroused him as completely as holding her in his arms.

They didn't talk much. They gazed into each other's eyes a lot. Every once in a while, she gave him a shy smile, and he stroked her hand. This kind of foreplay was new to him and erotic as hell.

The four-piece orchestra began playing as they sipped coffee. Finally Logan couldn't stand sitting across from Meg when he wanted to feel her pressed against him. He pushed back his chair, stood and held out his hand to her. "C'mon. Let's dance."

She placed her hand in his with a smile that could make a stormy sky turn blue. Logan protectively curved his arm around her and led her to the dance floor.

Taking Meg in his arms seemed as natural as breathing. At first he left a few inches between them. Her brown eyes locked to his were enough. But slowly, with each heartbeat, he drew her closer…too close to dance, almost too close to breathe.

Her hand slipped out of his, and she linked her arms around his neck. He caressed her bare back, feeling the tremors course through her. Smiling, he rested his jaw against her temple, savoring the response of a beautiful woman in his arms.

After Travis was born, sex had been a duty to Shelley, a duty she'd used for her own benefit. She'd used her pregnancy and their hasty marriage as grounds to keep her distance. And he'd been a fool to believe commitment could stand in for feelings that had never matured or deepened. As always, Logan tried to push the guilt away and didn't succeed.

Meg released a soft sigh, and her breasts pushed against his chest. The lightning-quick response of his body had to be obvious. But she didn't pull away.

He brought his hand to the back of her neck and rubbed in a small circle. Lifting her chin, she waited.

Bending his head, he kissed her. The music wound about them, her perfume intoxicated him and her taste aroused him. They were the only two people in the world, and all he could think about—

Beep, beep…beep, beep.

Beep, beep...beep, beep.

Meg pulled back.

Logan swore. "I told Cal not to page me unless he had an emergency. I have to call."

He escorted Meg to their table, then went to the phone at the reception desk. "Cal? This had better be good. What's going on?"

"Someone broke into the high school. You'd better get over here."

Logan looked over at the table where Meg sat. So much for the night he'd planned. Damn. He had to shut down his libido and wake up his sixth sense instead of his baser ones. "I'll be there in fifteen minutes. Don't touch anything."

"I know better than that."

"Sorry, Cal. I'll get there as soon as I can."

"You droppin' Meg Dawson off first?"

Logan sighed. He wasn't going to even ask how his deputy knew. There were few secrets in Willow Valley. "Yes, I am."

He hung up and crossed to Meg. Usually he liked his work. Usually, he didn't hesitate to go when duty called. But tonight *duty* was a four-letter word he'd rather wipe from his vocabulary.

Chapter Nine

An hour later, Logan stood in the principal's office, waiting for Michael Holden to answer his question.

Michael ran his hand through his brown hair. "The change is gone from the cafeteria office. Fifty dollars. The individual classrooms don't seem to have anything missing. Do you want me to call the teachers tomorrow and have them come in and check?"

Logan surveyed Michael's office for the tenth time, interested in anything that might look suspicious or out of place. "That would probably be a good idea. What about in here?"

"I keep it locked—too much confidential information."

Logan peered into the full waste can. "When does the janitor clean?"

"Early Monday morning while I'm in the building."

Logan respected the way Michael ran the school. "But he cleans the rest of the school on Saturday?"

"That's right."

Logan rubbed his chin. "From what I can tell, I think the thief snuck in this afternoon while the janitor was cleaning. Mrs. Konnecut saw someone leaving by the west door, and that's why she called us."

"Did she recognize who it was?"

"No. And she keeps track of everything and everyone she can. But her sight is failing. Cal's at her place now. I'm going to stop there to question her, too, and to see if I can pick up any more details. Do you have any ideas who broke in?"

"Not offhand. But I'll circulate Monday and have the teachers keep their ears open. If someone did it for a prank or a dare, he'll brag."

"No one tampered with your office door."

"And that means...?" Michael asked.

"I think it means the thief thought your office would be too much trouble. He wanted easy pickings and he probably knew where to get them."

Logan walked out into the main office area and narrowed his eyes, staring at the computer on the secretary's desk, the long counter where students stood to wait for information or directions. He'd gone over everything at least ten times.

Michael followed, going behind the counter and looking over the area again.

"I'll come in tomorrow and talk to your teachers. There's nothing more we can do here now," Logan decided.

Michael crossed to the door and switched off the light, then walked with Logan down the hall. "The school is updated but old. I've debated about getting an estimate on a security system, but it's never been necessary. But after this break-in, I'm sure someone will bring it before the board.''

"I hate to see Willow Valley change, but we're getting bigger. Now some people do lock their doors. It's reality.'' Logan checked his watch. Eleven o'clock. Even if he didn't have to interview Mrs. Konnecut, it was too late to pick up the evening where he and Meg had left off.

Michael locked the front door of the school. ''Cal said you and Meg Dawson were having dinner when he paged you.''

Logan swore. ''I might as well have taken out an ad. I'd like to know where Cal found out in the first place.''

Michael grinned. ''It seems a friend of his wife talked to Meg when she was buying a dress for the occasion.''

Logan shook his head.

"So you and Meg are going out now?'' Michael asked, his interest obviously more than casual.

"That's my intention,'' Logan responded, jealousy pricking at him. He had no doubt if he was out of the picture, Holden would make a move of his own.

Michael shrugged. ''Just checking. She's an intriguing woman.''

"That she is.'' Logan wasn't about to discuss anything about himself and Meg.

The two men descended the steps and went to their cars. Logan called to Michael, ''After I stop at Mrs. Konnecut's, I'm going to the office to file a report. If you think of anything else you think I need to know, I'll be there.''

Michael opened his car door. ''Good luck.''

"With Mrs. Konnecut?"

"With Mrs. Konnecut and with Meg."

Logan didn't quite know what to say to that, so he got into his car. He couldn't ever remember a rival wishing him good luck. Either Michael Holden was a genuinely nice guy or a man to watch. Logan decided he'd better watch.

Only a few minutes of daylight remained when Meg saw Logan's car coming down the lane. He'd dropped her off last night with a quick but thoroughly devastating goodbye kiss that she'd felt long after he'd gone. The evening had been exciting and perfect up until the moment when Logan's pager had beeped. She could read his disappointment as they'd hastily ended their date as much as she could feel her own.

Yet maybe Providence had intervened. Maybe she wasn't supposed to get involved with Logan any more than she already was.

"Looks like you've got company," Ned remarked with a sly wink as he hung a lawn chair on a hook in the garage. When he'd told her he wanted to clean out and straighten up, she'd offered to help to keep herself busy. Her uncle added, "We can finish this tomorrow."

"Maybe Logan's here to visit you and Lily."

Her uncle chucked her under the chin. "You're a lot younger and prettier than we are. I don't think there's any doubt as to who he's here to see. But Lily and I will be inside if you two younger folks need the wisdom of a few years." Ned waved to Logan as he walked toward the back door.

Meg rounded her uncle's car and met Logan at the path to the house.

She smiled.

He smiled.

Then he pulled her into his arms for a hug. "Do you know how difficult it was to leave you last night?"

"I can guess."

He rubbed his chin against the top of her head. "I was tied up all day today at the school."

Leaning back in his arms, she asked, "Did you find out anything more?"

"Not much. Nothing else was missing. Mrs. Konnecut thinks she saw a blond teenager in jeans, but she admits her cataracts make her unsure."

"You don't have much to go on."

"No, but Michael thinks scuttlebutt will produce information."

"The kids respect him. If anyone knows anything, they might tell him outright."

Logan shook his head. "They won't snitch on each other. Not at that age. It's their code of honor."

Silence fell between them. Logan's gaze left hers, drifted over her nose, settled on her lips. "What do you think of Michael Holden?"

It was the last question she expected. With a shrug, she said, "Michael is—"

"Meg! Logan! Come here quick. Something's wrong with Lily," Ned yelled from the porch, waving his arms.

Meg and Logan both took off at a run. Logan got to Lily first. The older woman was sitting on the sofa, as pale as the white doily on the coffee table. Perspiration stood on her forehead, and she clutched her chest.

Logan helped Lily stretch out on the sofa. Pulling

the afghan from the back, he covered her with it. Then he said to Meg, ''Open her collar. I'm going to make sure the rescue squad is at home base. If not, I'll take her to the hospital myself.''

Ned stood by, helpless, his face stricken, as Logan made the call. Afterward he slammed down the phone and crouched down beside Meg's aunt. ''Hold on, Lily. They'll be here in about four minutes.''

It was the longest four minutes of Meg's life. She and Logan encouraged Lily, making her as comfortable as possible as Ned held her hand. Logan went outside when he heard the siren. In a matter of minutes, paramedics transported Lily to the rescue van. Logan drove Ned and Meg to the hospital in Lynchburg.

After what seemed like an eternity in the waiting area of the emergency room, Ned dropped his head into his hands. ''Meg, what am I going to do if something happens to her? She's my life!''

Meg laid a comforting hand on her uncle's shoulder although her fears mirrored his. She couldn't imagine life without her aunt. ''She's a fighter. You know that. Heart attacks don't have to be fatal. There's so much medicine can do now.''

Logan had been calm and collected since Ned had called to him. He stoically sat next to Meg, waiting with them. Abruptly he stood. ''I'll see what I can find out. Flashing a badge might help.'' He strode off before Meg could thank him.

When he returned, he said, ''They've taken her up to the coronary-care unit. Doc Jacobs is already up there.''

Meg felt tears prick her eyes. ''Did you call him?''

"From my car after the paramedics arrived. I thought a friendly face might help."

Trying to blink the tears away, Meg said, "Thank you."

Logan curved his arm around her shoulders. "Let's go upstairs."

A nurse motioned Ned and Meg to a small private waiting area. Doc Jacobs stood by the sofa.

Logan said, "I'll wait outside."

Meg took his hand. "I'd like you to stay, but it's up to you."

He rubbed his thumb across the top of her knuckles. "Whatever you want."

Doc Jacobs cleared his throat. "I spoke to the cardiologist. He was called back to the emergency room. He'll be glad to talk to you later if you'd like." The doctor gestured to the sofa. "Why don't we sit?"

Ned sat but said, "Just tell us, Doc."

Logan guided Meg to the cushion beside her uncle.

"Lily did have a heart attack, but we believe the damage is minimal. We are, of course, going to watch her very closely, especially the next twenty-four hours. She is stabilized for now, and I'm hoping that status won't change. But the human body is unpredictable. The cardiologist wants to wait until tomorrow before he makes a decision about further tests."

"Will she have to have a heart bypass? You've got to do everything you can...."

Compassion glowed in Doc's eyes. "We *are* doing everything possible. And we're taking good care of her. You can go in to see her, but only for fifteen minutes. I'll be able to answer your questions better tomorrow, and so will the cardiologist. I want you to stay calm so Lily stays calm. Understand?''

Both Ned and Meg nodded.

''All right. Then let's go tell her to rest so she doesn't think she's the one who has to take care of everyone else.''

Meg and Ned followed Doc to the cubicle where her aunt lay. After kissing Lily, holding her hand for a few minutes and murmuring hopeful thoughts, Meg said to her uncle, ''I'll let you spend the rest of the time alone with her.''

Meg stepped outside the cubicle and immediately started shivering. Winding her arms around herself, she put one foot in front of the other and walked toward the waiting area. She stopped inside the door and leaned against the wall.

Logan stood at the window, looking out but not seeing. He recognized the tightness in his gut as the worry that had haunted him all the days he hadn't known Travis's whereabouts. Lily and Ned were as integral to Willow Valley as the World War II monument in the park, as Gibson's Grocery, as the willow trees that had given the town its name. Logan knew nothing in life was permanent. His years as a cop in Philadelphia, Shelley's pregnancy and death, Travis running away, had proved to him again and again that life could turn on a dime.

But somehow the stability of his life in Willow Valley was connected to the people who lived there. And to think of Willow Valley without Lily...

He heard footsteps and turned in time to see Meg sag against the wall. Without a moment's hesitation, he hurried to her and enfolded her in his arms. ''Has something happened?''

She shook her head against his shoulders. Her breathing was uneven, and he knew shock had set in. Stroking her hair, he said, "Let it out, Meg. It's okay. Just let it out."

When sobs shook her, he held her tight.

He couldn't tell her everything would be better in the morning, because he didn't know if it would. So he offered her his physical strength, a shelter for the moment, and hoped that was enough.

Finally, she raised her gaze to his. "I'm sorry."

"There's nothing to apologize for."

"But I have to be strong for them. I can't—"

"You *are* strong. You've had a shock and you're afraid of losing someone important to you." He wiped the tears from her cheek and tugged her toward the sofa. Keeping his arm around her shoulders, he sat with her and waited, never before feeling so protective about a woman.

By the time Ned returned, Meg had composed herself. The straightening of her spine, the squaring of her shoulders, signaled her dependence on Logan for support was about to end.

When Ned came in, she immediately went to him and hugged him. "She's going to be all right. She has to."

He nodded and swiped at the moisture in his eyes. "I'm staying here tonight. Why don't you let Logan take you home?"

"No, I'm staying here with you."

Logan took a deep breath, knowing he was about to fight an uphill battle. "Now, wait a minute. Both of you. How are you going to take care of Lily if you get run-down?"

"Logan, we don't want to be a half hour away," Meg explained.

He offered a solution. "There's a motel—"

"I'm staying right here," Ned said stubbornly.

"And I'm staying with him," his niece agreed.

"You two are a pair."

Ned put his arm around Meg's shoulders. "Family has to stick together."

Logan shook his head. "All right. But at least let me get you some pillows and blankets."

Meg smiled weakly and took Logan's hand. "Those we'll accept."

Logan looked at Ned's arm around Meg, her hand entwined with his, and he felt Lily's presence though physically she lay in another room. He experienced a connection with all of them, a connection he'd really never felt before. Suddenly he had the urge to include Travis in the circle. But he didn't know how.

The sun hadn't yet broken the horizon when Logan took the elevator to the coronary-care unit the following morning. When he entered the waiting room, he found Ned stretched out on the long sofa and Meg curled up on the shorter one. She lay with her hands tucked under her cheek, her elbows close to her body as if she were cold.

Logan set the carrier of coffee, juice and food he'd bought on the low table littered with magazines. Then he pulled Meg's blanket up to her chin, annoyed with himself for thinking about touching her creamy skin and kissing her pink lips when she obviously needed attention of another kind. This was not the time to think about steamy nights, long, wet kisses and satisfaction of his physical needs. Except he couldn't help imagining it and longing for it.

When he smoothed the blanket under her chin, her eyes opened. She propped up on an elbow, trying to orient herself.

Logan crouched down beside her. "Hi, there. Did you get much sleep?"

She smiled. "I'm used to sleeping in strange places. Though usually they're hotel rooms."

He couldn't resist leaning forward and sealing his lips to hers. He meant it as a light, caring gesture, but it took on a life of its own.

Kissing Meg took him on an adventure of self-discovery. He never knew he could need so much, or expect so much, or want something so elusive that the sensation almost terrified him. Even here, kissing her on a waiting-room couch, time stopped, the universe spun and dawn broke through the black night. She'd brought light into his life…and forgotten passion.

After breaking away, he tenderly caressed her cheek.

She ran a hand through her hair and sat up. "I'm glad Uncle Ned finally fell asleep. The doctor let him sit with Aunt Lily through some of last night. Those two can't bear to be separated from each other."

"I checked at the desk. Your aunt is sleeping comfortably." He lifted the box from the coffee table. "So how about a little nourishment?"

She wrinkled her nose as if eating was an abhorrent thought.

"Come on. I have a few fast-food breakfast sandwiches and doughnuts."

She looked at the waxy bag with a little more interest.

"Chocolate honey glazed?"

Logan laughed. "Ah-hah. I've discovered the woman's weakness."

"Addiction. I rarely turn down chocolate."

He opened the bag and lifted out the chocolate doughnut and handed it to her. "I'll remember that."

Meg couldn't remember a man ever bringing her breakfast. Logan was dressed in his uniform, his dark brown shirt and tan slacks looking crisp and pressed. "Thank you."

"For stopping for coffee?"

"No. For being here. Last night. This morning. I don't know what's going to happen but..." Her voice caught.

"Hopefully your aunt is going to recover, and life will go on. Will this change your plans for returning to D.C.?"

"I don't know. I'll have to wait and see."

Logan's jaw tightened. He picked up one of the coffees, flipped off the lid and took a few sips. Then he capped it again. "I have to get going. I told Michael I'd drop by the school. My presence might shake up whoever stole the money. I don't want anything worse to happen."

"Worse?"

"If this was a prank, that's one thing. But if someone *needs* money, the crime could escalate. I don't want that to happen. So I'll probably be giving a few lectures on solving problems by looking at all the options rather than taking the easiest one."

"Have you talked to Travis about what happened?"

"He was too occupied with a new CD and headphones."

"Does he know you're going into school today?"

"No. And he's not going to like it, but he'll have to live with it. Call me if there's any news about Lily. They can page me."

Logan seemed to have distanced himself. Because of talk of her leaving? Yet he knew she couldn't stay. She was already making lists, preparing herself to get back into circulation. The reception for the Native American Museum Fund in three weeks would be the perfect opportunity. "The cardiologist said he'd be here around eight. We should know more then. I'll call you."

Logan studied her for a few moments, and she felt self-conscious. What was he thinking? What was he feeling? More than desire?

He nodded to the doughnut. "Don't forget to eat."

"I won't."

He left then, and she felt...alone.

The late-morning sun shone on Meg and Lily as they sat on the front porch two weeks later. Meg examined her aunt's face, looking for telltale signs of fatigue or overexertion.

"Uncle Ned will be out here in five minutes to check if you're getting chilled. Are you sure you don't want a sweater?"

Lily frowned. "I love that man dearly, but he's driving me crazy."

Meg chuckled. "You gave us quite a scare."

"I know, but I'm very fortunate. If I take the heart attack as a wake-up call, I can be healthier than before."

The cardiologist had kept Lily in the hospital for a week. At the end of that time, he'd ordered a stress test. The results were encouraging. He'd also ordered a nutritionist to counsel Lily and a cardiac-rehab specialist to explain the types of exercise that would benefit her the most. But life-style changes never came easily.

"Uncle Ned seems to like the new diet."

"Don't you try to pull the wool over my eyes, young lady. He might not mind eating turkey instead of roast beef, but he misses his sweets. I know he snuck off to the bakery yesterday."

"And how do you know that?" Her aunt was right, but Meg felt a certain loyalty toward protecting them both.

"Because when he came home, he had powdered sugar on his shirt!"

Meg laughed. "Uncle Ned should know after all these years he can't hide anything from you."

"What he should know is that he shouldn't try." Her aunt pointed to the lane. "Look who's coming."

Meg didn't have to look. She knew the sound of the sedan's tires on the gravel. The truth was she was perturbed with Logan yet had no right to be. She'd called him from the hospital the day after Lily had been admitted to tell him her aunt's condition. He'd called and spoken to Ned twice since then, not asking for Meg. Meg had decided she wasn't about to call him.

Logan mounted the porch stairs, a bouquet of flowers in his arms. After presenting them to Lily, he sat on the top porch step. "How are you feeling?"

"Fine. But nobody will believe me," she grumbled as she smelled the flowers.

Logan grinned. "You have lots of people who care about you. Let them pamper you a little."

"They're pampering me until I'm suffocating." She pointed to her niece. "This one, for instance, thinks she has to cook and clean and do all the laundry. I'm going to have to get a note from my doctor so she'll let me load the washing machine! She even postponed volunteering at the adoption agency. I told her she's going tomorrow morning if I have to push her out."

Meg shook her finger at her aunt. "Your doctor said no heavy lifting. You're to walk and build up your strength. After your next checkup, we'll talk about the laundry. And we'll talk about tomorrow when tomorrow comes."

Lily looked toward heaven. "She's worse than a drill sergeant." Suddenly a twinkle sparkled in her eyes. "I have a great idea, Logan. Why don't you take her on a picnic? She could use a break."

"I don't need a break," Meg murmured, embarrassed her aunt was backing Logan into a corner.

"See? She's prickly. Meg never gets prickly. So she definitely needs a break," Lily assured Logan with a smile.

Logan's gaze fell on Meg. "Would you like to go on a picnic?"

"I wouldn't want to force you into anything." The comment just sort of popped out.

Logan's brows arched. "No one forces me into anything. If you can find a blanket, we can stop at Gibson's and get what we need. I know the perfect spot."

Logan did know the perfect spot. Laurel grew along the bank of the stream. Willows swayed low, their branches whispering with the breeze. He often drove the few miles out of town and sat on the bank of this stream. He'd thought about seeing Meg again constantly for the past two weeks. But he knew she was distracted at first with worry about Lily and then with her aunt's care.

Logan studied Meg as she pushed her purse to the corner of the blanket. It fell over, and the clasp popped open. Ignoring it, she reached into the deli bag and took out the sandwiches. They'd only talked about what they should buy for lunch. He could sense Meg holding back, and he wanted to get to the bottom of it.

"You've been very quiet."

She raised her gaze to his. "I wasn't sure if you came to visit Lily or me."

He tried to suppress a smile. "Both won't do?"

Avoiding his gaze, she set a turkey sandwich before him. "I haven't seen you for two weeks."

"You were busy. I didn't want to interfere."

"Just say it, Logan. You changed your mind. You lost interest...whatever happens to men when they don't call back."

He clasped her wrist. "Don't lump me with everyone else."

Her gaze locked to his. "Why not if you act the same way?"

"Act the same way? The last date we had, I couldn't keep my hands off you. Why would I lose interest?"

She pulled her hand out of his grasp. "Maybe you finally realized I'm going to leave and someone else could meet your needs better."

The passion inside him for Meg Dawson burst the restraints he'd carefully kept in check. He rose to his knees and cradled her head in his hands. "I want you. No one else. I haven't lost interest. But every time I hear your voice, see you, touch you, I want more. And you didn't have time for more with Lily on your mind."

He still saw the doubts, the sense of abandonment she carried with her from her childhood. And there was only one way he knew to make that go away.

Pulling her up to him, he sought Meg's lips, and he didn't hold back. With her gasp of surprise, he plunged his tongue into her mouth, intending to erase each of her doubts and assure her he wanted her more than he'd ever wanted anyone.

Chapter Ten

Logan's mouth was possessive and hard on Meg's. He turned his head and, with an urgent thrust, pushed his tongue into her mouth again. The dark sweetness of her increased his need, and the desire to show her that his interest had reached new heights, rather than diminished, was foremost in his mind. He searched and stroked and possessed until her arms wound about his neck, and he was sure she understood that he wanted her in the primal way a man wants a woman.

Suddenly she returned his desire. She took it, made it her own and gave it back to him with flames that licked at his body, intent on consuming him. He groaned, his arousal straining for freedom, his body dying for her touch. But the kiss was too intense to break, the pleasure too great to cut off. He wanted it to go on forever. Yet he knew he couldn't last. He was too close to the edge now.

He breathed in the scent of roses and Meg. Searching her mouth for every bit of sweetness, he ran his hands over her shoulders, down her arms. His senses reeled.

As his fingers danced over her skin, she became more daring. Her tongue dashed to the corner of his lips. When he tried to capture her, she evaded him, kissing his bottom lip, then the upper, then meeting him again lips to lips and tongue to tongue while her fingers dug into his hair.

Logan wrapped his arms around her and stroked her back. He felt the heat under the cotton blouse, and he wanted it at his fingers. He pulled her blouse from her skirt and unhooked her bra. The buttons evaded his trembling fingers as he tried to unfasten them, all the while kissing her harder, trying to assuage some of the need.

The last button tore, but it didn't matter because finally he filled his hands with the softness of her breasts. The sounds she made encouraged him. As he rubbed over her breasts with his thumbs, she bit his lip, and the intensity of their passion was almost a physical blow.

He broke away and, when she cried out in protest, he bent his head to her breast and swirled his tongue around her nipple. She grabbed at his shoulders, and her fingernails dug through his shirt. When he took her nipple between his lips, nipping and nibbling and licking, finally suckling in a mating rhythm that was driving them both insane, she clawed at his shirt, dragging it up his back. Finally her fingers touched his skin, and he shuddered.

Pulling back, he separated from her for only a moment and tugged his shirt over his head. Then he kissed her again, taking her down on the blanket. Her gaze met his, and there was no turning back.

He couldn't get enough of her satin skin, golden in the reflection of the sun's rays. Looking and tasting, he devoured her and coaxed broken moans from her that drove him on. Her breasts swelled under their dusky rose peaks. He bit gently, and she grew more restless, reaching for him, murmuring his name. He felt powerful...invincible...and whole.

Meg's hands felt like soft, branding instruments of sweet torture as she caressed his chest. When her thumb slid over his nipple, he sucked in a breath and wondered how much more he could take. Her hands danced over his shoulders, his chest, his stomach, in restless abandon. Beads of sweat broke out on his forehead, and his breathing became ragged.

Cupping Meg's head, Logan kissed her with the desperate need building inside him. He searched for the hem of her skirt and brushed it up her thigh. She was silk and heat, and he was dying to plunge himself inside her. But she had to be ready. He had to make her ready.

He nibbled down her neck and stroked her inner thigh. She was so hot there...so soft. She undulated toward him, and he explored higher until he met a silky barrier. When he played his fingers over it, she cried out. He dragged in a breath, trying to rein in his body's need. Wherever they were going to go, he had to take her with him. He had to.

Meg couldn't seem to breathe in enough air to help her think coherently. Logan's kiss had started a spiral of desire and need and longing that was taking her somewhere she'd never been. His need was hers; hers was his. There was an intangible connection between them, deeper than the passion lacing their kisses and touches.

Logan's tongue on her nipple brought tears to her eyes. The sensation was so beautifully erotic. His taste and texture and scent were everywhere, surrounding her, making her long for more. But any more would almost be too much, wouldn't it? How much pleasure could she absorb without losing herself in him?

When he cradled her head, and the passion seared the depths of her soul, all she wanted was more of him in her arms. She wanted to feel his body against hers, his skin against hers. He glided his hand up her thigh, and she realized skin against skin would never be enough. She wanted him inside her, touching her core, reaching a place that was isolated…alone… waiting.

When he found the juncture of her thighs, she wanted to touch him as intimately as he was touching her. She reached for his belt buckle. Logan helped her, stripping off his jeans and briefs, coming back to her with a kiss that made her forget they'd been separated even for a moment. As he stretched out on top of her, his hips met hers. She could feel his arousal through her skirt, through her panties, and she wanted no barriers between them.

Arching up to meet him, she could feel more, but not enough. Apparently Logan understood the message. Leaning to the side, he swept up her skirt. But he didn't hurry to undress her. He simply laid his hand over her panties, arousing her until the core of her throbbed.

"Logan!"

"What, sweetheart?" His voice was raspy and deep.

"It's not enough. It's…"

In a deft motion, his long fingers and large hand ridded her of her undergarment. "It's not enough for me, either."

While he kissed her, he caressed her thigh, inching higher and higher. She couldn't stand the anticipation, the waiting, the suspense. She wanted to cry out in frustration. Her body screamed, *More, more, more.* And then his fingers parted her and she felt as if she'd explode. He knew how to touch…and where to touch. She melted around him and kissed him as he took her deeper and deeper into passion and taught her the recklessness of desire.

She clutched at his shoulders, feeling the same glistening slickness on his skin that she felt on hers. The warmth of the sun penetrated the canopy of leaves above them, but she knew that her heat and Logan's came from the two of them together, a ball of fire that ignited inside them when they were together—inside of them, not outside. Her fire and his fire were coalescing into one. When they joined, she was afraid she wouldn't care if she ever burned alone again. There was something magical about their desires uniting, becoming more powerful, fed by each other, so much more together than separate.

The hungry yearning of her body centered in her womb, under Logan's deft fingers. When he found the silky nub, hidden, waiting for him, his touch was so sensually slow and erotic, she cried, "I want you, Logan."

He took her at her word, meeting her hips with his, joining his lips to hers, resting at the entrance where her need for him was greatest. She felt the tip of him, the scalding heat of tangible passion, and knew he was waiting for her consent.

Nothing in this world could stop the fire between them now. Nothing in this world could prevent Meg from giving her heart with her body. Nothing could keep her from raising her hips and inviting Logan to possess her.

And possess her he did. He took her hands and held them above her head. Intertwining his fingers with hers, he murmured, "Raise your knees."

The huskiness in his voice, the green depths of emotion in his eyes, the trembling of their hands that was neither his nor hers but theirs, urged her to do as he demanded.

When she did, he thrust into her with all the power of his need.

"Logan!" The sensation was sublime. She could feel his heat, his heartbeat, his pulsating desire. He withdrew and she protested.

He caught her protest and her breath with a scalding kiss as he thrust into her again.

Quickly she closed her knees and gripped his hips, taking him deeper, prolonging the pleasure. He tore away. "Meg, I can't hold on when you do that. Let me..."

"Don't hold on." She contracted around him, and he groaned. With another powerful thrust, he stoked the fire. Each time he drove into her, she rose to meet him until they moved as one, burning into each other.

The fire became liquid, flashing over her in waves, melding them together. Each wave became more intense than the one before. She couldn't think in words, only in feelings and senses. Logan's taste was on her lips, his scent mingled with hers, surrounding them, his hands closed and opened with hers in cadence with his thrusts. The fire danced in front of her eyes, first red, then orange, then silver white—white heat that licked and swelled and finally burst into an explosion that rocked the universe. She couldn't breathe as the orgasm shook her, subsiding, swelling, subsiding, swelling until the prolonged tremors became Logan's, as well as hers. The ecstasy seemed to last forever.

Finally she needed air, and she drew in a deep breath. Logan's body was still on top of her.

He lifted himself on his forearms. "Are you okay?"

Gazing into his eyes, realizing what had happened, her mind racing ahead, asking *what happens next?* she answered, "I'm not sure."

"I hope you don't have regrets."

How could she regret something so wonderful? Yet...

He frowned and separated from her. "I only have one regret."

"What?"

"Are you on the pill?"

Her eyes widened, and the full impact of his question hit her. "No."

He laid on his back beside her and stared up at the leaves blocking the blue sky. "I wouldn't want either of us to be trapped into something we don't want."

Would she feel trapped? Obviously Logan would. Because of a pregnancy, he'd been trapped in an unhappy marriage. "We should have known better."

"*I* should have known better." He rolled toward her, studied her face and pushed her damp hair from her brow. "But when I'm with you, I feel like a teen-ager again. Apparently with about just as much sense."

"You don't sound happy about it."

"Are you? Do you burn every time we get within a foot of each other? Does the sound of my voice turn you on? Does an inadvertent touch make you need?"

She heard his frustration, but she heard vulnerability, too. "Logan, yes. I wanted you as much as you wanted me. How could you doubt that after the way I…?"

"Some women can pretend real well."

"Logan!"

"It's true. Shelley—" He stopped.

"Tell me," she requested softly.

He stared up at the leaves above them. Finally he said, "After Shelley became pregnant, she was less than enthusiastic about sex. I thought we just needed time. But after Travis was born, she didn't want any more children. It was always a point of contention between us and colored whatever happened in the bedroom. When we made the decision to move to Willow Valley, I asked her if we couldn't start over, consider having another child. She agreed. After we moved, I thought our marriage was better. She seemed to enjoy sex again. Then I found out it was an act to cover up for her guilt."

Meg moved her leg closer to Logan's. Her arm brushed his. She wanted the physical contact to let him know he could tell her whatever he was thinking and feeling.

"One evening I saw something sticking out of her dresser drawer. I opened the drawer to stuff it back in, and I felt a package at the edge, the reason it wouldn't close. It was a packet of birth-control pills with some missing.''

Turning on her side, Meg watched Logan's chest rise and fall and wondered if he'd ever told anyone about any of this or if he'd kept it inside all these years.

''I confronted her with them. We started shouting. Saying things we shouldn't have. I don't even remember them now. But I do remember her telling me she never should have married me—not for a baby's sake. She said I'd ruined her life. Then she ran out, and an hour later I got the call. She was speeding, lost control and ran the car into a telephone pole. She was killed on impact.''

Logan's expression manifested anguish, as if it had just happened, as if he blamed himself. Instinctively Meg reached for him and held him tight.

His body was rigid, as if he couldn't accept her comfort. After a few minutes, he kissed her. The sparks burst into flame again, but this time he pulled away. ''We'd better not tempt fate twice,'' he said in a husky murmur. ''Let's have lunch.''

Meg felt awkward dressing, putting her clothes in order. But as Logan zipped his jeans, he smiled at her. Not sure what he was thinking or feeling, she proceeded cautiously. ''Remember I told you I have to go to D.C. for a fund-raiser?''

Logan nodded.

Noticing the top button of her blouse was torn off, she decided not to worry about it. A little cleavage at this point didn't much matter. ''It's next weekend. Saturday night. I wondered if you'd like to go along with me as my escort.''

''Black-tie?'' He buckled his belt.

She couldn't seem to move her gaze from his hands, the fly of his jeans. Her body was still tingling, and the thought of being with him again...

"Meg?" The sexy, knowing smile on his face made her blush.

"Uh, yes. It is. We could stay at my apartment."

His smile turned into a full-fledged grin. "I'll have to make sure Travis has somewhere to stay. But he has friends besides Kyle. It shouldn't be a problem. When do you want to leave?"

"Saturday morning around eight?"

"Sounds good." He sat down beside her. "But what sounds even better is a night at your apartment."

"Logan, I don't know where we're headed...."

He caressed her cheek. "I don't, either. But until we get there, let's just enjoy ourselves. Okay?"

She nodded.

Meg couldn't remember when she'd enjoyed an impromptu picnic more. Of course, she'd never been on a picnic quite like this one. She still couldn't believe... She sneaked a surreptitious glance at Logan—at least, she thought it was surreptitious—as he took a bite from an apple. His jaw was so strong and well chiseled. His cheekbones were high. The long lines beside his mouth deepened when he smiled. And his mouth...

He caught her looking, and the green of his eyes deepened. Leaning toward her, he offered her a bite of apple. "It's juicy," he said with a wink.

She'd never thought of Logan as a ladies' man, but she realized he could be devastatingly charming without half an effort. She took a bite and the juice ran down her chin. When she reached for a napkin, Logan took it from her.

"Let me."

Bending to her, he licked the apple juice from her chin. He didn't stop there, but settled his lips on hers. When he ended the kiss, she wished the picnic would never end.

He smiled. "Would you like the apple? I have another one."

Maybe if she crunched on the fruit, she'd forget about what else they could be doing. She took it from him.

He reached to the corner of the blanket for the grocery bag. Her purse lay open with the contents spilled out. First he picked up the lipstick and tossed it inside. Then he gathered the pen and small notepad. When he glanced at it, he frowned. "What's this?"

She could protest he had no authority to poke into her things, but there was no point to that. "It's a list. I make them all the time. They help me stay organized."

"This one looks important. Names. Numbers. All D.C. area code."

"People I'm going to call next weekend."

"Friends?"

She took the notepad from him and pushed it into her purse. "No, my contacts and colleagues who should know when I'm returning."

"You've made a decision?" There was a strain in his voice.

"I want to make sure Aunt Lily's okay. So I'm going to tell them I'll return January 1."

"You sound sure."

"I am sure."

He lifted her chin. "And what about what happened today? How does that figure in?"

She searched his eyes and her heart. "I don't know."

"Do you think it was a mistake?"

He was forcing her to look at them and make some kind of decision. She had to admit, "Maybe it was. Our roads are different, Logan. I have to go back to my work. You know that."

Dropping his hand, he shook his head. "I don't understand you. You have people here who love you."

Was Logan including himself in those people? "But I also have my career. It's part of who I am. Just like being a cop is part of who you are. Could you quit?"

"That's not the same thing, Meg. You know as well as I do long-distance relationships can't work. Me here. You in Washington and God knows where else."

Avoiding his gaze, she dropped her purse in her lap. "We haven't known each other very long. You can't expect me to make a decision about us because of a few weeks."

"I expect you to make a decision about us because of us."

"Logan, I'm still trying to find my bearings. I—"

"You're running away from people who care about you because you're afraid they'll let you down—like your parents did, like another man did."

She lifted her eyes to his. "So you're a psychologist now?"

"In my line of work, I'm a little bit of everything."

"You think you understand me, but you can't understand your own son. Have I got that right?"

His jaw tensed, and his voice was curt. "That's a low blow, Meg."

She'd never meant to hurt him. But he was hitting hard at her insecurities.

He gathered the remains of their picnic and stuffed them in the bag. "I'll take you home."

Why couldn't he understand her life couldn't revolve around one person? Why couldn't he see the danger in that? "Logan…"

Frowning, he stood. "It's all right, Meg. You call it as you see it. We just don't see it the same way."

He drove her back to Lily and Ned's in silence. They didn't seem to have anything else to say. Meg hurt. She'd been so close to Logan when they'd made love. But now he didn't even want to talk to her. When she climbed out of his car at her aunt's, she didn't know if she'd ever see him again. And she didn't ask because his answer might hurt too much.

Fully expecting to drive to Washington alone Saturday morning, Meg opened her back door and tossed her overnight case inside of her car. Most of her clothes were back at her apartment, so she didn't need much. When she heard tires on the lane, she turned in surprise.

Logan. She hadn't heard from him since the picnic a week ago. After their argument, she presumed he wouldn't want to go with her.

He pulled in beside her car and got out. With each step he took, bringing him closer to her, her heart beat faster.

"My car rides better," he said in a neutral tone.

"I didn't think you'd want to go with me after—"

"I keep my commitments, Meg, even though I make a mess of them sometimes."

His attitude rankled. "This isn't an important one, Logan. If you'd rather not go, you don't have to."

"Meaning I'm easily replaced?"

She was sure she could find an escort among her acquaintances in D.C. Annoyed with his attitude, she responded quickly, "Yes."

His green eyes became hard as his jaw tensed. "Well, I don't want to be replaced, so let's go."

She could tell this was going to be a *fun* trip. But she'd rather have Logan beside her, even when he was pulling his caveman routine than not have him with her.

The ride to D.C. was awkward. Although Logan switched on a soothing radio station, the vibrations inside the car kept Meg from relaxing. As they neared Chevy Chase, she directed him on which exit to take. Her apartment building was easy to find.

The doorman smiled at her. "Welcome back, Miss Dawson. How are you feeling?"

"Pretty good, George. How about you? Is Mary Claire walking yet?"

"Just last week. Now that she's got the ground covered, she's climbin' on everything."

Meg laughed.

Her smile faded as she stepped into the elevator beside Logan and his gaze met hers. She pushed the button for the fourth floor.

Logan remained silent while she unlocked her apartment. Once inside, he asked, "Where do you want the bags?"

She knew what he was asking, and she was tired

of pussyfooting around. "Where do *you* want the bags?"

Apparently he was, too. He dropped them on the floor and crossed to her, his face granite hard, his eyes boring into her. "I don't give a damn where we put the bags. But I want to spend the night with you, in your bed. Is that what you want?"

She reached up and stroked his jaw. "Yes."

The tension between them snapped. Logan wrapped his arms around her, and his lips crushed hers. When he broke away, they were both breathless.

He took her face between his palms. "I don't know how to deal with an independent woman."

His admission and the frustration in it made her want to cry and laugh at the same time. "Is that what I am?"

He grimaced. "Unfortunately, yes." Dropping his hands, he paced across the room like a caged tiger. "I'm not used to dealing with a woman like you. You're strong enough to tell me what you want, what you need. Apparently Shelley wasn't. And I have to wonder why. Maybe if I could have let *her* make the decisions, if I hadn't pushed to have more children—"

"Logan, all the what-ifs in the world won't change the past. You're a strong man. I imagine you've always known what you want."

He shook his head and faced her. "That's no excuse for not listening. Maybe you were right. Maybe I don't know my own son because I don't really listen to him, either."

Meg crossed to Logan and wrapped her arms around him in a hug. He stood rigid, as if he didn't know how to accept the comfort. Finally he enfolded her in his arms.

She twined hers around his neck and stroked his nape. "You can start listening anytime."

"Not when you're doing that," he growled, and swept her into his arms.

Since Meg only had one bedroom, finding it wasn't a problem. Logan lowered her to the bed and opened the top button on her blouse. "This time we're going to take it slow." When he finished with her blouse, he went to push it from her shoulders.

She caught his hand to stop him.

"What's wrong?"

"The last time I...wasn't completely undressed. My shoulder...it's not pretty."

He lifted her chin and rubbed his thumb over the point. "Everything about you is pretty. Sit up so we can take this off."

Meg sat up and pulled her blouse from her jeans. Logan helped push it from her shoulders. For a long moment, he studied the red lines. Then he leaned toward her and, with incomparable gentleness, kissed each line, each scar, until she knew they truly didn't matter to him.

Logan helped strip off Meg's clothes slowly, kissing her arms, her fingertips and, a few moments later, her knees and calves. Each piece of clothing melted away under the firmness and heat of his lips, the stroking eroticism of his fingertips.

When she was naked before him, quivering from his kisses and caresses, she said, "Now it's your turn."

His brows arched as he smiled. "And that means?"

She sat up and pulled his shirt free of his jeans.

''That there are advantages to keeping company with an independent woman.'' After the first button, she kissed his chest. After the third, she splayed the plackets open and rubbed her fingertips over a dark nipple.

He shuddered.

Smiling, she unbuttoned the rest and placed a slow, wet kiss above his navel.

''Meg. What are you trying to do?''

Her hands worked his belt while she looked up and teased, ''Didn't you say you wanted to do this slowly?''

The green of his eyes deepened with the desire evident in his taut muscles, his husky voice. ''I never realized it would be such torture.''

When she answered Logan by cupping him, he groaned and took her by the hands. ''That's it.'' He stripped, took foil packets from his pocket and lay beside her on the bed. Then he dropped the packets on the nightstand.

They gazed at each other, absorbing the other's presence, just relishing the moment. Meg brushed her hand over his shoulder. ''I was afraid I'd never see you again.''

''It crossed my mind,'' he said honestly. ''Especially when you didn't call.''

''When *I* didn't call?'' She withdrew her hand.

He caught it and brought it to his lips. Gently, with a sexy grin, he nibbled and kissed her palm until she sighed. ''The more I thought about *not* seeing you again, the more restless I got. Then I started thinking about my history with women and your history. You needed your independence to survive emotionally, and you have every right to make decisions you feel are right for you. I might not agree, but that's my problem. Too often I forced my opinions on Shelley. Or else she just wasn't confident enough to stand up for what she believed."

Meg tried to keep herself free of the sensual haze Logan induced and paid attention to his words. She knew they were important. "It sounds as if you've done a lot of thinking."

"I have. And it all boils down to the fact that I'm not ready to give you up." Leaning toward her, he kissed her tenderly, letting the passion build.

With soft words and feverish caresses, he kissed and touched her everywhere until she was trembling from head to toe, needing him in the most elemental way. But this time she wanted to touch him, too. His back was smooth to his waist, where she discovered a few silky hairs. Every inch of him was strong and muscular and hot. And when she stroked his thigh higher and higher until she curled her fingers around him, she knew she'd found an intimacy with Logan of which she'd been afraid to dream. She could feel the beat of his pulse in her hand, and when she stroked him, he made a deep sound in his throat and closed her tight in his arms. She'd never felt more safe or more cherished. If only the feeling could last forever.

But Logan had other feelings in mind. Drawing her on top of him, he entered her slowly. Then he let her set the pace. Tears came to her eyes. He was telling her she was his equal and that they could share their passion, not compete, not make promises they couldn't keep. He held her waist, kept his eyes on hers and joined her in their ascent up the mountain.

Just when Meg thought she'd reached the top and could grasp the pleasure and hold on to it, it exploded all around her, shaking her and frightening her. Because the moment before the ecstasy overtook her, she realized the deepest truth of all—she loved Logan. Heaven help her, she loved him. The realization scared her to death, because if she loved him, she'd have to trust him. She wasn't sure she could trust anyone.

After Todd, she'd promised herself, no matter whom she met or what situation she got herself into, she would only trust herself. But trust went with love, didn't it? Yet how did independence and trust fit together?

As she leaned forward, laying her cheek on Logan's shoulder, feeling his heart beating, she realized she was more frightened than she'd ever been. In Costa Rica her life had been in danger, but here...now...her heart was on the line. Did she have the courage to give it to Logan and trust him to keep it safe?

Chapter Eleven

A waiter offered Logan a glass of champagne from a silver tray, but he declined, keeping his gaze on Meg. Ever since they'd walked into the ballroom, one person after another had greeted her. Mostly men. What man wouldn't look at her in that dress? It was emerald green and molded to her much too well from her breasts to her ankles. The slit halfway up her thigh made it sexy as sin.

To be fair, the men looked at her, all right, but they talked to her, too. She was obviously well respected. And here she was in her element. She glittered and glowed, more than the gold earrings swinging on her ears. For all his talk of accepting her independence and the decisions she made, he regretted how well she seemed to thrive in this atmosphere. He was hoping she'd return to D.C., see the emptiness of it and want to spend the rest of her days in Willow Valley. That was a foolish pipe dream on his part.

After they'd made love this afternoon, she'd changed, becoming quiet and distant. He'd asked her if anything was wrong. She'd just smiled and said, "No." But there was something in her eyes. If he didn't know better, he'd think it was fear.

She'd been talking to the same guy for fifteen minutes. Suddenly her gaze connected with Logan's. After another minute or so, she walked toward him. Once she was beside him, she asked, "Are you bored?"

"I can think of other things I'd rather be doing," he drawled.

She smiled coyly. "Walking on the mall?"

"We did that this afternoon."

Tilting her head she offered, "I'd suggest visiting the Smithsonian, but it's closed."

"Not quite what I had in mind, either." He stuffed one hand into his trouser pocket. "Who was that guy?"

She looked toward the man who had engaged her in conversation. "He's a journalist."

"Known him for long?" Logan asked, unable to keep the edge from his voice.

"About five years." She studied him for a long moment. "Logan, are you jealous?"

"Hell, yes, I'm jealous. You're my lady now, and I don't particularly relish watching while other men undress you with their eyes."

He thought she might get her hackles up. But instead of getting angry, she laid her hand on his arm and said, "But I only let *you* undress me."

The husky desire in her voice, the sincerity in her

wide brown eyes, aroused him. He tapped one of her dangling gold earrings. "Do you intend to mingle much longer?"

"Not if you'd rather go back to my apartment."

"You're certain?"

"I'm positive."

Meg was so unlike Shelley—so sure of herself, what she had to do, what she needed. "Then let's go, pretty lady. Because right now there's no place else I'd rather be."

Back at the apartment, Logan took off his tuxedo jacket and tossed it over a chair. Meg's apartment, even at night, was very much like her. Flowers and vines in rose and green on white covered her love seat and chair. The wicker tables added lightness to the small area. The kitchen was painted yellow and white with touches of green here and there. *Vibrant, warm* and *alive* were words that came to Logan's mind.

After making sure all locks were in place, he went to Meg's bedroom. It was simple but elegant—an off-white spread, ruffled curtains that crisscrossed the windows. Meg stood at the dresser removing her earrings. She smiled at him in the mirror.

He came up behind her and wrapped his arms around her. "How would you like to go hiking next Saturday with me and Travis?"

"Maybe the two of you should go alone."

His eyes stayed on hers. "I'm afraid he won't go if it's just the two of us. He seems to like you."

"So you want to use me as a buffer."

Logan dropped his arms and stepped back. "I can understand if you'd rather not go."

When she turned to face him, her voice was gentle.

"I didn't say that. I just don't want Travis to think I'm invading his territory."

He should have known Meg would think about Travis, too. "All right. I'll ask him if he wants you to come along. Maybe it'll get some honest conversation going between us."

"And you'll tell me the truth about what he says."

Logan nodded. "Always." He ran his fingers along the edge of her dress above her breasts. "Do you need help getting out of this?"

Slipping her arms around his waist, she unlatched his cummerbund. "If you need help getting out of this."

Logan lifted her off the floor, bringing her lips to his. His answer was in his kiss.

Meg's restlessness woke Logan. She tossed from side to side. When beads of perspiration dotted her forehead and she said, "No, no. Don't shoot!" Logan knew she was having a nightmare rather than a dream.

He clasped her arm. "Meg. Wake up. It's only a dream."

Not hearing him, she clutched her shoulder and moaned. She was shaking all over.

Quickly he slipped his arm around her. "C'mon, sweetheart, wake up. Meg. Wake up."

Her eyes fluttered open.

Logan stroked her tears away. "It was a bad dream. You're awake now."

Recognition dawned in her eyes.

"Do you want to talk about it?"

She shook her head, and her lower lip quivered. "Would you just hold me?"

Wrapping his arms around her, he settled her

against his chest. After they'd made love, they'd fallen asleep in each other's arms. With Meg tucked against his shoulder, Logan had fallen asleep easily. But holding her then and holding her now were two different things. She trembled against him, but not from desire. The kidnapping still haunted her. Suddenly he realized her decision to return to work might be something she had to do for her emotional survival.

A week later, Meg glanced at the darkening sky, hoping the expedition Logan had planned wasn't a mistake. The hiking trail wove through wooded terrain like a thin ribbon. As the incline became steeper, it was only wide enough for one person at a time. Meg glanced at the sky again. The day had started out sunny. They'd been hiking about an hour when the sun had disappeared behind a cloud.

Logan trudged along first. Meg followed, with Travis bringing up the rear. He'd been sullen throughout the morning, and Meg wondered if Logan had bribed him to come today. Maybe she could get father and son talking to one another when they ate lunch.

Stopping for a moment, Meg looked over her shoulder. Travis hiked about twenty feet behind her. "Are you getting hungry?"

He gave her a very slight smile. "I'm *always* hungry."

At least he talked to her in more than monosyllabic sentences. Maybe if she could *keep* him talking… "I packed liverwurst."

"You what?"

She grinned. "Just kidding. Ham and cheese and turkey and cheese."

They trekked on in silence a few more minutes. Suddenly she sensed he was right behind her.

"I talked to Mr. Holden about the exchange program."

She moved to the side to make room for him on the trail. "And?"

"He said if I keep my grades up, it's a possibility second semester next year."

She clapped him on the shoulder. "That's terrific."

"I was wondering…" He seemed hesitant to continue.

"What were you wondering?"

"Well, this is my third year of Spanish. But like you said, school learning's not the same as actually speaking it with someone. I wondered if while you're in Willow Valley, you and me could practice. If you have some spare time. I heard you telling Dad about working at the adoption service. If you're too busy, I understand."

"For now I'm only working there in the mornings. I want to make sure Aunt Lily doesn't overdo. But if you want to stop by after school a couple of days a week, that would be fine."

"You mean it?"

She saw the doubts in Travis's eyes. "Yes, I mean it."

"Because of Dad?"

Travis was trying so hard to assert his independence. She understood what he was asking her. She laid her hand on his arm. "Your dad and I are seeing each other now. You know that, right?"

"Yeah. I knew Dad was going to Washington with you."

"No matter what does or doesn't happen with me and your dad, you and I can still be friends. Got it?"

He grinned, a real full-fledged grin. "Got it. Is Monday afternoon okay?"

"Monday's fine."

The path narrowed even more, and Travis dropped back again.

A short while later, Logan stopped before a sharp rise and waited for Meg to catch up. "How are you doing?"

They'd managed little time alone since the past weekend. Wednesday night, they'd stolen an hour away in Lily and Ned's barn. Afterward, laughing, they'd brushed the hay from each other's hair. Remembering, she smiled. "I'm fine."

He offered her water from the bottle hanging on his belt. After popping the lid, he held the water out to her. When she took it from him, his fingers purposefully slid over hers, telling her he wanted to touch her more. She took a few swallows and handed it back to him. He sipped from the spot her lips had touched.

Meg wondered if the bond growing between her and Logan was making matters worse instead of better for him and his son as Travis came up to them and frowned.

Logan reattached the bottle to his belt. "Once we climb this hill, we can stop and eat."

Travis shrugged. "Whatever. I just want to get back. I have plans to meet Kyle at the Pizza Shop for supper."

Meg could tell Logan was counting to ten. As Travis started off in front of them, he said, "No progress so far."

"The day's only half-over," she soothed.

He slid his hand under her hair and stroked her neck. "Always an optimist."

Closing her eyes, she relished the feel of his fingers and wondered why she loved his touch so. Maybe because she loved him. She was getting used to the idea...slowly.

By the time they'd finished lunch, Meg felt like tearing her hair out strand by strand. Travis met Logan's attempts at conversation, as well as hers, with brooding silence. She was about ready to take Travis by his ears and shake him, and she realized this was probably how frustrated Logan felt on a daily basis.

When they took to the trail again, she guessed all three of them had a common goal—get the day over with. As they hiked up a steeper, rocky incline, her mind sorted through all the possibilities of things she could say to get through to Travis. Thinking about taking him aside for a heart-to-heart when they returned, she wasn't as careful as she should have been on the path. She lost her footing.

One minute she was upright; the next she'd let out a yelp and was sliding down the packed earth on her bottom.

Travis got to her first and slid his arm around her shoulders to help her sit up. "Take a deep breath if you can. You probably got the wind knocked out of you."

Logan appeared by her side seconds later and snapped, "Don't move her until I find out if she's all right." He took her hand and gentled his voice. "Does anything hurt?"

Travis's arm was still supporting her shoulders, but it was rigid with tension.

She sat up on her own, moved her arms and legs and took a few breaths. Her right forearm was sore, and she realized she'd scrapped it on the slide downward. "I'm fine. Tomorrow might be a different story."

Logan directed, "Bend your arms and legs."

She did, and winced when she bent her arm.

"Let's take a look." He unbuttoned her cuff and rolled up her sleeve. She'd scraped the skin.

Travis shifted his backpack from his shoulders. "I have a first-aid kit." Quickly he found it and opened it. After taking out a small plastic bottle of peroxide, he unscrewed the lid.

Logan took a cotton patch from the little box and took the peroxide from Travis. "I'll do it."

Travis slapped the box on the ground. "Fine. You do it. Like you do everything!"

"Travis. Watch your mouth."

"What are you going to do if I don't? Oh, I know. Send me to military school. Well, that couldn't be any worse than living with you. You don't want me there, any more than you want me here today. Anybody can see you two'd rather be in bed together."

"You apologize to Meg. Now." Logan's expression was so fierce, Meg was afraid he'd slap his son.

"Do I have to apologize to you, too? What for? Telling the truth?"

The two males stared each other down until Meg couldn't stand it anymore. "Will you two please *talk* to each other?" When only silence met her question, she asked the teenager, "Why do you think your dad doesn't want you around?"

Travis pushed himself to his feet. "He just doesn't.

I *know* it." He looked at the hill and said, "I'll meet you at the top."

After he scrambled off, Meg said to Logan, "Go after him. Talk to him."

"He won't listen to me, Meg."

"You're not listening to each other!"

Thunder rumbled, and they both looked up at the darkening sky. Logan poured peroxide onto the cotton patch. "Let's get you fixed up and home. If you soak in a hot tub tonight, you might not feel so sore to-morrow."

Meg was ready to bop both MacDonald males over the head with something heavy. They were more alike than they knew.

Lightning flashed, and drops of rain began to fall. Logan had been keeping a sharp eye on Meg as Travis led their trek. She seemed fine, but he wanted to make sure she wasn't hiding an injury so he wouldn't worry.

The rain fell in earnest, and Logan called to his son, "Travis, hold up."

Logan untied his jacket from around his waist. When he caught up to Meg, he put it around her shoulders. "This will keep you drier than your sweater."

"Travis, I said hold up," Logan repeated as his son kept walking.

Travis called over his shoulder, "The only way we're going to get back is to keep going."

Logan ran up ahead and caught his son by his arm. "I said stop."

"I don't want to stop. I told you I have plans."

"I'm not going to let us get soaking wet because

you have plans. There's a lean-to around the next bend. We'll wait it out there.''

Lightning shot through the sky, and the blast of thunder followed.

A few minutes later, the three of them sat on the floor of the lean-to while the rain came down steadily on the roof. Travis had wound his arms around his long legs and rested his chin on his knees.

Logan wished he could get through to him. He wished... "What are you and Kyle going to do tonight?"

"Nothing illegal," Travis answered sarcastically.

"When I ask a civil question, I expect a civil answer."

Travis lifted his head and stretched out his legs. "I'm not a suspect, Dad. So leave me alone."

Anger and pain beat in Logan's chest. "I will not leave you alone. You're my *son!*"

"And you wish I wasn't."

Travis's statement hit Logan between the eyes. "What?"

"You heard me," Travis mumbled, looking at his sneakers.

"Where did you get an idea like that?" Logan asked, wishing he could read his son's mind.

"From you."

Logan reached out and grabbed Travis's arm. "You can't believe that. What did I ever do or say to make you think it?"

Travis hesitated a second, then murmured, "Plenty."

He tried to pull away, but Logan wouldn't let him. "Tell me, Travis. Tell me what's going on with you.

I've asked you before, and now I want the truth. Why did you run away?''

''Your rules and regulations, curfews—''

Smoke and mirrors—the same thing he thought they'd been fighting about for four years. ''The truth, Travis.''

Travis wrenched away, and his green eyes smacked into Logan's. ''All right. You want the truth. I'll tell you the truth. You never loved Mom. And you never wanted me. I heard you fighting that night. I'd come home from a game and was standing on the deck. If you didn't love her, you shouldn't have married her! You shouldn't have had me!'' With that, Travis jumped up and ran from the lean-to into the pouring rain.

Logan put his hand on Meg's knee. ''I have to go after him.''

She nodded. ''Of course you do. Go.''

Logan found Travis running along the path. He clasped his son's elbow. ''You're wrong. I have *always* wanted you. I married your mother *because of you.*''

''You shouldn't have. Not if you didn't love her. The two of you should have just gotten rid of me.''

''No!'' Logan shouted to Travis and the world as rain dripped from his face. ''I didn't love your mother as I should have. But I was committed to her, committed to you, committed to our life as a family. My mistake was trying to convince your mother to want the same things I did.''

''What things?'' Travis clenched his hands at his sides.

Logan had always tried to protect his son. Maybe it was time to stop. ''More children, for one. I thought

when we moved to Willow Valley, we could revital-
ize our marriage. I thought we'd try to have more
children. But your mom and I didn't agree. We argued about it that night and she ran out. Don't you
think I blame myself for her death as much as you
blame me?'' The guilt and anguish Logan had felt
over Shelley's accident poured over him with the rain.

The question hung between him and his son as the
drops pelted down.

''You do blame me, don't you?'' he pressed, knowing if he and Travis were going to have a relationship,
it had to be based on honesty.

''It's your fault she ran out. Every time I miss
her…'' Travis's voice broke.

''You blame me,'' Logan finished.

Thunder rolled. Travis's eyes flashed defiance.
''Yes.''

His son was breaking his heart. But he deserved it.
Somehow he had to make peace with it so they could
both go on. ''I can't fault you for that. And I can't
be angry with you because of it. But I am angry with
myself because I didn't know what was going on in
your head. Travis, no one is as important to me as
you. Can you believe me?''

''I dunno,'' he mumbled.

''I have always wanted you. From the moment
your mother told me she was pregnant.''

Travis raised his chin and, as the rain dripped down
his face, he asked, ''What about Mom?''

Logan couldn't tell Travis the truth about that. Besides, eventually Shelley did want and love their son.
''You know your mom loved you.''

Travis searched Logan's face. After a while, he

said, ''Yeah, she did. But that night, why did she say she shouldn't have married you?''

''Because she didn't want to get married. I talked her into it. I thought we'd be happy. I thought I could make her happy. But I couldn't.''

''Is that why she said you ruined her life?''

''Travis...''

''Dad, tell me the truth,'' Travis pleaded, his green eyes large and deep and hurting.

Logan couldn't ignore his son's plea. ''Yes.''

Comprehension dawned in Travis's eyes. ''*She* didn't want me.''

His son's pain was Logan's, too. ''Only at first. She was younger than I was. She found out she was pregnant and panicked. But she did love you, Travis.''

''*You* made her keep me.''

Logan took his son by the shoulders. ''I convinced her to marry me. That might have been a mistake. But keeping you and having you was not a mistake. The problems were between me and your mother.''

Travis looked confused. ''Do you miss her?''

''Yes, I miss her. And I ache because she died the way she did. It shouldn't have happened.'' More than anything, Logan wanted to hug Travis. But there was still a wall around the boy that he wouldn't let his father penetrate. They stood there for what seemed like hours, letting the storm swirl around them.

The rain plastered Logan's shirt to his body, and Travis was just as wet. Finally Logan said, ''We're soaked. And Meg's probably worried. Let's go back.''

Travis looked toward the lean-to, then nodded. They walked back together, not touching and not speaking, but Logan felt they'd opened a window.

Maybe now some air and sun could get in. If not today…maybe soon.

When Meg spotted them, her eyes widened but she didn't scold. Rather, she shrugged out of Logan's jacket, then stripped off her pullover sweater, leaving only her cotton blouse.

"You'll get cold," Logan chided.

"And you two will catch pneumonia if you don't get out of at least some of those wet clothes. I know you're both stubborn, but believe me, I can be just as stubborn."

Logan checked his son's face.

Meg handed the jacket to Logan. "Shirt off, jacket on. No arguments."

He knew Travis might follow his lead. "You're tough," he grumbled.

"You don't know the half of it," she responded, holding the sweater out to Travis. "The same goes for you."

Logan's confrontation with Travis had left him shaken but hopeful. Maybe with everything out in the open, they could start fresh. Trying to establish a connection between them, he asked, "Do you think we should make her turn around?"

Travis shrugged, and then his lips turned up in a small smile. "She *could* close her eyes, though."

With an exaggerated but patient sigh, Meg did.

Mighty rolls of thunder continued to echo through the lean-to. Lightning cracked close by. None of it seemed to faze Meg. Logan knew Shelley would have cowered close to his side. Yet he remembered Meg waking up from her nightmare, asking him to hold her. She was strong but vulnerable, and he felt more for her each day. How would his relationship with Meg affect his son? Of course, if Meg didn't stay…

As they sat munching on trail mix in a stilted silence, Meg asked, "Have you discovered anything more on the break-in at the high school?"

Logan knew she was trying to make conversation to cover the awkwardness. "Dead ends every way we look. No gossip. The kids aren't talking."

"The kids don't know anything," Travis mumbled.

"How do you know?" Logan asked. After all, Travis was on the scene, in the midst of it.

His son shrugged again. "I don't for sure. But the school's not that big. Even if someone's covering for somebody else, they usually slip. Nothing is going around. Zilch."

Logan frowned. "That means either someone outside the school did it or else someone in the school is intending to do it again."

"How do you figure?" Travis asked.

"If it was a prank, someone would know something because there's pride in carrying it off. Whoever did it must need the money."

Travis looked thoughtful. "When I was on the streets, no one told anyone anything. It was too risky. You didn't even tell where you were going to crash that night."

"Where did you crash, Travis?" Logan had tried before, unsuccessfully, to get his son to talk about his experience.

Travis looked defiant for a moment, but then the defiance faded. "Wherever I could. Garages. You wouldn't believe how many people use 'em for storage instead of their cars. Factory warehouses. Security is lousy on most of them."

"Travis, did you ever get hurt other than the mugging?" Meg's caring voice was a request for information rather than a judgment.

Logan waited for the answer, every muscle in his body tense. It was the question he'd wanted to ask ever since Travis had come home.

Although Meg had asked the question, Travis directed his answer to his father. "No. I got a few bumps and bruises now and then when someone tried to steal my stuff, but I never got hurt. Not till the mugging."

Logan let out his pent-up breath. "Thank God."

Meg took his hand, and Travis saw it. But he didn't comment.

A short time later, the rain let up. Logan watched Meg carefully as he let Travis lead and he followed Meg. The wet rocks and mud made the going slower than usual. Every fifteen minutes or so, Travis checked behind him to make sure he wasn't getting too far ahead.

Logan had time to think as they hiked. The full impact of Travis's misconceptions hit him. He couldn't believe that for four years, his son had believed that not only was Logan responsible for Shelley's death, but that he'd never wanted a child to begin with. No wonder Travis's behavior had been such a trial. No wonder he held such hostility. Logan had compounded the problem by cracking down harder, thinking more discipline had been the answer.

What kind of a father knew so little about his child that he couldn't see the signs, that he wasn't intuitive enough to get to the bottom of the problem? Travis had a right to be angry, resentful and distant. They'd lost so much ground. Logan wasn't sure they'd ever be able to recover. Now that he knew the root of the problem, he still didn't have the answers. All he could do was try to be as open and honest with his son as he could, and hope Travis would do the same.

He couldn't help asking himself if he and Shelley should have divorced. Would she be alive today if they had? The guilt for coaxing her into marriage sometimes seemed like a ten-ton weight. All those years, there had been a separateness between them, a tension that he thought they'd hidden but obviously not well enough. Travis had felt it on some level. That's why now he believed so easily that he'd been a mistake, that they'd never really wanted him.

As Logan, Meg and Travis arrived at the area where Logan had parked the car, they were quiet. He guessed Meg just wanted to soak in a hot tub. His own jeans were wet and uncomfortable, and he figured Travis itched to get home, get changed and go meet Kyle. The silence lasted as they climbed into the car and Logan drove down the winding road that led out of the trail area. They'd only traveled about a quarter of a mile when Logan spotted the felled tree blocking the narrow road.

He stopped and considered their options. Opening his door, he said, "I'm going to take a look."

A few minutes later, Travis and Meg stood beside him. Thinking about the way he'd handled his son over the years, instead of making a unilateral decision Logan asked, "What do you think?"

The teenager looked surprised that Logan wanted his opinion. He shrugged. "We might be able to move it."

Logan smiled. "If we're lucky, it's hollow."

"No such luck," Travis mumbled as he gave the trunk a shove with his foot.

"What can I do?" Meg asked.

"Get back in the car and relax. Travis and I will see what we can do."

When she hesitated, Travis encouraged her. "Go on. Dad and I will take care of this."

Relieved her help wasn't needed, relieved the two MacDonald men seemed to want to work together instead of backing away from each other, she settled in the front seat and laid her head against the headrest. A wave of nausea washed over her. She was tired. So tired.

The nausea subsided. This had been an emotional day. More so for Logan and Travis, but she'd felt caught in the midst of it. She didn't know what the two MacDonalds had said to each other out in the rain, but something was different—especially the way they looked at each other. Now they seemed to *see* each other.

For Logan's sake, as well as Travis's, she hoped they could find some common ground.

Fighting her fatigue, she lifted her head and watched. Travis and Logan used a long branch as a lever, then rolled and pushed the tree trunk back far enough that the car could fit through. When they returned to the car, they wore satisfied expressions, as if they'd accomplished something.

Logan drove Meg to Lily and Ned's. As he braked, Meg rested her hand on his arm. "You don't have to get out. You two need hot showers as much as I need a hot bath."

But Logan wouldn't let her go that easily. Surprising her, he leaned close and gave her a quick kiss. "I'll call you."

With a peek at Travis, she realized he looked pensive rather than defiant. She hopped out of the car and told them both goodbye. Maybe Travis would stay home tonight and talk with Logan. Maybe they would begin to realize they were more alike than different.

Meg insisted on cleaning up after supper so Lily and Ned could take an evening stroll. The sky had cleared, becoming pale blue before the sun set. Finally, when she'd clicked on the dishwasher and headed upstairs, she realized her right hip was as sore as her arm. As she soaked in the tub, she almost fell asleep. The sounds of her aunt and uncle returning from their walk urged her to leave the now-lukewarm water.

She'd wrapped herself in her robe and was drying her hair when her aunt opened the bathroom door. "I'm perturbed with you, young lady. Logan's on the phone. He told me you took a spill today."

"I'm fine, Aunt Lily. I slipped. That's all." She hadn't wanted to give her aunt anything to worry about. Although Lily was recovering nicely and had resumed many of her activities, the doctor had told her to try to keep stress to a minimum.

"You should have let *me* clean up the kitchen," her aunt chided.

"*You* made supper," Meg argued.

"I stuck a chicken in the oven with a few vegetables." Lily looked her over. "Are you sure you're okay? You looked pale at supper."

Meg slipped by the woman who loved her like a mother. "Don't worry. A good night's sleep is all I need.'' A few moments later, she picked up the phone in her room. ''Logan MacDonald. Why did you tell Aunt Lily about my fall?''

''I merely asked how you felt. I didn't know if you'd tell me.''

''Why wouldn't I?''

''Because you think you can handle everything yourself.''

She sighed. ''I think you know me a little too well.''

''Not nearly well enough,'' he responded in a deep, sexy voice that almost made her forget her fatigue. Knowing they couldn't spend the night together but longing to cuddle in his arms, she asked, ''How are you and Travis?''

He allowed the change of subject. ''I'm not sure. We're both watching what we say and how we say it. But something happened out there today, Meg. Even though it hurt like hell, we got the raw truth out in the open. Now all I have to do is make him believe that he's important to me and always has been. He thought Shelley and I never wanted him, that it would have been better if he hadn't been born.''

She could hear the pain and regret in Logan's voice. ''He'll believe you. Just take it slowly.''

''I've had sixteen years and suddenly I feel as if I'm starting from square one.''

''You are. But he'll come around.''

''You've made a difference.''

''Logan...''

''You have. You were right. I needed to see his point of view. After today, I think I can.'' Following a pause, Logan asked, ''You know what I'd like to do this very moment?''

"What?"

"Make love to you."

There was almost too much desire in his words, too much feeling in her heart. Fear tapped her on the shoulder again. Closing her eyes, she tried to will it away. When she couldn't, she pretended a lightness she didn't feel. "In the barn?"

"Anywhere at all."

With a shiver of passion attached to the love flowing through her, she took a deep breath, realizing that leaving Willow Valley would be even more difficult than standing on her aunt's porch when she was twelve and watching her parents drive away.

When Meg raised her arm to knock softly on Victoria Lee's office door Monday afternoon, the sleeve of her blouse brushed her scrape, and she winced. Then she ignored the soreness as she had all morning. It would heal.

"Come in."

Meg stepped inside. "I spoke with our contact in Guatemala. Everything is finalized on the Conlin adoption. They leave tomorrow and pick up the baby on Wednesday. They're ecstatic."

"They've waited two years to adopt."

Handing the file to Victoria, Meg said, "Mrs. Conlin was crying. Did you know she and her husband went through procedures for five years, and none of the surgeries or fertility drugs worked? For seven years, she and her husband have prayed for this child."

Victoria laid the manila folder on her desk. "I know. A lot of our couples have a similar history." She gestured to the chair in front of her desk. When

Meg was seated, she asked, "You're enjoying your work with the agency, aren't you?"

Meg was beginning to love her work here. The past week, she'd thought more and more about staying in Willow Valley. Logan was becoming part of every fiber of her life, as well as her being. If she enjoyed helping couples adopt, if she gave in to her feelings for Logan, the nightmares would disappear. Wouldn't they? She felt safe when Logan held her. Her love for him grew each day. But she hadn't told him yet. It was so soon. So new.

"I *do* enjoy my work here."

"The liaison position is still open. I've held off interviewing anyone else, hoping you'd change your mind and accept my offer."

Meg brushed her hair from her cheek. "I can't make the decision yet. I'm sorry."

Victoria leaned back in her chair. "I'm going to take the chance that placing babies with loving couples will be more valuable work to you than any you've experienced. So I'm going to give you until Christmas to decide. Fair enough?"

Meg thought about Logan and smiled. With a joyful feeling in her heart, she agreed, "Fair enough."

Chapter Twelve

The sun peeked over the horizon, casting the earliest rays of daylight onto the barn. Meg sat in her bedroom Thanksgiving morning, staring into the backyard. She'd been awake most of the night. She had to pull herself together, she had to stuff the turkey, she had to…

She had to talk to Logan.

Her life had never been more complicated, and there were no simple answers. Would Logan be angry? Upset?

Meg placed her hand on her stomach, sensing the life there, loving it, knowing for certain she'd never abandon this child, call it a mistake or give it any reason to believe it wasn't important, valued, loved. She would never call this child an accident, although the first time was the only time she and Logan hadn't used birth control. What was the phrase? *Love child.* She loved Logan and she'd love this child.

She didn't know if Logan loved her. He desired her, but passion was not love.

A month had passed since their hike. She'd missed the signs of pregnancy at first—fatigue, the late-afternoon nausea, a missed period—blaming all of it on the trauma of being kidnapped and wounded. Enjoying her time with Logan, whether they talked or stole away to make love, she'd gotten caught up with being in love. Until the day before yesterday, when supper had been a chore to eat and she'd lost it soon afterward. She'd made an appointment with Doc Jacobs. He'd put the symptoms together immediately, taken a blood sample and given her the results. She was pregnant.

Lily had invited Travis and Logan to Thanksgiving dinner. Meg had looked forward to this day. But now part of her wished she could go back to bed, pull the covers over her head and not get up again until she knew exactly what to do about everything—her career, possibly accepting a position with the adoption agency, but, most of all, Logan.

Meg wouldn't let Lily do anything except mash potatoes. It was difficult keeping her aunt in line. Yesterday, when Meg had returned from Doc Jacobs's, she found Lily taking two pumpkin pies from the oven. So Meg had made her aunt promise to behave today. Except Meg's idea of behaving and her aunt's were entirely different.

Finally, when Logan and Travis arrived in the early evening, Lily let them take her place in the kitchen.

Logan came to Meg as she put the finishing touches

on a salad, put his arms around her and kissed her on the neck. "Happy Thanksgiving."

His touch, his voice and the knowledge she now carried brought tears to her eyes. She swallowed hard and managed to reply, "Happy Thanksgiving."

Travis pulled out a chair and sat at the table already set with Lily's best china. "Are you two going to cook or make out? Some of us are getting hungry."

When Meg turned around, she saw Travis's grin. She'd seen a change in him over the past month. His hostility had given way to an honest friendliness to her and a more accepting attitude of his father. Over the past few weeks, she'd seen Logan relax more with his son. They still didn't talk much, but when they did, they seemed to be more willing to listen to each other.

She couldn't help but think of the child she was carrying. How would Logan relate to him or her? Did he want to be a father again? And if not...

Travis's grin faded, and he was looking at her as if wondering if he'd said something wrong.

Summoning up a smile, she responded, "We're almost finished cooking. If one of you strong men would like to lift the bird out of the oven—"

The phone rang, and Meg reached for it. "Hello."

"Meg, darling, it's your mother. We just got back to the village and received your messages about Lily. It sounds as if the crisis is over."

When Meg had tried to reach her parents after Lily's heart attack, she'd been told they'd left for an archaeological dig. She'd called their base site each week, leaving a message with an update of her aunt's condition so they'd have it when they returned. Old sadness surfaced when she heard her mother's voice.

But anger soon followed. Anger like she'd never known.

Even when they'd learned of Meg's ordeal and injury, they'd made two solicitous phone calls, discovered she'd recover and gone back to their work. She found herself angry not only for herself but for her aunt. "Yes, the crisis is over. For now. What I'd like to know is how you would have felt if she'd died and you were just calling in now?"

"Margaret Elizabeth. How dare you speak to me like that?"

"I dare because it's the truth. Would you like to speak to Aunt Lily?"

"Yes, of course. But first, how are you?"

Pregnant, Mother. And believe me, you'll be the last to know. "I'm terrific."

"Good. Good. I just wanted you to know we'll be back in the States in about a month. It's time to raise funds again, so we'll be doing a tour of colleges and private companies."

"Are you and Dad well?" As much as she didn't want to, she still loved her parents and cared about their welfare.

"Yes, of course."

Silence extended between them. They had no more to say. "I'll get Aunt Lily. Hold on."

When Meg returned to the kitchen, she listened to make sure her aunt had picked up, then replaced the phone on its cradle. Logan and Travis were looking at her as if she'd grown two heads. She opened the oven door and pulled out the rack.

Logan crossed to the stove. "I'll get it."

She stood back and let him lift it to the top of the range.

He lifted off the lid and asked casually, "That was your mother?"

"Yes. They'll be coming back to the States around Christmas."

Travis stood and joined her by the sink. "You don't sound too happy about it."

Whether it was hormones or the tension she felt because of the news she had to give Logan, she just wanted to cry. "I'm not happy or unhappy about it. What they do no longer affects me."

"You can't mean that," Logan chided.

"I know exactly what I mean and how I feel." She faced Travis. "If you want to see an example of parents who really *don't* care, just drop by when they're here."

Logan and his son exchanged a look that said they didn't know what had gotten into her. She wasn't entirely sure herself. But she did know she loved her baby already, and her protective instincts had revved into overdrive from the moment she'd heard her mother's voice. She would never, ever hurt her child as her parents had hurt her. She would never abandon her son or daughter.

This tension was driving her crazy, that's all. As soon as they finished dinner, she'd tell Logan about the baby.

Lily and Ned loved having more people in their house for the holiday. Conversation flowed around the table as Meg struggled to keep her mind on it and answer questions when someone addressed her directly. Every once in a while, she caught Logan's gaze on her. She pushed her food around her plate, managing a bite or two.

After dinner, Travis left to join friends. Lily and

Ned insisted on helping Logan and Meg with cleanup, though Meg would have preferred to work with Logan and ease into the conversation they needed to have. Finally Meg washed the roasting pan and sighed with relief as Ned and Lily went to the living room.

Logan quickly dried the pan. "Do you feel like getting some fresh air?"

Meg jumped at the chance. "I'll get my jacket."

A few minutes later, they walked along the path in the backyard. A whippoorwill sang into the night. The stars, brilliant against the black sky, twinkled through the bare branches. So many changes in the past month. She could already feel the changes in her body, now that she was aware of what was happening.

"What's wrong, Meg?" Logan's tone was gentle, but also held that determination that was innately his to cut to the bottom line.

Stopping, she faced him, not knowing how to say it the best way. "I'm pregnant."

Silence. The light from the back porch reached only far enough to cast shadows, but she could see Logan's jaw tense. Finally, as hours seemed to pass, she heard him blow out a breath.

"Say it," she said.

Still, he remained silent.

"Go ahead, Logan. Tell me how you feel…as if you're in the middle of history repeating itself."

"How do you feel?" he asked without responding to her statement.

She wasn't sure what she expected, but this wasn't it. Had she expected Logan to suddenly declare his undying love? Maybe she hadn't expected it, but searching her heart, she had to admit that had been a

KAREN ROSE SMITH 205

hope. "I'm confused and scared. I just found out yesterday, so it hasn't had time to sink in."

"You don't have to go through it alone." There was sincerity in his voice, but distance, too.

Any hope she'd entertained about happily-ever-after wilted. She should have known better. She should have known she couldn't count on anyone but herself. Despite Logan's halfhearted promise of support, she knew she had to make decisions that were more than convenient—they had to be right for her and her baby. She'd never depended on anyone; she wasn't about to start now.

"I won't place any demands on you, Logan. I have to think about what's best in the long run."

He clasped her elbow. "Now, wait a minute. I'm this child's father. Any decisions we make, we make together."

She wished she could see his face in the shadows. "And what if my decisions don't coincide with yours?"

"Dammit, Meg. You've just thrown me a hand grenade. Let me absorb this. I haven't done such a great job of being a father to Travis, but I won't let you cut me out."

"You won't *let* me? *I'm* the one who's pregnant. *I'm* the one who will carry this child, decide where I want to raise it."

"Where? You can't be thinking about going back to D.C. and that life. Not with a baby."

"I don't know what I'm thinking about. But I do know that I'll never for one moment let this child think it was an accident...or a mistake. I felt like that all my life. With or without you, I'm going to love this child every minute of every hour of every day.'' Shivering, she suddenly felt cold from head to toe.

Logan slid his hand from her elbow to her fingers. ''You're cold. Let's go inside.''

Pulling away from him, she said, ''I haven't told Lily yet, and I don't intend to. At least, not right now. I don't want her to worry. She doesn't need the stress.''

''Meg, she knows you. She'll be able to tell something is wrong.''

Meg's teeth chattered, and she couldn't seem to be able to do anything about it.

''Let's go to my place. Travis won't be home for a few hours. We'll talk this through....''

Contrary to her usual opinion, talking wouldn't help this. His first reaction had been the important one. It was obvious he wasn't happy about her news. It was obvious he didn't love her. ''I think you should go home. Give us both time to sleep on it. I didn't get any sleep last night, and my thoughts keep going around in circles.'' One thought. She loved Logan. Logan didn't love her.

''Are you sure that's what you want?''

What she wanted and what she'd get were two different things. She loved Logan so much it hurt. Standing here, pretending her heart wasn't breaking, was simply too difficult. ''That's what I want.''

They walked back to the house, not touching, not talking. When Logan left, he didn't even kiss her good-night. Her past experience had taught her that love hurt. But she'd never, ever imagined it could hurt this much.

Logan drove and drove, trying not to think, but most of all, trying not to feel. What he wanted to do was return to Meg to tell her he'd handled everything all wrong. He'd known it as soon as he'd walked away.

Yet he wasn't sure how to handle it right!

Every instinct inside him had screamed, *Take her in your arms. Ask her to marry you.*

Another voice conflicted with instinct. The voice of the past reminded him of his mistakes, the tension, the heartache, of a marriage that didn't succeed because he'd forced his opinion on Shelley. It reminded him that Travis had been hurt and was still feeling the effects of a marriage that hadn't been strong enough.

And then there was Meg. A woman who was so damn strong and independent, she wouldn't let anyone make decisions for her or tell her what to do. But God help him, he wanted her and he wanted this child! Marrying Meg would give him so much joy....

He pushed his foot down on the accelerator. What kind of marriage could they have if she wanted to return to her career? He couldn't move to D.C. right now. He couldn't uproot Travis again. They were finally finding each other.

Damn it all to—

Logan let up on the gas. He wanted to marry Meg. Period. Somehow he had to convince her that was what she wanted, too—him, a family and a life in Willow Valley. He wouldn't stand by and let her waltz out of his life. Together they'd find a way through this. The right way.

Friday evening, the wash basket tilted over, and the clean laundry spilled onto the laundry-room floor.

Meg stooped over and plopped it back in. She'd gone to the adoption agency this morning, hoping to keep herself distracted. But that had been a silly idea. There, couples wanting children and children needing parents surrounded her.

All day she'd been haunted by a familiar sadness she'd carried with her as a child. Then she'd think about the life inside her and experienced indescribable joy. Down…up. Up…down. What a day. And then trying to get through supper, pretending her life wasn't in chaos…

Suddenly Meg heard footfalls in the kitchen. They didn't belong to her aunt or uncle. If she could have fled, she would have. But the small room off the kitchen was a dead end, and she was trapped.

Logan stood in the doorway for a moment. But when she stooped to lift the wash basket, he moved. "Where do you want it?" He took it from her.

"Logan, it's not that heavy…."

"Where do you want it?"

When his jaw tensed like that, there was no point in arguing. "On the kitchen table. I have to fold it." She followed Logan to the kitchen.

He set the wash basket on the table, the lines around his mouth cutting deep as he said, "Let's go to the movies."

"What?"

"I want to take you out somewhere."

Sometimes she really believed men and women were from totally different planets. "I don't want to be taken out. If you're not ready to talk about the things we need to talk about…"

"I'm ready, all right." His eyes were the darkest green of a rain forest and just as impenetrable. "But

I'm more worried about you. You're pale. You seem tense. I thought maybe we could relax, then go get something to eat and talk then."

"I don't know, Logan."

In a lightning-quick movement, he was before her clasping her shoulders. "We were friends before we were lovers, weren't we?"

She wanted so much more than friendship and being lovers. She wanted the kind of love she'd witnessed between her aunt and uncle. Studying Logan's face, loving him, she couldn't stop hoping.

The movie theater, built in the strip shopping center with a large food store, jewelry store and a few smaller shops, didn't seat many moviegoers. Several people who knew Logan stopped him to chat, and his good intentions for the evening were fast fading away. Meg was already withdrawn. Each acquaintance who stopped him, usually asking about Travis, pushed her further into her shell. All he wanted to do was kiss her and remind her of the feelings between them.

As soon as they took their seats in the theater, the previews began. Meg sat stiff and straight beside him. He took her hand and tucked it into the crook of his arm. When she didn't pull away, he was relieved.

The movie was a comedy. He thought laughter would be a good icebreaker. But the shenanigans were slapstick, and he didn't laugh. Neither did Meg. Yep, this had been a *lousy* idea.

As the theater emptied after the movie, Meg stood beside Logan. "I'm really not hungry."

"Meg, you have to eat."

"This isn't a good time of day for me, Logan. I'd rather just go back to Lily's and get a few crackers."

He'd never even asked if she had morning sickness. "Fine. We'll go back." After they climbed in the car and headed to Lily's, he asked, "Do you have morning sickness, too?"

"No. Just afternoons and sometimes in the evening."

"Have you seen Doc?"

"Yes. So, I'm sure if that's what you're asking…"

"I didn't doubt you. Shelley knew almost right away—"

"I guess she was a few steps ahead of me."

He never should have brought up Shelley's name. Damn, he was handling this badly. As he drove down the lane to the farm, he asked, "Did Doc give you vitamins?"

"Logan, I know how to take care of myself and my baby!"

Pulling to a stop, he switched off the ignition. "This is *my* baby, too."

"I'm not about to forget." She unsnapped her seat belt.

He unsnapped his. "Then why are you pushing me away?"

"I'm not pushing you away. I'm trying to make it clear that I'm an intelligent woman. I love this baby already and would never do anything detrimental to it or me!"

In the rays of the porch light, he could see her independence but also the shimmering vulnerability. Without a thought of the consequences or all the things they needed to discuss, he slipped his hand behind her head and caught her lips before she could say anything else.

She tried to pull away for an instant, but when his tongue eased into the corner of her mouth, she surrendered. Logan pushed between her lips, too frustrated by the wall she'd erected to use finesse. He felt his control slipping from the first stroke of his tongue on hers. She returned his desire by inviting him deeper. He thrust inside with a primal rhythm, symbolizing the union he truly wanted. He wanted to possess all of her, coax her to open to him, to need a future with him as much as he needed one with her.

He splayed his fingers into her silky brown hair, imagining their bodies uniting again in sweet harmony. She hadn't buttoned her jacket. He needed more than kissing. When his hand slipped under her sweater, she moaned and pressed against his hand. He thrust his tongue against hers over and over, trying to show her how much he cared, how much he wanted this child…*their* child.

Her fingers clutching at his shoulders drove him on. He cupped her breast in his hand. It felt fuller. It felt…

He swore a blue streak in his mind. What in the name of good sense was he doing? Meg was pregnant with his child. This wouldn't give them answers. In fact—

Tearing away, he tried to get control of his breathing and his thoughts.

"What's the matter?" she asked in a soft voice.

"I'm sorry. This isn't going to get us anywhere. It's what got us into this mess."

For those few moments when they'd been entangled in each other's arms, the distance had faded away. Now it was back along with the night chill, which was getting frostier as each second ticked by. But even with Meg's withdrawal, he didn't expect her to suddenly throw open the car door and hop out.

Before he could reach for her, she said, "I thought we did have something to talk about. But I was wrong. I absolve you of this mess, Logan MacDonald. It's *my* mess now. And probably the best way for me to handle it is to handle it alone." She slammed the car door so hard it rattled, the echo surprising Logan almost as much as her words and her exit. By the time he'd climbed out, she'd already gone into the house and closed the door. He didn't need gut instinct to tell him she wouldn't open it again to him tonight.

When Meg sagged against the back door, her first sob broke loose. All she could do was wrap her arms around herself and let the tears fall.

Suddenly the light went on, and Lily stood in front of her. "Meg, honey. What's wrong? Did you and Logan have a fight?"

"I'm pregnant, Aunt Lily. I thought I could handle this alone. I didn't want to worry you." Her tears felt hot on her cold cheeks, and she tried to brush them away, but they were falling too fast.

Her aunt wrapped her arms around her niece. "You don't have to handle anything alone. Especially not this. What did Logan say?"

"He thinks it's a mess. He doesn't love me."

"Did he say that?"

"He didn't have to. When I first told him…he didn't say anything. And then tonight… What is it about me? Mom and Dad couldn't love me. Neither could Todd. And now Logan…"

Her aunt stroked Meg's hair as she'd done when her niece was a child. "Unconditional love is a miracle. We can't earn it, honey. It just is. You've known too few miracles in your life. But I do think Logan cares about you. Very much."

Meg pulled away and swiped at her tears with her hand. She wouldn't let a man, not even Logan, do this to her. Apparently he had wanted to play. He'd wanted sex. As attracted as they'd been to each other, they'd given in to their desires. Well, now, she was left with more than desire. Her heart hurt, but he'd given her a gift.

Just as long ago, she'd accepted her parents' abandonment and found joy in her aunt and uncle's love, so now she'd accept the fact that Logan's passion was that and nothing else. Now she'd find joy in the child growing inside her. Her child would know the miracle of unconditional love.

"If Logan calls, I don't want to talk to him."

"Do you think that's wise?"

"For now it's the wisest thing I can do. I have decisions to make, Aunt Lily. I have to center my energy on them and the baby. So, please, if he calls, tell him I'm busy. I have to pull myself together before I can face him again."

And as she had as far back as Meg could remember, Lily gave her niece unconditional love. "All right. But you *will* have to face him again—and soon. Knowing Logan, he won't let you hide very long."

"Don't be so sure. He might want me to hide forever."

Lily just shook her head and gave Meg another hug.

This time she didn't pull away.

Chapter Thirteen

Meg stood in the front yard and admired her uncle's handiwork as he looped cedar garlands wrapped with twinkle lights across the front porch's banister. Lily sat on the swing bundled in a corduroy coat, watching her husband, making sure he did it "right." The pine cone wreath on the door Lily had made herself years ago. This year it wore a gold bow. After a hug for her aunt and a "good job" and a wink for her uncle, Meg went inside and hung her coat in the foyer closet, thinking about her day at the adoption center.

Her professional and personal interest in the job was becoming more involved. She enjoyed it—both the worthwhile feeling of accomplishment in placing children with loving families, and the people she worked with. It wouldn't be a stretch to imagine herself taking the position as liaison permanently. Yet, she didn't know if that decision would solve problems or create more. Did she want to stay in Willow Valley if Logan didn't love her? If he didn't truly want this child?

After she fixed herself a cup of tea, she sat at the kitchen table, trying to think about something other than children and Logan. When the doorbell rang, she peeked out behind the kitchen curtain. No sheriff's car. No navy sedan. During the past few days Logan had called several times. But she wasn't answering the phone.

As Meg opened the back door, she didn't find Logan, but rather his son. Travis had been dropping in twice a week for practice sessions, but she hadn't seen him since Thanksgiving, two weeks ago.

"Hi. You busy?" he asked without his customary smile.

She wondered what, if anything, Logan had told him. "No. I just got home. Come on in."

Shifting his backpack to the side, he lifted it off and set it on the table. "Did you and Dad have a fight?"

Before answering, she went to the cupboard and took out two glasses. "It's more complicated than a fight. I think you should ask your Dad."

Travis, as well as Logan, had become comfortable at Lily and Ned's house. The teenager pulled a carton of milk from the refrigerator. Seeing that it was skim, he turned up his nose and found the regular quart. "Dad's been a bear. I don't think he'd like a bunch of questions." After he opened the carton, he didn't pour. "Do you want me here? I mean, if you're mad at him and you'd rather not do this…"

"Travis, I told you before. You and I can be friends no matter what happens with me and your dad."

He studied her for a moment, then poured the milk. "It's about you going back to Washington, isn't it?"

"It's about a lot of things."

Travis pulled out a chair with his foot and sat at the table. "Dad and I have been getting along better. I mean, he still thinks he should run everything, but he's not so…I don't know. At least he doesn't jump down my throat when I go out now."

Meg knew how difficult it had been for Logan to give his son some space.

"You and Dad…you're not fighting because of me, are you? Another year, and I'll be gone."

Was this the reason Travis had really stopped by today? Meg sat across from him and didn't evade the probing question in his gaze. "Travis, you have nothing to do with my problems with your dad."

"For sure?"

She nodded. "For sure."

Travis visibly relaxed as he leaned back in his chair. "Are you going to the square dance Saturday night?"

The second weekend in December, Willow Valley fire company hosted a Christmas bazaar during the day and a square dance in the evening. Meg told Travis the truth. "I really haven't thought about it."

"Dad has a sheriff's meeting in Lynchburg, but he'll probably be back by evening."

"Is that a warning?" She smiled, not sure where Travis was headed.

"Sort of. He usually goes. I thought you'd want to know."

So now she knew. What she'd do about it was another matter entirely.

* * *

The booth beckoned to Meg on Saturday morning as she passed one stand after another displaying Christmas ornaments and handicrafts. This particular booth held a stack of homemade baby bibs, quilts and sweaters with bootees and caps. Meg picked up a tiny white crocheted sweater that was as soft as Leo's kitten fur.

"Are you going to buy it?"

Meg turned and found her uncle at her elbow. "It's a little soon."

"It's not too soon to plan and dream. I guess you know Lily's as excited about this baby as you are."

Her aunt *was* excited. She loved to nurture. "Aunt Lily and you should have had ten kids."

Ned shrugged. "It wasn't to be. When we were trying to have a family, there were no fertility drugs or in-vitro-fertilization procedures. We probably should have adopted. But we always struggled with the farm. And then again, we had you."

"And I had you."

He nodded to the baby sweater in her hand. "Now you're going to have a child of your own. That makes us proud."

"Even though I'm a single woman?"

"From what Lily tells me, you're not giving Logan much of a chance to make it otherwise." He frowned and gave her a look she'd seen before, a look that said she might be acting foolish.

"Uncle Ned…"

"Are you going to the square dance tonight?"

She knew as well as anyone else she couldn't avoid Logan forever. Tonight, in the midst of a crowd of people, would probably be the best place to see him again. They wouldn't have to "talk" unless they both made a concerted effort.

Whenever she thought about Logan, she ached for what might have been. "Yes, I'm going tonight. You and Aunt Lily would probably carry me if I said I wasn't."

Her uncle chuckled and gestured to the sweater. "So, are you going to buy that?"

Meg smiled. It *was* time to dream and plan, at least about her baby. "Yes, I am. And I might buy a few bibs, too. I hear babies go through quite a few."

Logan's tie had gotten tighter as the day-long meeting had droned on. Finally at home, he tugged it loose and tossed it over his bedroom chair. His shirt followed.

Travis stopped in the doorway. "I'm leaving."

"For the square dance?"

"We'll get there eventually. A couple of stops first."

Logan opened his mouth, then closed it again.

Travis grinned. "Very good, Dad. You didn't ask if we were stopping for booze. I gotta split. If I pretend I don't know you at the fire hall..."

"I know. I shouldn't take it personally."

Travis tapped his fingers on the doorframe. "You're learning, Dad. See ya."

Logan unbuckled his belt and unzipped his trousers. Yeah, he was learning, all right. Very slowly. The problem was that learning took patience, and he was about out of patience where Meg was concerned. He knew he should tell Travis that Meg was pregnant. But he was supposed to be a role model for his son. Until he and Meg reached some kind of agreement...

Agreement. Yeah. When she wouldn't talk to him. Well, that was going to end tonight. And if she didn't put in an appearance at the dance, he'd drive to the farm and insist she talk to him. He wouldn't leave until she did. He didn't blame her for being angry. But she'd misinterpreted what he'd meant. Granted, *mess* hadn't been the best term to use, and he'd kicked himself for the past two weeks for using it.

He understood her anger at his insensitivity, but he didn't understand her withdrawal. They'd always been able to talk. She'd always been open, coaxing *him* to lay everything out on the table. Without Meg, he might have lost his son. Maybe he hadn't told her often enough how grateful he was. How glad he was she'd come into his life. Out of all the things he should have told her, the one very important one was that he was glad she was carrying his baby. Maybe once she knew that, marriage wouldn't be such a big jump. After all, maybe he needed to court her.

What did a man wear to court a woman?

He'd think about it in the shower.

In a few hours, the social hall of the fire company had been transformed from a Christmas bazaar into a festive, barnlike atmosphere with bales of hay, cedar garlands, red ribbons, and holly centerpieces abounding. Meg sat beside Lily and Ned at one of the long tables. Friends of her aunt and uncle sat at the table with them. The band tuned up, and soon the caller stood at the microphone directing the dancers.

Meg kept her eyes on the door. Logan hadn't yet appeared. But suddenly someone stood behind her chair with a hand on her shoulder. She turned and found Michael Holden, his jeans and red plaid shirt giving him a different persona than his principal's white shirt and tie.

The chair beside her was empty. He nodded to it. "Do you mind?"

"No. Have a seat. How are you?"

"Good. Is Logan here?"

She shrugged as nonchalantly as she could manage. "Not that I know of."

He looked at her curiously. "Is something wrong?"

His concern made her give him an honest answer. "Nothing I want to talk about."

Smiling, he said, "All right. Then I'll assume you came tonight to have fun. Are you having it yet?"

Michael really was a nice man, and she had to smile back. "Not quite yet."

He laughed. "Would you like something to eat? They have quite a spread over there. Hot dogs to popcorn."

"Just some soda. Something without caffeine."

After Michael brought them two glasses of soda, he asked, "Would you like to join a square?"

She'd asked Doc about exercise. He'd told her what she'd suspected—keeping fit was the best way to keep problems during pregnancy to a minimum. "Yes, I would."

As Meg do-si-doed with Michael, she remembered the fun she'd had as a teenager when she'd gone to square dances. It was the challenge of hearing the calls and keeping her feet moving in the right direction. It was the mixture of male and female, brushing elbows, laughing and misstepping that put everyone in a congenial mood. But when the caller directed her to promenade with her partner and Michael took her hand, she longed for Logan beside her. She longed to be sharing the moments of fun with him.

On a deeper level, she realized she wanted him beside her through her pregnancy and during the birth of their child. Her heart ached because she knew she wanted something from him he couldn't give. Because of Shelley. Because of Travis. He'd probably never expected to be a father again. With the heartache and turmoil he'd gone through the past few years with Travis, contemplating the responsibilities of fatherhood again was probably just too painful. Yet she knew Logan was the type of man whose sense of responsibility was as vital to him as his sense of duty. Essentially that's why she'd been hiding from him. She was afraid his sense of responsibility or duty would trap him again in a life he didn't want.

For that reason, she'd kept the idea of going back to D.C. as an option. On the other hand, if she took the liaison position with Victoria's adoption agency, Logan would have access to his child if he wanted it. As much as she'd thought about what was best for her and the baby, she'd thought about what was best for Logan, too. Because she loved him.

But loving him only added confusion to questions that seemed to have no answers.

When the song was over, Michael nudged her elbow. "You stopped smiling. For a while there, I thought you might be having fun."

"For a while, I was. Do you think scientists have ever done a study on how detrimental thinking can be to a person's health?"

He took her hand and positioned her across from him in another square. "The secret is to keep too busy to think. Now, what do you say we try this again until you get it right?''

Michael's patient amusement was contagious. "All right. Let's give it one more try."

He squeezed her shoulder. "That a girl."

Before the music started again, Cal walked by the square, saw Meg and Michael facing each other and frowned. Stepping closer to Michael, but not so far away that Meg couldn't hear, he warned in a low voice, "She's the sheriff's lady, Holden. You better not get any poaching ideas if you know what's good for you."

Meg stood stunned.

Michael responded to the deputy sheriff calmly. "Then I guess the sheriff should be a little more attentive to his lady if he expects other men *not* to get any ideas."

Cal scowled, but when Michael wasn't intimidated, the deputy arched his brows at Meg and walked away.

Meg finally found her voice. "I don't believe he said that."

"One thing Cal is is loyal."

"Loyalty is one thing. That kind of…of…outdated chauvinism is another."

"We're in Willow Valley, Meg."

The music started; the caller called the dance. And Meg made up her mind she was definitely going to have fun.

The fun stopped cold when she felt Logan's gaze on her. How could she tell he'd arrived when the room was full of people? The question was moot. She just could. He stood beside a stack of bales of hay, his arms crossed over his chest. His black jeans, gray, western-cut shirt and black boots made him look tall, dangerous and as sexy as she could ever remember him looking. Her hormones were just in a whirl from her pregnancy. That had to explain why, out of all the men in the room, she only felt an overwhelming attraction toward Logan. She ignored it. She was having fun.

Sure, it was lots of fun to see Cal stop beside his boss and mumble something to him. Logan frowned, looked at Michael, then back at her. Not hard to imagine what *that* was about.

It was lots of fun to wonder if she'd split a seam. She'd worn the puffed-sleeved turquoise blouse and matching full skirt, knowing it would be comfortable if she felt like dancing. Logan was looking at her so hard...what was the phrase he'd used at the fund-raiser? *Undressing her with his eyes.*

And it was the most fun to imagine what would happen when the dance was over. Would he come to her? Should she go to him? It was a shame she knew how to square dance so well. Obviously she wasn't busy enough to stop thinking.

When the dance ended, she didn't have to imagine what would happen next. Logan pushed himself away from the bales of hay and headed right toward her, a scowl drawing his brows together.

He stopped a few inches from her. "Do you think you should be doing this?"

As if Michael sensed something in Logan that could be intimidating, he protectively laid a hand on Meg's shoulder. "Why shouldn't she?"

Logan's gaze pointedly stayed on Michael Holden's hand. "Because she's pregnant, and this kind of activity could be harmful to our baby." There was the slightest emphasis on the word "our."

Meg was mortified, and Michael's look of astonishment didn't help. "Logan! I can't believe you'd embarrass me like this. If you think this macho behavior is going to help anything, you're mistaken."

Michael dropped his hand from her shoulder.

Logan curved his arm around her and nudged her toward the closest exit. "I want to talk to you."

She dug in her heels and wouldn't move. "Maybe I don't want to talk to *you*."

"Do I have to pick you up and carry you?"

One look at his face told her that's exactly what he'd do. "All right."

He guided her toward the back exit, out onto a landing. She shivered and rubbed her arms.

"We should have gotten your coat."

"I'm fine."

"You're *always* fine. That's the problem!"

"And just what is that supposed to mean?"

He looked as if he wanted to shake her…or kiss her. She wasn't sure which. "It means you don't always have to handle everything yourself. It means that this is *our* child you're carrying. It means I want you to marry me."

It was a demand, not a request or a proposal. Hurt, she said the first thought that came to mind. "The same way you wanted Shelley to marry you?"

He exploded. "No!" With a slash of his hand through the air, he said angrily, "You're not Shelley."

"No, but I bet the reasons you want me to marry you are the same ones that made you ask Shelley."

"No."

"Logan, the situation is the same."

He stuffed his hands in his pockets. "I want to give

our baby a family. I know I've made mistakes with Travis, but I won't repeat them with this child.''

Logan's intentions were good, but his motivation lacked what she needed most—his love. ''You can be a good father without marrying me. I won't keep the baby from you. I couldn't—''

Logan's pager beeped, then beeped again. The string of epithets he uttered should have scandalized her. But they didn't. He was angry and frustrated. She felt like yelling a few choice swear words herself. Maybe then she wouldn't feel like fleeing to her room at Lily and Ned's and having a good cry.

''I have to call in. Go inside where it's warm. I'll find you.''

''Logan, do you know how to do anything but give orders?''she flared.

He clasped her chin with his thumb and index finger. ''Yes. I know how to kiss you and touch you until you want me as much as I want you.''

His honesty excited her and created pictures of the two of them together she'd never forget. But right now that picture hurt so much.... ''There's more to life than sex,'' she said in a low voice.

Blowing out a breath, Logan opened the door and waited for her to go inside.

A few minutes later, he found her sitting with Lily and Ned. ''There's been another break-in at the high school. This one's messier. Broken glass everywhere. I've got to go. If I'm tied up too late tonight, I *will* see you tomorrow. And I won't accept excuses from Lily.''

With that promise, he headed for the exit.

Lily leaned her shoulder against Meg's. ''I think

Logan's jealous. You should have seen his face when you were dancing with Michael.''

Frustrated and angry herself, she crossed one leg over the other and swung it. ''He told Michael I'm pregnant.''

A hint of a smile played on her aunt's lips. ''He's laying claim.''

''He embarrassed me!''

''You won't be more embarrassed when you start showing and everyone knows?''

Small-town thinking at its finest. She expected her aunt to be more broad-minded. ''That is *no* reason to get married!''

''Married? Did I mention marriage?'' Lily asked innocently.

''No, but Logan did and…'' Her aunt's expression was expectant. ''Never mind. I'm going to get another glass of soda.''

Lily patted Meg's hand. ''When you want to talk, honey, I'll be here.''

''I appreciate it, Aunt Lily. Everything just hurts too much right now.''

At the snack stand, Meg saw Travis. But he didn't see her. He was shifting from one foot to the other, watching the front door.

''Travis, are you looking for your dad? He had to leave because of a break-in at the high school.''

Travis avoided her gaze. ''Yeah, I know. I'm waiting for some friends.''

Intuition she'd relied on over the years made her ask, ''Kyle?''

''Uh, yeah.'' Travis was fidgety. He pulled down his T-shirt and stuffed one hand in his pocket.

''What's happening?'' she asked.

"Nothing," he mumbled.

"Have you been drinking?"

"No!" He glanced at the door again. "If I tell you anything, you'll tell Dad."

"Maybe *you* should tell him."

"No way. I don't rat on friends."

She grabbed his arm. "Travis…"

Pulling away, he shook his head. "I said too much already. Forget it, Meg. Please?"

She didn't want to lose his trust. Her friendship with Logan's son had become important to her. "Only if you promise to call me if you need help with something."

"I don't need help."

"Promise me, Travis."

He didn't deny it again, but nodded. "All right. But now I gotta go."

His reassurance didn't make her feel any better, and she suddenly realized worry would be a constant part of a mother's life.

Meg had been holding her breath since she'd awakened Sunday morning, expecting to hear Logan's car crunch down the lane. But the crunch she heard didn't belong to Logan. She took a look out the back door and called to her aunt and uncle, who were reading the Sunday paper in the living room.

"Aunt Lily. Uncle Ned. Come here. It's Carmen and Manuel." Meg ran out to the truck.

Manuel hopped out first and went around to the other side of the truck to help his wife. Meg reached the truck just as Carmen handed Tomás to her husband.

Seeing Meg, Manuel grinned. "We promised we'd stop on our way to Florida."

Meg gave Carmen a hug, then turned to the baby who'd brought her and Logan together. "Yes, you did. I can't believe how much he's grown. Can I hold him?"

Without hesitation, Carmen said, *"Sí. Tú le eres especial."*

"He's very special to me, too," Meg responded, her eyes filling up. Babies were hope and joy and laughter. So why did she feel as if her heart were tearing in two?

An hour later, she'd finally handed Tomás back to his mother. While Ned, Lily, Carmen and Manuel visited in the living room, Meg offered to make tea. She was taking low-fat muffins out of the pastry holder when a knock came at the back door. Her stomach tightened.

When she opened the door, Travis stood there. And he didn't look good. She pulled him inside. "What's wrong?"

"It's Kyle. I think he's gonna do something stupid."

"How do you know?"

"Last night, before the square dance, he'd been drinking. He said he had things to do and couldn't go with the rest of us. When I heard about the break-in, I was afraid he'd done it. But I didn't know. I was hoping he'd show up at the dance. But he didn't. Then he called me this morning and said he might not see me again for a while. He wouldn't answer my questions about where he was last night. Just said he was stopping at Gibson's, then taking off. I might be all wrong, but I think he needs money. Everybody knows old man Gibson keeps Saturday and Sunday's deposits till Monday morning.''

"Why didn't you go to your dad?"

"Because I don't know where he is. He got in late last night and left a note for me this morning saying he had to talk to me but he was following up on a lead first. I didn't want to alert the whole sheriff's department. Maybe Kyle's just going to buy stuff, and then I'd look like an idiot...."

"Wait right here. I'll tell Aunt Lily I'm going out for a bit. We'll go warn Mr. Gibson, then find your father."

Chapter Fourteen

When Meg opened the door to Gibson's Grocery and walked inside, she felt as if she'd traveled back in time. All those weeks ago. Costa Rica... She saw Olan Gibson's face and remembered the panic, the terror, the nightmares. Before she could prevent Travis from coming in behind her, a voice came from her right.

"Don't move, or someone will get hurt."

She automatically went still.

"Kyle, what the hell...?" Travis turned toward the voice.

When Travis started for Kyle, Meg grabbed his hand and said, "Stop, Travis."

The teenager wore a ski mask and raised the gun in his hand. "Very good, Miss Dawson."

Travis moved toward his friend again. "You don't know what you're doing!"

Kyle raised the gun and shot at a row of canned goods at Travis's left.

Meg wanted to scream, but instead she caught Travis's elbow and held him in place with every ounce of strength in her body.

The sound of the shot had startled Travis, and he finally froze.

She laid her hand protectively over her stomach. Somehow she had to protect her baby and Travis. Somehow she had to get them out of this. What she'd feared most had happened, and she hadn't even gone back to work. One of life's ironies. She needed a clear head. She had to take one step at a time.

"What do you want, Kyle?" she asked calmly, although every nerve in her body trembled.

He tore the ski mask from his head. "I wanted this to be nice and easy. I just wanted Gibson's money, that's all."

The teenager looked as if he'd been drinking. That could slow his reflexes, but also make him more volatile.

"So, take it and go," she suggested reasonably.

He smirked. "Yeah, right. With all of you knowing who I am. I wouldn't get a block."

"You won't get a block anyway, not when my dad finds out what's going on." Anger emanated from Travis.

"Travis, cool down," Meg advised.

"While someone who's supposed to be my friend is holding a gun on me?" he snapped.

"She's right, MacDonald. You'd better pipe down till I figure out what to do." He waved the gun at Olan. "Over here with them, old man. And don't do anything you're going to regret."

* * *

Logan was asking Kyle's mother questions and listening to her problems when he got the call. His blood turned to ice as Cal gave him the specifics as he knew them. Meg, Travis and Olan Gibson were locked in the store with Kyle. Kyle had already fired a shot, and Logan didn't want to think about what that could mean.

He took off at a run and jumped into the sheriff's cruiser. Then he took his gun and holster from the locked glove compartment and strapped it on. Chances were he was going to need it. Calling the rescue-squad dispatcher, he gave instructions for them to drive to the grocery store without sirens. In case someone had been hurt, he wanted them there. But he didn't want to shake up Kyle or give him any reason to shoot again.

As Logan switched on his flashing lights and sped to Main Street, he thought over his conversation with Kyle's mother. A father who'd walked out. A mother trying to make ends meet for herself and three kids on a secretary's salary. Kyle being frustrated by not having the things he saw other teenagers had.

Last night, as Logan had interviewed witnesses concerning the second high-school break-in, he'd discovered someone had recognized Kyle running from the school. But Kyle had never returned home last night. Logan tried to will his heart to slow, tried to wipe the pictures from his mind of Travis or Meg wounded...or worse.

Life could turn on a dime. Just last night, he'd asked Meg to marry him. Just last night, he'd hoped...

He still had hope. He wouldn't lose her or either of his children.

A crowd had gathered outside the grocery store. Logan parked along the side of the building, rather than in the front. He could do this one of three ways. He could try to make contact with Kyle by phone and talk him into some kind of trade. He could surround the store in a SWAT-team-like maneuver and hope for a clear shot. He could use the back entrance of the store, go in and try to disarm Kyle himself.

On-site, he instructed five of his deputies to surround the front of the store but to wait for further orders. Then he told Cal he intended to go in the rear entrance and asked him to cover him and act as a backup. Cal followed Logan inside.

Guns drawn, Logan and Cal eased through the storeroom, careful not to make a sound. Logan stopped behind the swinging door and listened.

"So tell me why you need the money, Kyle."

That was Meg's sweet voice, calm without a quaver. Surely she was okay if she sounded like that.

"I need to get out of here. To go to Richmond like Travis. There was practically nothing in that school last night. Change. Five bucks in petty cash at the secretary's desk. Cripes, it wasn't worth the commotion of getting in."

"I told you before, Kyle, Richmond's no dream place. Even if you get a few hundred dollars, it won't go far," Travis warned.

"You managed four months on a little bit of nothing. I'll get a job," Kyle argued.

"You don't have a high-school diploma," Meg argued softly. "What kind of job are you going to get?"

"Shut up," Kyle yelled.

The silence almost killed Logan. He edged closer to the window in the door and peered through.

The teenager shook the gun at Meg. "I saw the sheriff kissing you. He'll pay to get you out of here. Hell, if he could afford a private investigator for Travis here…"

Logan watched Kyle swing the barrel of the gun near Meg's chin. All he wanted to do was lunge out of that storeroom and take the kid down. But he knew better. At least, his head did. His heart was screaming for him to act. If anything happened to Travis or Meg… Lord, how he loved them both.

Love…love…love.

The word echoed, making his head spin and his heart pound even harder. Of course he loved her. That's why he wanted to marry her. Couldn't she see that? Couldn't she see…

He fought against the swell of feelings.

Right now he needed to alert her to his presence.

When he carefully checked the window again, Kyle's back was to him. Logan stood at the small window, praying Meg would look beyond Kyle and see him. But all her attention was riveted on the teenager.

He couldn't make a sound. That would alert Kyle. But if he could make some small motion… He tested the swinging door. No sound. He pushed it a little farther. Still no sound. Now, if she would just look.

Suddenly Meg lifted her chin a fraction of an inch. Her gaze went from the doorframe to Logan's face at the window. Then she dropped her gaze again to Kyle's gun.

"Kyle, if you want money, then you're going to have to do something about it. Why don't we go over to the phone and call the sheriff's office? If I could talk to Logan and tell him we're all fine..."

She was a sweetheart, all right, giving him the information he needed to hear most.

"Why are you in such an all-fired hurry to help me?" Kyle exploded.

"Because I'm afraid. And Travis and Mr. Gibson probably are, too. That gun's dangerous, Kyle."

"Yeah, and I know how to use it."

"I can tell Logan that. I can tell him..." She stopped for a moment. "I can tell him you don't want to hurt us, that you just want to get out."

Kyle looked confused. "I need a car."

"I can tell him that, too. In fact, you can tell him. But we have to go over there to the phone."

Logan caught on to what she was doing. She was putting their lives in his hands. To get to the phone, she and Kyle would have to pass the door. He'd have a split second to take Kyle down before he could hurt anyone. Meg trusted him that much. Yet she didn't want to marry him.

"C'mon, Kyle. Let's get this over with. You don't want to hurt us. I know you don't," Meg urged. Her soft voice, her wide brown eyes, her caring attitude, seemed to work on the teenager.

"You're not trying to trick me," he said as if he was trying to convince himself.

"No tricks. I don't know any tricks, Kyle. But I do want to ask a favor. Why don't you let Travis and Mr. Gibson leave? You don't need them. You have me."

"You *are* trying to trick me."

"I'm staying with you," Travis announced with the same protectiveness Logan felt.

Meg was trying to get Gibson and Travis out of harm's way. But it wasn't working. Logan's quick glance at Olan Gibson told him the older man was shell-shocked. He was probably afraid he'd do or say something that would make matters worse.

"All of you are staying," Kyle decided, waving the gun. "Gibson, Travis, you move and I shoot. You got it?" he demanded.

Olan nodded, but Travis said between clenched teeth, "So help me, Kyle, if I ever get my hands on you…"

"Yeah, well, you're not going to, Travis. C'mon, Miss Dawson. I want five thousand dollars and a car. In an hour. A sheriff should have enough clout for that."

"You could just put down the gun, Kyle," she suggested. "It would go a lot easier for you."

"Quit yakking. Let's make the call."

Logan readied himself. All of his years in law enforcement, the rigors of keeping fit, the afternoons at the shooting range, his love for Meg, their unborn child and Travis, boiled down to this one moment. He wouldn't have another. She'd done all she could as the intelligent, gutsy woman she was. Now he had to make this maneuver work or regret it the rest of his life.

Meg passed the door first, as Logan knew she would. He caught a glimpse of her hair through the window. And then he listened and watched for a shadow…

All at once, Kyle stepped in front of the door. Logan slammed it open into the teenager with the force of a tornado. A shot hit the wall.

"Everyone on the floor," Logan yelled.

Then Logan pinned Kyle's arms behind his back, and Cal was there, cuffing the teenager. Olan Gibson must have opened the front door, because the other deputies rushed in.

Meg was sitting on Olan's stool behind the counter, her face pale, her hands gripping the counter.

As the deputies escorted Kyle out, Logan hurried to her. "Are you all right?"

She looked up. "I'm fine. I…"

"Dad!"

Logan threw his arms around his son. "Are *you* all right?"

He held on tight, thinking about how close he'd come to almost losing the two people he cared about the most in this world. Holding on was more important than breathing or talking or anything else.

Finally Travis pulled away. "That was so cool, Dad. Did Meg know you were there? How did she…"

When Logan looked over at Meg…she was gone! "Where did she go?"

"I don't know. She was here."

They both rushed outside and caught a glimpse of her in the front seat of someone's car as it drove away. Logan's heart pounded as it had when he'd stood behind the door. "She probably wanted to get home so Lily and Ned would know she's all right."

"What's going on with you two, Dad?"

Logan took a deep breath, feeling as if he needed a few hundred more to slow his adrenaline. "Meg's pregnant."

"Wow!"

"Yeah, wow," Logan repeated wryly.

"Ya know, Dad, maybe you and I should have a discussion about the birds, the bees and condoms."

Logan could feel his cheeks flush. "Things got out of hand, we got caught up in the moment."

Travis grinned. "I think I've heard that stuff from a few guys I know."

"Look, I know I'm a lousy role model where this is concerned."

Travis's grin faded. "What's going to happen? I mean, you said you didn't really love Mom when you asked her to marry you."

"I know. And at first I compared this situation to that one. But they're very different. I was committed to your mother, Travis, and I cared about her deeply. But with Meg...I *do* love her. How would you feel if we got married?"

"I like Meg. I think...we're friends. It would even be kinda neat."

Logan slung his arm around his son's shoulders. "Travis, I need to know exactly what happened last night and this morning, whatever you know about Kyle."

Travis looked up at his father. "You don't think I was in cahoots with Kyle, do you? Because I wasn't."

Logan knew his answer would shape their relationship for years to come. He looked into his son's eyes, saw the truth there and said, "If you say you weren't, I believe you. I just need you to fill in missing pieces if you can."

"You really believe me?"

"Yes."

Travis relaxed. "I'll tell you whatever I can."

As they walked to the car, Travis asked, "Dad, can you do anything for Kyle? He just wanted to get out of Willow Valley. I mean, I know what he did today was bad, but *he's* not. Do you know what I mean?''

Logan knew exactly what his son meant. If someone could have helped Kyle before he'd gotten this desperate… "I can't make any promises. But I'll try to get him some help. Okay?''

"Okay.''

When Logan removed his arm from Travis's shoulders, his son said, "You know, Dad, that's the first time you've hugged me since I was twelve.''

Logan's chest tightened. "Then it was long overdue. And I'm warning you right now, it won't be long till the next one.''

Travis grimaced, but Logan watched the grimace change into a small smile. His son was finally home.

Meg knew she had run away again, telling herself she had to get home so her aunt and uncle would realize she was safe and unharmed. And she did. But she'd also needed time to get her thoughts together before she talked to Logan.

She sat on the edge of the guest-room bed, watching Tomás sleep in his cradle, the cradle she'd once slept in. Family, friends and tradition meant so much. And the love that surrounded all of it…

So much had become clear to her the moment her gaze had met Logan's at Gibson's Grocery. She'd risk her life for Travis and the baby she carried; she'd risk her life for Logan. No love could burn deeper than that.

Logan had done his job this afternoon. Had it been more than his job? Had love shown them how to communicate, to make the split-second timing work? She wouldn't know until she asked. She wouldn't know until she found the courage to tell Logan she loved him and discovered how he felt in return.

And if he didn't love her?

Her heart would break. But she'd also hold on to the hope that staying in Willow Valley, parenting their child together, would eventually give him the freedom to love. She'd stay here and love him. But she wouldn't marry him unless he could offer her more than a fulfillment of responsibility.

Long ago she'd learned facing life's challenges required courage. She had the courage to stay in Willow Valley and stop running from whatever Logan did feel for her. Maybe someday it would turn into love.

The crunch of tires on gravel urged her to switch her gaze from Tomás to the window. Logan.

Now all she had to do was find the courage to tell him she loved him.

Still wearing his uniform, Logan sat on the swing on Lily's front porch absently gazing at the Christmas decorations, waiting for Meg. Lily had said Meg was upstairs tucking Tomás in for his nap. Logan wanted to see the couple and their baby, but first he had to talk to the woman he loved and give her a symbol of that love, along with the words he should have said before now.

His thoughts had been in turmoil since Meg had told him she was pregnant. He'd realized why today in the midst of the chaos. He loved her. The problem was—he hadn't offered her love. He'd offered her passion, caring, marriage. But Meg had needed more. She'd needed his love.

Suddenly this afternoon, with her life on the line, he'd figured out why she'd withdrawn from him when once she'd been so open. Essentially Meg's parents had abandoned her. Although she was a warm, compassionate woman, she didn't trust easily. Somehow, between the birth of Manuel and Carmen's baby and Logan's problems with Travis, she'd started to trust him. And hopefully love him. She'd never said it, and now he knew why. Her saying it would be the ultimate risk, a plea for her love to be returned.

Not only had her parents abandoned her, but so had a man she'd loved. Once again work, rather than emotions, had been important. When Logan had met Meg, both their guards had slipped. Desire and feelings had become inseparable. When she'd told him she was pregnant, he'd thought he was doing the best thing by not pushing her, by not *trapping* her. Yet his silence and distance had given her another message that she'd again read as abandonment, and if not that, his lack of love.

He could see it all so clearly now.

The most important question was, had he blown his chances with the lady he loved?

He'd soon know. The pine cone wreath rattled as the door opened. He stopped pushing the swing with his foot and drank in the sight of Meg in her colorful wool jacket and stirrup pants.

When she stepped down on the porch, he stood. "You ran away."

She blushed. "I realized so much in the midst of everything that happened. I needed time to think about it."

Where before he'd made a mistake by not telling her his feelings, right now he sensed she needed to talk about hers. "What did you think about?"

She searched his face as if she was looking for something special. "I'm no longer afraid to go back to work. I faced my worst fear today and did it successfully. I have a feeling the nightmares will stop, too.''

His heart did a nosedive and the ring he'd bought a half hour ago became a weight in his pocket. ''I see. Does that mean you'll be moving back to D.C.?''

She looked hesitant but took a step closer to him. ''No. It means I won't be moving back. When our lives were in danger today, I also realized nothing is more important to me than this baby…and you and Travis.''

Hope flared again, and he stepped so close to her they were almost touching. ''You trusted me with your life today, but I think you're still afraid to trust me with your heart. That's my fault, and I'm sorry. I just hope it's not too late.''

''Too late for what?'' she murmured, her brown eyes wide and soft and maybe just a bit hopeful.

''For me to tell you how much I love you. Yes, I want to marry you for the sake of our child, but also because we're good together in bed and out. We can talk and kiss and argue. I think that's because we love each other so completely. Travis was willing to stay in the situation and risk his life for you. You were willing to risk your life for Travis. And I wouldn't have had a life if anything happened to either of you. I'm asking you to marry me so I can give you the love you deserve—a love that accepts who you are and what you need, a love that will last forever.''

Tears fell down her cheeks. ''Lily calls that kind of love a miracle.''

He couldn't keep from wrapping his arms around Meg and pulling her into his body. Stroking her hair, he asked, ''What do you think?''

Meg lifted her head and tenderly traced his jaw. "I think I'm trying to get up the courage to stop running and hiding from you." Her lower lip quivered as she said, "I love you, Logan. More than I thought it possible to love anyone. Even after this afternoon, a little voice in my head kept saying, 'He only did his job.' But my heart knew better. It has all along. That's why making love with you is a miracle in itself."

He'd never known a woman more loving or honest or courageous than Margaret Elizabeth Dawson. Taking the ring from his pocket, he clasped her hand and slipped the solitaire diamond on her finger.

She looked at the ring with a radiant smile. "It's beautiful."

As her gaze returned to his with so much love it overwhelmed him, there was only one more way he knew how to tell her how much he loved her. He kissed her forehead, her eyes, her cheeks. When she lifted her lips to his, he took her tenderly until their love exploded into passion they couldn't deny. Sweeping her off her feet, he carried her to the swing, where he held her in his lap. Their eyes sent loving messages, their tongues explored, their hands crept to warm places until finally Logan raised his head.

Surrounding her with his arms, loving her tucked into his body, he said, "You haven't answered my question. Will you marry me?"

She held his face between her hands, running her fingers along his jaw. "Yes, I'll marry you."

Suddenly she looked worried.

"Sweetheart, what's wrong?"

"Travis. How do you think he'll feel?"

Logan passed his hand up and down her arm, almost afraid to believe his heart's desire was within his grasp. "He approves. And he understands that I love you. He understands we're not getting married just for the sake of the baby."

"You told him?"

He lifted her chin and smoothed the pad of his thumb over the delicate point. "I'm ready to tell the world."

With the sweetest smile he'd ever seen, she set her lips on his, traced their outline with her tongue, then pulled away. "There's a town-council meeting tomorrow night. We can do it then," she teased.

"I'd rather do 'it' right now."

Her expression was smug and thoroughly seductive at the same time. "Why, Sheriff MacDonald! We're on the front porch of my aunt and uncle's house."

He lowered his lips to her ear and said in a low voice, "I'd remedy that and carry you to the barn if you didn't have company."

Bracing her hands on his chest, she promised, "You can carry me to the barn later, after we visit with our company."

"Do you think Lily and Ned will let us borrow their barn after we're married?"

"I'm sure of it."

He looked into her eyes, so full of everything he wanted to see and more. "I love you, Meg. Will you marry me soon? Before the holidays so we can share Christmas with everyone we love as husband and wife?" He couldn't keep the husky note of possession from his voice.

"Nothing would make me happier than sharing Christmas with you as your wife."

Logan found her lips again...giving, taking and sharing their love—their miracle.

Epilogue

Meg clapped her hands and tried to keep her tears in check as Travis received his college diploma. "I'm going to miss him," she murmured to Logan.

"Sweetheart, he's been gone for four years," her husband responded reasonably.

Four-and-a-half-year-old Suzanne, sitting on her mother's lap, clapped her hands, too. "He's goin' *far* away."

Logan slipped his arm around his wife's shoulders. "He's wanted to go back to Spain since he spent half of his senior year there in high school. Only now he'll have a job. Remember when *you* used to enjoy traveling?"

Travis had earned a degree in international finance, as well as majoring in Spanish. The two had gotten him an entry-level position with an American corporation based in Spain.

Chun Won slipped from the folding chair and tried to wave at his brother as he came down from the platform set up in the center of the football field. Even from the considerable distance, Meg saw Travis give them a thumbs-up sign.

She smoothed her hand over Chun Won's coal black hair. After Suzanne was born, Meg had worked part time at Victoria's agency, taking her daughter along with her. Then one day, two years ago, Chun Won's file had come across her desk. Meg had read that he'd been abandoned at birth and left at a Korean orphanage. She and Logan adopted him. He'd needed tons of love and affection, something she and Logan had plenty to give. From the day he'd arrived in the United States, she'd decided to stay home full time, although she still helped Victoria when she got into a bind.

Remembering her husband's question about traveling, she teased, "You and the children are enough of an adventure." She felt the familiar kick of the newest member of their family residing in her womb.

"When we get home, I have a surprise for you." Logan's smile was slightly off center and mysterious.

"What?"

"If I tell you, it won't be a surprise."

She laid her hand on his muscled thigh and gave it a squeeze. "Tell me."

Green passion, deep and exciting, intensified in Logan's eyes. It was still like that between them. A smile, a touch, and they wanted each other as much as they had the first time they'd made love, whether they were in their own bed or in her aunt and uncle's barn.

He chuckled. "Are you going to use coercion?"

"If I have to," she assured him with a coy smile that she knew would raise the stakes a notch or two.

Leaning toward her, he gave her a sound kiss that made the beautiful May day in Connecticut even more memorable.

When Logan pulled away, she asked, "Was that supposed to distract me?"

"No. That was supposed to tell you how much I love you."

He never forgot to tell her or show her...often. The past five years had taught her she could depend on love and believe in its power to solve any problem and forge a bond so strong Logan's heart and hers communicated without words.

Stroking her cheek, he smiled. "The plans are finished for the new house. We can pick them up from the contractor when we get home."

That was a surprise. She hadn't expected them for another two weeks. "Our dream house."

"And a house to dream in."

Logan understood her dreams as well as he understood her. Best of all, he shared them.

She remembered back to a day when she was twelve, standing on her aunt's porch. Then, she'd decided she belonged in Willow Valley. Now she called Willow Valley home, but she knew she belonged with Logan.

Until the end of time.

Suzanne laid her dark head on Meg's shoulder. Chun Won stationed himself between her and Logan, leaning against his father's knee. The graduation ceremony complete, Travis walked toward them, his robe flapping in the breeze.

Love blessed her daily with its miracles.

Logan took her hand and held it tightly in his. Their love was the greatest miracle of all.

*   *   *   *   *

Karen Rose Smith has a new novel out next month in Silhouette Special Edition. Look for Take a Chance on Me.

The Cowboy's Seductive Proposal

SARA ORWIG

SARA ORWIG

lives with her husband and children in Oklahoma, USA. She has a patient husband who will take her on research trips anywhere from big cities to old forts. She is an avid collector of Western history books. With a master's degree in English, Sara writes historical romance, mainstream fiction and contemporary romance. Books are beloved treasures that take Sara to magical worlds, and she loves both reading and writing them.

Sara has a new crossline series in Sensation and Desire, starting in February. Look out for the MISSION: MARRIAGE books listed below:

MISSION: MARRIAGE

Shut Up and Kiss Me – Desire, February 2005
Bring on the Night – Sensation, March 2005
Standing Outside the Fire – Desire, April 2005
Don't Close Your Eyes – Sensation, May 2005

To Hannah Elaine Slater, another little sweetie...

And with thanks through the years to
Dr Clifton L Warren.

One

Fifteen more minutes of peace. Faith Kolanko glanced at her watch and sighed. She could enjoy her lunch break a little longer before she had to return to her frenzied office at Graphic Design. This was her one chance during the day for solitude.

Even when it was almost uncomfortably warm like today, she loved this secluded area of Harrington Park in downtown Tulsa. In addition to a redbrick wall, a tall hedge of blooming spirea bushes hemmed in the niche where she sat. Higher than her head, the white wall of spirea divided the quiet hideaway from the rest of the park.

"Ah, darlin', isn't this a gorgeous day?"

Beyond the spirea bushes a rich bass voice floated on the air. Figuring the couple would move on, Faith paid little heed to their murmurings. A glance at her watch showed twelve more minutes of tranquillity.

She didn't want to return to the office one minute shy of her hour break. She had worked until ten o'clock last night, and then her day had begun at six this morning. She needed quiet before returning to the Bradley account.

Bushes rustled and noises on the other side of the spirea caught her attention again. She heard the snap of a blanket being shaken and then the pop of a can being opened.

"Lie down there, honey, and look at that blue sky. Can you believe this day?"

Faith sighed. Knowing her solitude had to end, she folded the morning paper, brushed crumbs off her blue skirt, then straightened her blue blouse. The couple on the other side of the bushes sounded as if they were going to stay for a while. She closed her thermos and slipped it into the brown paper bag.

"Oh, darlin', I love you so much! I never would've guessed it possible."

As she listened to the masculine voice that softened with tenderness, Faith's brows arched, and she became aware of the cooings and murmurings on the other side of the bushes. The only way out of this corner of the park was a gravel walk that curved right past the amorous couple. She prayed they would pick up and move, but they sounded pretty comfortable.

"I love you."

Faith heard the whispered baby talk, along with kisses and coos and deep-throated noises. She didn't want to even imagine what was going on. But if the woman began screaming with pleasure, Faith wasn't going to sit quietly. Didn't they know there were people around?

They obviously didn't care, because the noises increased.

Faith frowned at the spilling fountain of white blossoms, the green foliage almost hidden by the spirea blooms. She glanced at her watch. Nine more minutes before she absolutely had to start back to the office. Should she make a loud noise or try to creep past them? It didn't sound as if they would notice her. Or care even if they did notice.

"Honey, wait a minute. There," the man said. "Let's get rid of this dress, darlin' blue eyes. Big, big blue eyes.

Oh, what long lashes you have! You're my precious sweetie...."

What would make perfectly sane adults resort to such ridiculous baby talk? Never in her life had Faith felt inclined to talk in such an absurd manner to any male she had dated. Nor would she ever.

The man's voice faded, replaced by sounds that made Faith blush. She didn't want to hear the noises, but now she certainly didn't want to walk past them. And to get out of her hiding place, she would have to do just that.

She looked at the brick wall and contemplated going over it. The vision of herself in heels and hose and a tight cotton skirt sliding over that wall in front of the busy intersection killed the notion instantly. The only other way to avoid the couple would be to crash through the spirea hedge, and she could just imagine how she would look returning to work with flowers and leaves in her hair.

She glanced at her watch. She had heard about couples having sex in the park, but she had dismissed the rumors as frivolous. All she had ever encountered were other business people and a few transients.

Seven minutes. The gurgles and growls and giggles made her cheeks burn. She debated what to do. Were they stark naked? she wondered.

How many times had her friend Leah warned her that they were too isolated when they came to this spot? Next time she would listen.

"Oh, honey, I love you!" came a whisper. Then more kissing sounds and cooing. "Yum, yum, yum. Take a li'l bite here...."

"For corn's sake!" Faith whispered. She looked at her watch. Five minutes. She bit her lip and frowned. Maybe if she just ran past them, they would never notice her. But could *she* avoid noticing *them?* Sex was not a spectator event.

The sounds became more primitive and garbled, and she

could too easily imagine what might be happening on the other side of the spirea.

"Oh, God! Oh, darlin'!" Unidentifiable sounds she didn't want to hear disturbed the quiet.

Faith wanted to scream. She wanted to yell to them that they were in a very public place and could get arrested for what they were doing. "Get a room!" She silently mouthed the words.

"Darlin', what's the matter?"

In the midst of her mental tirade, Faith realized the man's voice held terror. The woman sounded as if she was gagging. Or having a seizure. The woman might be having an attack of some kind!

"Oh, Lordy, Lordy," the man cried out. "What do I do? What should I do? Merry, darlin', can you breathe? Oh, Lord, help."

He sounded desperate. Faith had CPR training. Knowing she couldn't stand by and ignore someone who was hurt, Faith clamped her jaw, prepared to face two naked lovers, and plunged through the spirea, scattering white petals like a rain shower in springtime.

She spit out spirea blooms and froze in momentary shock, staring into dark brown eyes as a man on his knees looked up at her. Sunlight splashed over broad bronzed shoulders that gleamed with a faint sheen of sweat. Shaggy black hair fell around his face. A muscled chest tapered to a narrow waist.

For one brief moment they stared at each other and then Faith's attention shifted. In his arms he held a baby who was choking. A *baby*. She wore a diaper and a pink ribbon in her tiny black curls, and her little face was screwed up in agony.

"She's choking," the man said, but Faith needed no explanation. The coughing and gasping signaled the baby's distress.

Faith reacted instinctively and with the experience of having dealt with a younger brother, sisters, nieces and nephews. She took the choking baby from him and quickly positioned the child face-down across her lap. With the heel of her free hand, she struck the baby on the back between the shoulder blades. On the second blow, something squishy shot out of the little girl's mouth.

The baby instantly gasped for breath and screamed.

Standing, Faith placed the tyke on her shoulder, patted her back, hugged her close and talked softly to her as she jiggled her gently.

"Thank God!" the man exclaimed. "Oh, thank you, thank you!"

Watching the slender blonde quiet his baby, Jared White-wolf experienced a kaleidoscope of emotions: shock when the woman appeared out of the bushes; terror over Merry's choking; swift relief when the woman cleared Merry's throat of the obstruction. Then his relief transformed into curiosity. Who was the pretty lady covered in white blossoms? Merry was snuggling in the woman's arms, quiet now except for an occasional hiccup.

Jared couldn't have been more dazzled if the sun had dropped halfway to earth. This woman knew how to handle a baby. A bona fide, world-class champion baby handler. Probably a mommy with three kids. His gaze ran down her slender figure, noticing her ringless fingers when she turned her profile to him. Her blond hair, sprinkled with white petals, was fastened with a clip behind her head. A practical watch with a leather strap circled her slender wrist. The blue skirt ended above great knees and long, shapely legs.

Jared stood, wiped his brow and hoped his heart would stop racing. The woman turned to face him.

"Thanks," he said. "That's the biggest scare I've had in years."

"What did you feed her?"

"I gave her a banana."

The woman glanced at the baby in her arms, then frowned at him, and he knew he had blundered. "She's too little unless it's mashed up. You didn't let her have the whole banana, did you?''

"Well, not a whole one, but too damned much," he answered perfunctorily, his thoughts moving on. Merry was twiddling with the woman's silver hoop earring, as blissfully happy now as if the whole incident had never occurred. This golden-haired rescuer really knew how to care for a baby.

He thought of the few disastrous dates he had had since Merry had come into his life. He hadn't met a woman yet who could cope with Merry for more than an hour and never in a crisis. And until today, he had never had a crisis that had been life-threatening.

"She's very pretty," the woman said softly, looking down at Merry. The baby gurgled, smiled and stared at the woman. Jared's pulse jumped.

"You're really good with babies."

"I should be," she said without looking up, and he braced himself to hear she had a house filled with her own. She stopped to smile at Merry, both of them looking beautiful, adorable and contented.

"Why should you be good with them?" he asked, holding his breath.

"I grew up with three younger siblings, as well as an older brother. They are all married now with babies," she answered.

He moved closer, catching a fragrance more enticing than the spring flowers surrounding him. Looking into her wide green eyes, he felt a tension that he recognized instantly and was delighted to discover. The sexual chemistry was icing on the cake.

"Hold still. You have petals in your hair," he said, reaching up to pull white blossoms from the silky waves. His hand brushed her throat, and he felt a tingle that echoed through the emptiness deep inside him.

She reached back to unfasten the clip that held her hair

and gave a shake of her head, scattering petals over her shoulders and onto Merry.

"Here, let me help," he said, watching the woman as he placed his hands on either side of her head. While he looked down into her eyes, he slowly combed his fingers through her soft cascade of golden hair. Green eyes tugged at his senses. She drew a deep breath, and the tension between them sizzled, invisible, yet as tangible as if he had moved close to a blazing fire. Her eyes darkened, and her lips parted slightly as she gazed back steadfastly at him.

Never one for long, deep soul-searching, Jared knew inherently that this woman was special. She had dashed into their lives, and he wanted her to stay.

"I'm Jared Whitewolf," he said quietly, looking at her crystal eyes, flawless skin, full red lips. "You're holding my daughter, Merry—spelled M-E-R-R-Y." His speech was automatic. His thoughts were on her eyes, so cool and filled with a mysterious invitation that revved up parts of him hungry for a woman's touch.

"I'm Faith Kolanko."

"Thanks for coming to our rescue."

"You're welcome."

They stared at each other, and Jared didn't want the moment to end. He didn't feel compelled to talk to break the silence between them because it wasn't an uneasy quiet. Far from it. It was snapping, popping and sizzling with chemistry so hot it should be illegal. While he looked down at her, he saw another flicker in the depths of her eyes.

For the first time since he'd become Merry's father, he momentarily forgot his daughter—forgot everything—except the woman whose wide eyes gazed up at him. Faith Kolanko.

"We're having a picnic. Want to join us?" he asked. "Are you alone?"

"Oh, my soul! I'm late for work!" she exclaimed, glancing at her watch, the magic sparks spinning between them vanishing as if turned off by a switch. "I've got to go," she said, handing Merry to him.

Jared knew a good thing when he saw it, and he wasn't going to let Faith Kolanko slip out of his life ten minutes after she'd arrived in it.

"Hey, wait!" he said, trying to scoop up his boots and shirt and Merry's sundress and hold Merry at the same time.

Faith did not wait. She dashed around the spirea bushes and reappeared in seconds with a purse slung over her shoulder. "See you!"

She ran down the twisting gravel path and vanished beyond a stand of bright yellow forsythia.

"Darlin', we can't let that woman go," he said to Merry, placing her on the quilt he had spread. He yanked on his boots, pulled on his T-shirt. He dropped Merry's pink sundress over her head, straightened it and picked her up to run. He passed the forsythia, sprinting across the grassy park while he looked around, searching for a golden head of hair and a blue blouse and skirt.

Halfway around the park, the brick wall progressively shortened and then ended. There was a parking lot at the north end, and Jared scanned the few people getting in and out of cars for a blue blouse and skirt. He glanced to the east. Beyond the park and the wide expanse of sidewalk, past a fountain with silver water sparkling in the bright sunlight, up wide steps to a tall office building, he spotted fabulous legs, a blue skirt, blue shirt and golden hair. He tightened his grasp of Merry and ran.

Faith Kolanko disappeared through the revolving glass doors of the Harrington Tower. Since he suspected she would be out of sight in an office by the time he reached the revolving doors, he stopped running.

He looked down at Merry, who smiled at him. "You are a sweetie, and I'm sorry I fed you too much banana at once. I won't do that again, I promise," he said, kissing the top of her head. "The lady got away—for now, but not for good. Nosiree. Li'l darlin', we'll get our things and go look for the pretty lady. I'll bet half the men in that building can tell me what office she's in. You liked her, didn't you?''

Merry gurgled and blinked when sunlight splashed over her face.

"Well, so did I. She's special, Merry. I can just feel it down to my bones. Faith Kolanko. That's a pretty name. Merry and Faith. I like that.''

Merry smiled at him, and he settled her against his shoulder as he strode back to the blanket he had spread. He laid her down gently, her big blue eyes watching him solemnly until a bird flitted past, and then her attention shifted to the birds and trees.

Jared folded up their things, finished the can of pop he'd been drinking and put their trash in a nearby bin. He sank down on the quilt, pulled Merry into his arms and got a bottle out of a satchel. "Now, li'l darlin', here's your bottle. You drink up and have a little nap. Then, sweetie, we'll go find the pretty lady we liked so much.''

Jared watched Merry's tiny hands grasp the plastic bottle, and he felt his heart swell with love for this little person he held in his arms. "I'm sorry your real daddy couldn't know you, li'l darlin'. He was a good man and we're not going to forget him.''

Merry's eyes closed, thick black lashes a dusky shadow over her plump rosy cheeks. Jared snuggled her closer, careful not to disturb her as she drank her formula. He brushed a kiss across her forehead. While he watched her drink, he thought about Faith Kolanko. He wanted a date with her. He hadn't had a satisfactory date since Merry had come into his life. And though he had yet to try, he suspected he'd had so few dates that he could count them on the fingers of both hands. He just hoped he couldn't count them on *one* hand.

Whatever the number, it had been too damned few. He liked women and he missed their companionship. But nothing about his life was as simple as it had been before. He had to think about Merry now. He had to be friends with nice ladies who liked Merry and could deal with her. And until today, he hadn't met anyone who fit his criteria—and who fit him.

Faith Kolanko had been marvelous with Merry. She was the first female he had encountered who could really cope in a crisis.

While Merry sucked happily, fantasies danced in his mind. Jared pictured the slender blonde in absolute detail. The way her lips curved in a smile, the hint of curiosity in her green eyes as she looked at him. The cool, decisive way she had taken charge. The warmth she exhibited toward Merry.

He had learned at an early age that a man out in public with a horse or a puppy drew women like honey drew flies. In the last four months, he had learned that a man with a baby also attracted women. Wherever he traveled with Merry—grocery, park, rodeo, beach or mall—women came up to him to see the baby. But when he carried it further, it was different. A man and a woman who met over a horse or a dog could ignore the animal for a few hours. No such luck with a baby. When Merry demanded attention, Jared had discovered that most of the women he encountered either knew little about babies or already knew too much and didn't want anything to do with another one. Romance had gone out of his life almost as swiftly as fatherhood had come into it.

But then, springing forth from a hedge, had come a beautiful lady who obviously loved little babies. "My, oh, my!" he whispered aloud. He looked down at the baby in his arms. She had finished the bottle, and her breath was rapid, rising and falling evenly, telling him she was asleep.

"What a day we've had, eh, li'l darlin'? It will be downhill all the way from here." He placed Merry gently on the blanket. "We're going to get our things and go find the pretty lady. I suspect she isn't going to be able to resist you. We are going to ask Faith to dinner and to become part of our lives. We need her—I can feel it clear down to my toes,'' he said to the sleeping baby.

He paused and looked at the spirea bushes. Only a sprinkling of white petals on the ground indicated that anything had disturbed the flowers. He picked a little sprig and tucked it into the pocket of Merry's bag.

Jared stretched out on the blanket, folding his arms behind his head, and watched white clouds shift across the deep blue sky. He listened to the birds and enjoyed the slight April breeze while leaves caused shadows to dance across him. His thoughts were on Faith Kolanko. She had been calm, cool, efficient. And beautiful. Big green eyes, long legs. In his heart he gave another silent prayer of thanks for Merry's rescue and for Faith Kolanko sweeping into their lives.

All his life, there had been women around—until the last two months. He missed having a woman around. He had thought of marriage—something that had never crossed his mind until he'd become a father. Now he was ready to marry. But now, because of Merry, he couldn't get out and meet women with the ease he had known before. Well, Faith was one lady who had charged into *his* life, and he wanted to keep her there. At least, he wanted her there long enough to see if he wanted her there forever.

Two hours later Jared shook out the soft blanket, rolled it up, then bound it with leather before fastening it to a carrier on his back. Catching his shaggy hair, he fastened it with a leather thong behind his head. Then he carefully placed Merry in her baby carrier and secured her against his heart, brushing her soft hair lightly with his fingers.

''Sweetie, I didn't know how lovable a little baby could be until I met you.''

He brushed off his jeans, gathered his things and crossed the park. Whistling, Jared strolled to the Harrington Building and pushed inside. Moments later, he was describing Faith to the receptionist, who shook her head at him.

"I'm sorry, sir. There are a lot of blond women who work in this building."

"Faith Kolanko is about five feet eight inches tall. She has long blond hair, green eyes, a few freckles across her nose—"

"Miss Kolanko works on the fifth floor." A man in a white shirt and dark slacks appeared at Jared's side. "She's an artist and works for Graphic Design."

"Thanks," Jared said, eyeing the man as much as the man was eyeing him. Jared turned, looked at the directory posted near the elevators and spotted Graphic Design listed on the fifth floor.

"We'll have to wait until she gets off work, Merry," he said to the sleeping baby. "We'll come back about four o'clock so we don't miss her."

He strode out into the sunshine and back to the park, this time spreading his blanket in the shade where he could see two of the building's exits.

At four he went to his pickup, where he left the blanket and picnic basket, opting instead for Merry's umbrella stroller. "Now, darlin'," he said, buckling Merry into the seat and handing her a bright blue rattle, "we'll wait for Miss Kolanko to get off work." Hooking Merry's diaper bag over the handle of the stroller, he pushed her toward the Harrington Tower.

They sat in the cool lobby and watched people pour through on their way home from work, but Jared did not spot any tall, beautiful blonde. Five became six, the building emptied, and a security man in a brown uniform appeared.

"Sir, do you work in this building?"

"No, I don't."

"Well, unless you have some reason for being here, I'll have to ask you to leave. I need to lock up the building for the night," he said, switching off some of the lobby lights.

"I'm waiting for Faith Kolanko with Graphic Design."

"Miss Kolanko? Do you mind if I verify that?"

"No, go ahead. I'm Jared Whitewolf," he said, standing.

The security guard crossed the lobby to a phone and placed a call. Jared pushed Merry and the stroller closer.

"Whitewolf. He said he's waiting for you, Miss Kolanko. That's right, a little baby. Yes, ma'am. You're welcome." He replaced the receiver.

"She said to tell you she would be right down. Sorry for the inconvenience, sir, but we have to make the building as secure as possible."

"Sure. I understand. Thanks."

Jared pushed the stroller back to the bench that faced the elevators and sat down to wait, watching as glowing numbers above the elevator moved from five to one. He stood as the double doors slid open and the woman he was going to marry emerged.

Two

Rushed, annoyed that she had to take time to see why the man she met in the park was waiting downstairs, Faith glanced around. Her searching gaze was arrested by a tall cowboy wearing a wide-brimmed black hat with two feathers hanging over the brim, a white T-shirt and a big silver buckle on a hand-tooled leather belt. Jeans hugged his slim hips, and the tips of black boots showed beneath the frayed edges. For an instant she didn't recognize him. The lobby was dim; the hat hid his eyes. And the shaggy black hair she remembered from the afternoon was pulled behind his head, changing his appearance considerably.

The tall cowboy turned a stroller to face her, and she saw Merry Whitewolf. Faith knew the man she was facing was Jared Whitewolf.

"Mr. Whitewolf—"

"Howdy, Faith. And it's Jared. You saved Merry's life, so we're on a very personal basis."

"I have to get back to the office," she said as he approached. She looked down at the baby, who smiled. Faith couldn't resist smiling back. For just an instant the cares of the day fell away. "Hi, Merry," she said, leaning down slightly. "You are the friendliest little girl I have ever seen."

"That's because her daddy's friendly" came a slow drawl. "Sorry to interrupt your work, but we wanted to take you to dinner when you're through here."

"Oh, I'm sorry, I just couldn't!" Faith exclaimed swiftly, straightening to face him. He tilted back his hat, and she looked into dark eyes that seemed to reach down and grab hold of a little part of her soul. She didn't want to look away. She forgot work. She forgot where she was for a moment. In the park today, she had felt that same magnetic pull, but she had blamed it on the sweet baby, the magic of the outdoors on a sunny afternoon, the unusual encounter. And maybe an expanse of a fabulous, bare chest.

She couldn't blame her current reaction on any of those things, yet here she was barely able to get her breath, gazing up at a man who was staring at her as if he had been searching for her all his life.

"Yes, you can," he said quietly, touching a tendril of hair near her face. "You have to eat sometime. Have you already had dinner?"

She felt the faint brush of his warm fingers on her cheek. She knew she looked disheveled. The afternoon had been as hectic as she had expected, and plunging through the spirea bushes earlier had mussed her cotton skirt and blouse. "No, I haven't, but I'm not going to take time now. I have another hour's work to do."

"We'll wait," he said with a smile as he smoothed her collar. When his knuckles brushed her collarbone, she tingled. What was the matter with her? Had she worked until she was senseless? She was reacting to a perfect stranger in a very primitive way.

"No, you shouldn't wait," she argued, making an effort to look away from brown eyes so dark, she felt she was staring into a moonless night. "I can't go out with you. You're a complete stranger. I know nothing about you. And I have to get back to work."

"Faith," he drawled, his hand catching her arm as she started to turn away. His touch was feather light, and she paused, rooted to the spot. "We're not going to stay strangers. Are you engaged or involved with someone?"

"No, but that isn't the point. In this day and age it's dangerous to be friendly to strangers."

"I agree. So let's fix this stranger status." He retrieved a glossy program from his satchel and handed it to her. "Here's my picture. I'm riding in a rodeo at the arena tomorrow night."

She stared at the smiling picture of him and noted the statistics about his bull riding, saddle bronc riding and prizes he had won. "You're a three-time world champion bull rider," she remarked as she read.

With a flash of very white teeth, he grinned. "Somehow, I don't think that's a plus in your book."

"I can't even imagine it," she answered, looking again at his picture. She had to admit the man was not only handsome, he had a charm that was spellbinding.

"You can call out to the arena, and any of the boys will tell you about me. I own a home here in Tulsa. The house is on South Peoria. If Merry could talk, she would verify that I'm safe. And besides that—" he thrust the rodeo program into Faith's hands and pulled out a card from his frayed billfold "—this is my brother Wyatt. He's a detective with the OCPD. We'll go call him and he'll tell you I'm safe. C'mon."

"Oh, no! You don't need to call your brother."

"I'm not going to. *You* are. I have coins here and you can make the call yourself," he said, positioning the stroller in front of Faith while he tugged lightly on her arm. "There's a pay phone, so you'll know this isn't a setup job. You can call the OCPD yourself and talk to Wyatt. He'll tell you I'm totally safe to go out with. If he doesn't convince you, I have another brother, Matt. He's a farmer. Let's start with the cop.''

"This is ridiculous. I have work upstairs.''

"I know you do and I'm sorry to interfere, but some time tonight you'll have to stop work and go home. And you'll have to eat. Merry and I can help you unwind. Just a little dinner and I'll get you home, so we can start getting to know each other.''

"I don't think so,'' she said, facing him. He was handsome with prominent cheekbones, skin as dark as teak, lashes unbelievably thick, a firm jaw. And every time she received the full force of his dark-eyed stare, she felt weak-kneed and knew she was going to cave in to him. She took a deep breath, trying to summon a *no*.

"Merry really wants you to go with us. She just doesn't know how to say it.''

No vanished as he offered the handles of the stroller to her. Faith pushed Merry to the phone. Big blue eyes stared at her.

Jared placed the receiver in her hand, turned her to the phone and put the card in front of her. He plopped a bandanna on the shelf and untied it. Silver coins filled the red cloth. "Now, you just call the OCPD. There's the number. Ask for Wyatt, and then you ask him about my character and reliability.''

She turned to him. "I just don't think I have time in my life right now—''

He bent his knees slightly to be at her eye level, then he leaned closer. She caught a soapy scent that was pleasant. "Faith, I think you should,'' he said quietly. "I think we were meant to know each other. Sooner or later we will. So let's make it sooner.''

Her heart started a ridiculous drumming. Never in her life had she had this kind of reaction to a man.

"Call Wyatt,'' Jared commanded softly.

She turned and began punching numbers. Then she listened as the operator told her the amount of money required. Each coin made a metallic clink. Jared Whitewolf moved away, pushing Merry around in her stroller, and then he hunkered down to talk to the baby.

A deep male voice finally came over the receiver and Faith felt absurd. "Is this Detective Wyatt Whitewolf?"

As soon as he said yes, she launched into an explanation. "This is Faith Kolanko from Tulsa, and I've just met your brother Jared. He's asked me to dinner, and since we're complete strangers—"

She paused as the man at the other end of the line laughed.

"My brother is safe enough," he said, his voice filled with amusement. "With horses and with women he's a will-o'-the-wisp charmer. He's harmless."

"I met him this afternoon, and his little girl, Merry."

The explosion at the other end of the line made Faith hold the phone away from her ear, but she recognized the shock in Wyatt's reaction.

"Let me talk to him," Wyatt said in a tone of voice that had lost all casualness.

Jared must have heard Wyatt's response, too, because he turned and smiled, making her pulse jump. His grin was infectious, softening his masculine features. The man was incredibly appealing.

She held out the phone. "He wants to talk to you."

"I'll only take a second. Do you mind?" he asked, gesturing toward Merry. They switched stroller for receiver, Jared's hand brushing hers ever so lightly, but she was fully aware of the contact.

"Hi, brother. Yeah, I have a little girl."

Faith couldn't help but listen to the one-sided conversation while she wondered what had happened to Merry's mother.

"No. It's a long story, Wyatt. I'll tell you when I see you. Merry's four-and-a-half months old." Another pause, and then he said, "Yeah, it's great."

Jared's voice had softened to a buttery warmth that sent

a tingle dancing in Faith, and she knew he was talking about Merry. His tone changed whenever he talked about the baby.

"I'm riding in a rodeo here tomorrow night, and then we'll be in Oklahoma City for the rodeo next weekend, so we'll come see you then."

He paused and listened. "Yeah, she's with me. How are your girls? And Alexa? Good. Tell them hello. See you Saturday." Jared turned to her. "Faith, do you want to talk to him again?"

She shook her head, then watched as Jared turned back to the phone. With one hand splayed on his hip, he seemed so relaxed, so easygoing, yet there was an air of energy about him that she could feel every time he was near. She would go to dinner with him, she decided. It gave her a peculiar feeling, as if she was caught in a current carrying her along, out of control. Her life was order and stability and security. Filled with routine precision, it was as sure and certain as the hands on a clock. But ever since she had plunged through the spirea bushes and Jared Whitewolf had come into her life, she had felt off balance and out-of-step.

Merry began to fret, and Faith bent down to pick her up. "You have been a very good girl today. You really are a sweetie," she said, remembering that Jared had used the endearment earlier. She turned to find that Jared had replaced the receiver and was sauntering back to her. "Have you been waiting here in the lobby with this baby all day?" she asked.

"No. We spent the afternoon in the park and then came back about closing time."

"Your brother didn't know about Merry."

"No, but he does now. We don't write letters. Now, what do you say about dinner?"

"You'll have to wait around for a little while until I'm ready."

"We don't mind, do we, Merry?" he asked, and Merry smiled at him.

"She's the best behaved baby I have ever seen. She smiles every time anyone looks at her."

"That's because—"

"I know. Because *you* smile a lot," she said, finishing for him as she handed Merry back to him. He grinned while he fell into step beside her and walked with her to the elevator, pushing the empty stroller ahead of him.

"If you'd rather wait in our office, you may. It might be easier with Merry."

"Thanks." He held the elevator door while she entered, and then he pushed the stroller inside. He leaned back against a wall and faced her.

"What's your title?"

"Executive director of advertising."

"I'm impressed. And what do you do? Sell advertising?"

"No. I'm a graphic artist. I plan the layout and design, write copy, sometimes do the entire ad campaign or promotion. I have certain accounts I regularly handle, as well as others I do occasionally, and I have six people I supervise."

While she talked, she was aware of his steady scrutiny. She became more conscious of her appearance, knowing her hair needed combing and her makeup had long ago disappeared. Her blouse was wrinkled and she had a green stain on her collar, probably from the spirea. Jared looked relaxed, one knee slightly bent, his booted foot propped against the wall.

"Do you always work this late?"

"No. We're working on a big account, and the client wanted changes at the last minute, so we're rushing to get everything done. We present the pitch in the morning."

He nodded. "Have any particular food you like to eat?"

"Maybe Italian." She glanced at Merry. "Won't we be keeping the baby up long past her bedtime?"

Jared shook his head. "She sleeps off and on around the clock. And whether she's tucked into her bed or out with us, Merry will sleep. When she's ready to snooze, nothing will stop her. Don't worry, she won't lose sleep," he said, smiling.

"You know best," Faith replied.

The elevator doors opened and she led the way to a glass door that she unlocked.

"You can wait in here."

They entered a large reception area with beige carpeting, dark wood furniture and pots of green plants. Faith turned to him. "I don't know how long I'll be."

He shook his head. "Don't worry about it. We have all the time in the world. At least, until the rodeo tomorrow night."

Feeling the familiar sense of being caught in something she couldn't control, Faith left through a glass door and returned to work. She moved down the hall to a wide table where brochures and folders were spread. Nearby a colorful graph filled the screen of her computer.

Her co-worker and immediate supervisor, Porter Gaston, glanced toward the glassed-in waiting room and his blond brows arched. "Who's your friend?"

"Jared Whitewolf. We're going to dinner later," she tried to say casually, wishing the announcement would go unnoticed, yet knowing it would be as overlooked as a fire-cracker exploding in a prayer meeting. Without really see-ing it, she studied the brochure in front of her.

"You're kidding."

Looking up, she could see the incredulity in Porter's blue eyes.

"Who the hell is he? Where did you meet him?" he demanded.

"He's a friend. Shall we get back to work?" She stared at Porter, feeling a challenge rising. For the first time in her life she was doing something unexpected, unscheduled and uncharacteristic. While Porter looked at the reception area again, she turned to the computer.

"Faith, how long have you known this guy? I know I'm prying, but we're friends."

She turned to face Porter. "I haven't known him long, but I've talked to his brother, who is a detective. Jared is a nice guy."

"Well, damn. I can't believe you're going out with him. Here Madge and I have been trying for two months to get you and Kent together and you're always busy. Yet here in the middle of this project, out of nowhere you're going to dinner with some stranger."

"It's just dinner, Porter."

"How long have you known Whitewolf?"

"His name is *Jared* Whitewolf."

"Sorry. You're evading my question."

"I met him today."

"Good Lord! And now you're going to dinner with that ponytailed cowboy? Faith, the papers are filled with stories about women who get picked up by strangers and the terrible things that happen to them."

"Look, I already told you, his brother is a detective, and I spoke to him. The guy is safe. He seems nice. He has a sweet little baby. He has a house on South Peoria. I read about him riding in the rodeo. I've seen a program with a write-up about him. He's won a lot of rodeo prizes—"

"This is really you talking?"

Annoyed, she turned away. Porter was echoing her own thoughts and causing her regrets to multiply. She didn't know Jared Whitewolf. And even if he was as reliable and charming as his brother indicated, she should be practical and go home to catch up on much-needed rest.

"Sorry," Porter said. "I think I should meet him."

"We will in a minute. Let's finish this up."

She met Porter's quizzical gaze and then he shrugged. "All right. Look at the layout here."

She moved around the table, scrutinizing papers that held graphs and charts and slogans. In minutes she was concentrating on her work again and had returned to the computer, rearranging the information and design. As she moved back to look at a brochure, she glanced through the glass partition.

Jared Whitewolf had tossed aside his hat. He stood with his back to her while he looked at framed pictures of advertising layouts the company had done. Her gaze ran over his thick black hair and his broad chest. The T-shirt molded the sinewy muscles in his shoulders and upper back. His jeans hugged slender hips. He was as foreign to her life as an intergalactic being. And Porter was right. She should tell Jared Whitewolf that she would be working incredibly late and that she would be too exhausted to go anywhere except home. Alone.

She thought of men in her past that she had dated. Without exception, she had known them years before dating them. Buddies, school chums, childhood friends—even Earl Baines, a co-worker whom she had dated the longest. She didn't know anything about cowboys, bull riders or men who spent their afternoons in the park with a baby and wore jeans and T-shirts. She glanced at Porter, who was seated at his desk. He had shed his suit coat, but he still wore his tie and white shirt with well-creased navy slacks. He was the kind of man she knew—professional, ambitious, punctual, whose life was filled with schedules and routines as much as her own.

She would tell Jared Whitewolf goodbye. It was absurd to think of doing anything else.

"Faith, can you look at this?" Porter asked without glancing up. "I think we should move this slogan and the picture of the machinery to the top of the page."

She crossed to his desk and bent over the layout in front of him, forgetting Jared Whitewolf.

It was half an hour later, as she walked back to her computer with papers in hand, that she remembered her date. She glanced toward the reception room, knowing she should put the papers on her desk and send Jared home.

He sat on one of the chairs, and Merry was in his arms

while he gave her a bottle. His head was bent over her, and Faith could see his lips moving and knew he was talking to her. Merry reached up a tiny hand, pale against his dark skin, as her fingers explored his jaw. Something seemed to unfold inside Faith and longing swamped her. She tried to picture Porter holding a baby, giving it a bottle, but it was impossible.

It was equally impossible to imagine either of her brothers—or even her father—tending a baby. With five children, her father had still managed to escape giving one of them a bottle unless he had been settled in front of the late-night news and her mother had placed a baby and a bottle in his arms. Nor could she imagine any of the men she had dated spending the day in the park with a baby like Jared had unless pressed into the duty.

Everyone in her life was as predictable as the sunrise. The men were busy with careers; the women busy with home and children. She was the oldest female and the only unmarried one in her family. Restlessness and a growing dissatisfaction tugged at her while Faith watched Jared Whitewolf. And she decided that this was one night she would spend a couple of hours breaking out of her routine. For once, she would let go of her orderly existence and see what life would be like with someone like Whitewolf.

His head rose and he met her gaze. They stared at each other, and even with a glass partition separating them, her pulse jumped and she felt weak-kneed and fluttery.

She waved the papers at him and he nodded, then she hurried to her alcove to try to finish. They had only the last touches now, and then she and Porter would be ready for the presentation tomorrow morning.

Ten minutes later she looked up to find Porter standing in front of her, gazing down at the brochures and folders and layouts. "We're done!" she exclaimed. "Ten after nine. Not bad."

"It looks great," he said with satisfaction. "Damned good job. I think they'll go for it."

"Thanks," she said, carefully placing the work in stacks.

"I'll wind things up here and then we can go over everything again in the morning before we meet with them. Come on, introduce me to Whitewolf."

She got her purse, shut down her computer and took a last look around.

"You're through, Faith. Stop working."

She smiled at him and they walked to the reception room. Jared came to his feet.

"Porter, this is Jared Whitewolf. Jared, this is my supervisor, Porter Gaston."

"Glad to meet you," Jared said politely, shaking hands with Porter.

"Faith said you're taking her to dinner."

"That's right."

"Before you go, I thought maybe you'd want to look around the office, see some of her work. Faith, why don't you sit with his little baby while I show him our new promotion?"

Hearing the determination in Porter's voice, Faith knew it was useless to protest. And she knew he wanted Jared alone to question him. Porter was a family friend who'd been looking after her for years.

"Now I can see what you've been working on," Jared said easily, and followed Porter beyond the glass door.

Faith felt mildly annoyed at Porter's meddling, but she knew her entire family would be even more curious about Jared Whitewolf than Porter was. She sat down and looked at the baby who was sleeping again, slumped over in the stroller. She looked uncomfortable, so Faith leaned down to unbuckle the strap and carefully lift the sleeping child into her arms. Merry sighed and snuggled against Faith and Faith's arms tightened. She felt a hollow ache while the warmth of the tiny baby seemed to permeate to her heart.

Fifteen minutes later, the men returned and Jared took Merry from her arms. He picked up his hat and set it on his head, and then turned to extend his hand to Porter.

"It was nice to meet you. Thanks for the tour."

"Sure thing. You two have a good evening. I'll wind this up, Faith. If I see anything that isn't ready, I'll give you a call. You don't mind if I call anytime tonight, do you?"

"No. I won't be home for about an hour, but after that, it's fine."

"Good. I might have a question."

"Nice to meet you, Mr. Gaston," Jared said, and pushed open the door for Faith. He wheeled the stroller through the door and walked beside her toward the elevators.

"Sure that wasn't your dad?"

Smiling, she shook her head. "He's a close friend of my father and my uncle, Blake Kolanko. My uncle owns this business."

"Ahh."

"Don't say 'ahh' like 'so that's why you have your job.' I worked at another ad agency until last year when I came to work here."

"I didn't mean any such thing. I just understand better why Gaston was hovering. He didn't want you to go out with me."

"Well, you're not my usual date."

As they waited for the elevator, Jared looked down at her, then touched her collar, his fingers brushing her throat. He stood close enough that she could feel the warmth of his body.

"Who's your usual date?"

"I date men like Porter. They work at brokerage firms or ad agencies. They don't spend the afternoon in the park. And I've known them for years and years." She knew she was rambling, but his brown eyes were playing havoc with her thought processes and she was aware she had worked since six that morning. She smoothed stray tendrils of hair away from her face and wished she had taken more time to freshen up before leaving the office.

He caught her hand and rubbed his thumb lightly across

her knuckles. The touch made her draw a deep breath. Why did the slightest physical contact with him make her tingle?

"I don't see any ring from one of these guys you've known years and years. Who's the one in your life now?"

"Right now, there isn't one. I've been really busy with work for the past couple of months."

He gave her a crooked grin and ran his finger down her cheek. "Sounds like you're ready for a little change in your life."

The elevator doors slid open and he stretched out a long arm, holding the door open while she entered. He pushed the stroller inside.

She looked down at Merry in his arms. "You know, I really don't know you. If it weren't for this baby, I wouldn't be doing this."

Jared stretched out his arm, placing his hand against the wall beside her head and leaned close, bending his knees to look into her eyes. "I didn't have anything to do with your agreeing to go out?" he asked in a husky voice. "You don't feel any little zip of anticipation or curiosity when we talk?"

"Maybe," she answered cautiously, her whole body feeling little zips from his husky voice, his nearness and his question. As she gazed up at him, her breasts tightened and her heart raced.

"Scared to admit it?"

"I told you, this isn't what I'm accustomed to at all. I've never gone out with someone I just met."

"I don't blame you if it's a stranger you don't know. But you know a lot about me. You know I ride in rodeos. You've talked to my brother. And you've saved my daughter from choking. We'll get to know each other better, and tomorrow night you can come watch me ride."

She had to smile. "Too bad you don't have any confidence in yourself," she remarked.

"Faith, darlin'," he drawled, leaning closer and placing his fingers along her cheek, "my confidence is in what I feel and what I see in your green eyes when we stand close like this.''

The elevator doors slid open. As she stepped out and walked through the doors into the night beside Jared Whitewolf, she felt as if she were leaving more than her office and day's work behind.

They placed the stroller in the rear of the pickup and then buckled Merry in the carrier that was in the back seat.

When Jared drove out of the lot, Faith glanced back at the sleeping baby. ''She is the best little baby. What happened to her mother?''

''She didn't want a baby, so she packed and left Merry behind.''

Faith shook her head. ''I'm sorry,'' she said, wondering how badly he had been hurt. ''Having a new baby and losing your wife about the same time must mean huge adjustments. I'm sorry you lost your wife.''

''Oh, I've never been married. I'm not Merry's blood father,'' he answered quietly.

Three

As he drove along darkened streets, Faith stared at him. "You said she's your daughter."

"I adopted Merry when her daddy died," Jared said, his voice rough.

"You must have been close friends," she said.

"He was my best friend." Jared stared straight ahead as he turned into a graveled lot lighted by a tall pole lamp. He parked and cut the motor, still staring out the front window. She saw a muscle knot in his jaw.

"You know, life is strange. My family was such a mess growing up, I finally ran away. I've lived everywhere and done nearly everything, but when Dusty died, it got to me like not much else ever has. I think part of it has to do with Merry. Sometimes when I'm with her, I know what he's missing. It shouldn't be me watching her get her first tooth, it should be Dusty."

"Sorry, Jared. But it's wonderful you took responsibility for her."

"She's my life now," he said, reaching back to touch the baby's wispy hair. "Enough about the past. C'mon, let's eat."

As they stepped out of the car, Faith glanced around. Red neon burned over the door in a simple sign reading Eldon's Café. Across the street was a bar and pool hall, and down the block another bar.

"The area's not great," he said, as if he had noticed her inspection. "But they have the best spaghetti south of Chicago and it's quiet inside so we can talk. You said you like Italian."

"I do. I've lived in Tulsa all my life and I've never eaten here."

"This isn't your style, Faith. Those businessmen you date prefer other places. This is pretty simple," he said as he unbuckled the carrier and lifted it from the rear seat of the pickup. He closed the door and took her arm.

They entered a small, one-room café with wooden tables, an old-fashioned jukebox and men on stools along the bar at the end of the room. A few customers were scattered at booths and tables around the room. Jared led her to a booth and placed the carrier on the seat. He hung his hat on a peg before sitting down to face Faith. As soon as they had glasses of water and had ordered their meals, he took a drink of the beer he had requested and then lowered the bottle to study her.

"Tell me about yourself, Faith. How many brothers and sisters and nieces and nephews do you have?"

"I'm next to the oldest of five siblings. My brothers and sisters are married and all have children."

"So you're the career woman."

She looked down, running her fingers on the cold glass, and watched as little drops of water dripped to the table. "I am. To tell the truth, it's beginning to get a little stale."

"How so? You looked pretty dedicated back there."

"I used to love my work and couldn't wait to get to the office. It was fun and I was eager and it was exciting." She glanced up to meet his steady, disconcerting gaze. "I don't know why I'm telling you all this."

"Because I'm a good listener," he answered lightly. "If you feel that way, why don't you ease up? Go out more. Date. Maybe you're suffering burnout."

"I keep telling myself I don't have burnout, but I don't feel like I used to.... Anyway, now you tell me about you. Two brothers. Where are your parents?" She saw him arch one brow; otherwise, there was no indication she had struck a nerve.

"My parents, darlin', are no longer living. My grand-parents are full-blood Kiowa. My brothers and I didn't have the same fathers. Actually, we didn't have any legal fa-thers—all of them were common-law husbands. My blood father was alcoholic, verbally abusive—not a sterling char-acter."

"I'm sorry," she said, saddened by the knowledge that his past had been so vastly different from her own happy childhood.

He shrugged. "I have two older brothers who are great. Wyatt has grown up with a sense of right and wrong that is powerful."

"Did he get that from your mother?"

"Oh, hell, no." Jared paused as plates of spaghetti with thick red sauce were placed before them. The waitress set a basket with hot, golden breadsticks on the table.

"Can I get you anything else?" she asked.

"No, thanks," Jared answered when Faith shook her head.

"You were telling me about your brother Wyatt," Faith prompted, curious about Jared's family.

"Wyatt got his fine-tuned conviction of what's right and wrong from our granddad. We spent a lot of time on the farm with him. My grandparents live in southern Oklahoma, and they were the Rock of Gibraltar in our lives. We moved all over. I ran away when I was sixteen, so I didn't finish high school," he said, giving her a level look.

"And why do I suspect you have more than one college degree?"

Surprised he had guessed, she shrugged. "I didn't think it showed," she answered lightly. "I have my MBA and a degree in graphic art."

"So our life-styles and our backgrounds are different," he said, putting his fork down. He leaned across the table, sliding his hand behind her head.

She inhaled, his touch bringing a tingling awareness to her whole body. Her pulse raced, and she felt as if she was drowning in his dark eyes. "You have a fancy executive job while I drift across the country riding horses and bulls. Even with all these glaring differences, why do I suspect we have some very common ground between us?"

"I don't think we do have any common ground," she whispered, barely able to get her voice. He was like a magnet, stirring and pulling everything to him.

He leaned back and placed her barrette on the table. "I like your hair better that way," he said.

She touched her hair in surprise. "I didn't even feel you take that out."

Amusement sparkled in his eyes. "I have a practiced hand," he drawled. "A very sensitive touch." She suspected he was not talking about taking out barrettes, but she had never been into light flirting and double entendres, so she let the remarks drop.

"I'll tell you some common ground," he continued cheerfully. "You like Merry, and from the way you look at her, you like little babies a whole damn lot."

"Yes, I do," she said, trying to gather her wits and pick up the thread of his conversation.

"Tell me more about yourself. What do you want out of life?"

She couldn't recall the last time anyone had asked her that question. Or if anyone ever had asked her. She paused, her fork halting. "When I was a little girl, I collected dolls, and all I wanted was to grow up, get married and have

babies. Then I got older and began to want a successful
career in graphic art. End of ambitions.''

"You want to own the company?''

"Actually, no. I like doing the design and art work. I'm
not as interested in management.''

He smiled, a slight curving of his mouth, a satisfied glint
in his eyes that made her uneasy, as if she had just passed
a test.

"So tell me about your parents and how you spend holidays and where all these siblings live.''

"They all live here in Tulsa, very close to our folks and
one another. We spend holidays together, and with all the
little nieces and nephews it's fun and hectic.''

Jared finished his dinner and listened to her describe her
banker father, her attorney brother, Andy, her stockbroker
brother, Keith, as well as her two married sisters who were
home with their children. While Faith finished her spaghetti
and talked, Jared felt more sure by the second that this lady
was going to be special in his life. Every time she talked
about marriage and babies, she got a wistful note in her
voice. She might have a hell of a career, but the woman
wanted a baby, and it showed almost as plainly as if she
had announced it.

When Merry stirred, he picked her up.

"I'll hold her if she'll let me,'' Faith said, and Jared
handed Merry to her. Faith settled Merry in her arms and
smiled at the baby. She touched the baby's cheek. "How
did you get to know her father?''

"Rodeo. He was into bull riding and saddle broncs just
like I am. I knew Merry's mother, too. She was a good-
looking woman. Too damn good-looking. She never intended to get pregnant, and when Merry was born, she took
off. She never married Dusty, and she told him she didn't
want any part of their kid. Some mother,'' he said.

"So how did *you* become father to her? Or would you
rather not talk about it?''

"Dusty lost control of his pickup and he was thrown out.

He didn't wear a seat belt and his internal injuries were terrible." Faith sat quietly while silence stretched between them, and she knew he was having another struggle with his emotions.

"Jared, I didn't mean to pry," she said softly, reaching out to cover his hand with hers.

He turned his head away, pinched the bridge of his nose and wiped his eyes. "Sorry. It seems like yesterday. I got to the hospital as fast as I could. Dusty asked me to take Merry. I didn't want to. Hell, I felt inadequate to be a dad. I damned sure didn't have a good role model growing up."

"Sounds as if you did in your grandfather."

"Yeah, I did. Anyway, Dusty was insistent I take Merry because he was dying." Jared met her gaze and looked down at her hand lying over his. He opened his hand, his fingers closing around hers, warm and strong and sure. Why did every little thing with him seem special? This cowboy was playing havoc with her system, and she suspected she was going to remember this day and night forever.

"Dusty begged me to adopt her. When I agreed, he got a lawyer and we signed the papers. Dusty didn't live until morning."

"I'm sorry."

"Yeah," Jared said, staring beyond her as if lost in memories. He gave her hand a squeeze and released her. Picking up his beer, he took a long drink. "Was I lost at first! I'd never been around a little baby in my life. Never held one. She's an angel and she's blessed my life."

"That's wonderful that you adopted her," Faith said. She was amazed he had adapted so well to fatherhood after the vagabond life he must have led.

"Looks like they want to close," he said, gesturing to the empty café. "Let's get out of here. We can talk in the pickup or we can go to my place."

"My stars," she exclaimed, looking at her watch. "It's half past twelve! We've been talking for over two hours."

He gave her a crooked grin. "So we have," he said, with so much satisfaction, she had to laugh.

"Don't tell me you knew we would."

"I didn't say it." He had paid the check long before, and as he slid out of the booth he placed his hat on his head. He took Merry from her and picked up the carrier.

The night breeze was cool when they stepped outside, catching locks of Faith's hair and blowing them across her cheek. Jared fastened Merry's carrier onto the back seat, and said, "She's asleep again. The afternoon in the park must have worn her out even with her little naps." He slid behind the wheel and turned to Faith. "Give me directions."

She did so, and they drove across south Tulsa to Faith's condo, where Jared punched in the code to open black iron gates. Moments later, he stopped in her driveway and cut the motor.

"Want to see where I live?" she asked. She hadn't given thought to whether or not she would invite him in, simply because she hadn't expected to, yet when he'd switched off the motor, the words were out of her mouth before she could take them back.

"Sure. I'll bring Merry," he said, climbing out of the pickup. He reached into the back seat to gather the baby.

They entered Faith's apartment through a small hallway leading into her kitchen. She switched on a light while Jared placed Merry, still in her carrier, on an oval wooden kitchen table and dropped his hat on a chair. The spotless room contained cherry wood cabinets, tile countertops and a pale blue-and-white floor.

"This is nice," he said.

"I'll give you a tour." Hanging her keys and purse on a hook, she motioned to him, leading him through a formal dining area with a fruitwood table and sideboard, the surfaces gleaming. He thought of the tiny fingerprints smudged on the furniture in his hotel room, Merry's diapers and belongings and toys strewn over the room, and his own clutter.

The living area was equally immaculate with Impressionist paintings hanging on the white walls, muted pastel upholstery lending touches of color in the beige-and-white decor and more fruitwood furniture.

"Would you like a glass of tea or pop?" she asked.

"Whatever pleases you suits me just fine."

He followed her into the kitchen again and when she opened the refrigerator door, he quickly pushed it closed. He placed his hands on the refrigerator on either side of her, hemming her in.

Faith's heart jumped and she drew a deep breath as she gazed up at him. He stood close enough that she could see a faint dark stubble on his jaw. His skin was smooth and brown, his eyes pools of midnight. A faint, thin scar ran across his right cheekbone.

"I don't really need something to drink. Go with me to the rodeo tomorrow night. Come watch me ride."

"Jared, dinner was nice—"

When his dark gaze drifted down to her mouth, her refusal died in her throat. Her pulse drummed, and she could see his intention in his eyes. Her body tightened, heated. The magic chemistry that had flamed between them from the first moments burned hotter than ever. She wanted his kiss, wanted his arms around her. Defying all logic and past history, disregarding every sensible thing she knew, she wanted his kisses. He was an unknown quantity, a temptation to discover secrets life had so far withheld from her. She closed her eyes and tilted her face.

Jared's heart thudded. He saw the invitation, knew she was responding to him the moment her words died.

He knew full well they were as different as a flower from the equator and a glacier in the Arctic, yet a sizzling attraction burned between them. She was wonderful with Merry, and since when had he ever held back because of fear of the unknown?

He slid his arm around her narrow waist, feeling the suppleness of her body, and watched her almost visibly melt into his arms. Her scent was a bouquet of spring flowers. Soft and tantalizing like all the rest of her.

Her hands came up to rest gently on his shoulders—a feather touch—yet the contact jolted him straight to his heart. Her eyes opened to watch him. He could see the questions in their cool, green depths, see the willingness, the invitation that made him shake with anticipation.

His mouth covered hers, tasted, sought and found a heated sweetness that shattered barriers he had built up around his heart too many years ago to remember. His arm tightened and his world shifted, and he wondered if it would ever again be the same. This woman was special to him. They barely knew each other, yet he wanted her. Needed her.

He didn't stop to question whether his feelings were right or wrong any more than he had stopped to question his actions at sixteen when he had run into a dark night, leaving family and home behind.

And he'd felt as if he was searching for something all those years, running, drifting, always seeking. In Faith's sweetness and searing kisses, he felt as if he was home. Yet what could he offer her in return? She was accustomed to business types with their methodical planning and driving ambitions, not rough-hewed cowboys who took each day as it came.

While his heart thudded, he fitted her against his body, one arm tightly around her, his other hand tangled in her silky hair. He felt a chance for a future with her, yet was he pushing his dreams too far? She clearly loved little babies and responded to Merry, yet she might never come to love him.

He gave a deep growl in his throat. He was a man of action, not one to spend time debating the wisest course. She felt right in his arms. She was a marvel; her kisses, her warmth were perfection. Even if he was just a cowboy, she was responding to him. She seemed ready for something more in her life, too. *Take a chance,* his heart whispered.

Her slender arms wrapped around his neck and her hips thrust against him. When she trembled and moaned softly, his temperature soared. He wanted her with every inch of his being.

Faith had never known kisses like Jared's, kisses that made years of loneliness fall away. Nor had she ever experienced the dizzying passion that burned into her, igniting responses she didn't know she had. She felt drawn to this enigmatic man. She sensed a desperate need in him that sought fulfillment as much as the empty void she felt in herself.

Her sane, logical, routine world was torn apart in the raging storm of his kisses. Time hung in the balance. For this moment he was all she knew and, for now, all she wanted to know.

His lean, hard body pressed against her, and she felt his arousal. He raised his head and she opened her eyes, dazzled and befuddled. Kisses weren't supposed to be life-changing. And his kisses had ended too swiftly.

She looked up into smoldering dark eyes that caused her heart to thud.

"Ah, Faith," Jared said softly, running his finger along her jaw. "Will you marry me?"

Four

"Marry you?" Faith gazed up at him, uncertain she had heard him correctly.

Reality came crashing in. Startled by his proposal, she shook her head. Her logical way of viewing a problem surfaced. "Marriage is absurd. We don't know each other at all!" She thought about all the times she had dreamed of marriage. In all those fantasies she had always imagined dating someone for a long time, then getting engaged, followed by months of planning for the wedding.

Too aware of the slightest contact with him, she dropped her hands to her sides. Jared still held her firmly, his arms around her waist, even though she wiggled to move away. "We can't marry," she continued. "If I ever marry, I will be wildly in love. I will have dated him for a long time and known him even longer. My family will know him. We'll like the same things, have the same background—"

"That's not what your kisses just told me," Jared whispered, brushing a kiss across her temple that made her pulse jump again.

"How many women have you proposed to?" she snapped, flustered.

"Only one, just now," he said so solemnly it took her breath away.

"We're strangers and we're not in love."

"I need a mother for Merry. I want a woman in my life. I'm ready to settle down, and you're perfect."

She closed her eyes, her mind reeling. "Get a nanny. Get out and date. You can't know that I'm perfect for you."

"Yes, I do," he answered quietly, and with a firmness that made her want to grind her teeth.

"Well, even if all that is so, there's nothing in it for me. I don't want to marry. I don't know you. You're not perfect for my life—far from it. You're so unlike me. By your own admission, you're wild, a drifter, a cowboy. What makes you think you're ready to settle?"

"Merry. Because of her, I know I'm ready to settle. Darlin', I've seen the world and done everything I wanted to as a single guy. That life is done and over. I've grown up."

She wiggled again, and he released her. She moved a few steps away and turned to look at him. He stood with his hands on his hips, waiting, looking patient and satisfied. And so damnably sexy!

"We don't know each other! I don't even know how old you are."

"Twenty-six."

"Oh, my word!" She reeled at his answer. "There! That's reason enough. I'm older than you."

He stepped close again, and her breath caught in her throat. He tilted her face while he shook his head. "In years you may be older, but not in experience. You thought I was older, didn't you?"

"Yes." The word was a whisper because she knew he had won this argument. She looked at the scar across his cheek, the tiny lines that fanned from the corners of his eyes, the knowledge held in his dark eyes, and she knew that of the two of them, anyone would think he was the older. And when he kissed her, she felt like a young, inexperienced girl.

"How old are you?"

"Twenty-nine," she answered grudgingly.

"Ahh, the thirtieth birthday approaches. How soon is it?"

"Six months." She glared at him, because that milestone had been worrying her more and more often.

"Your biological clock is ticking, Faith. Now I've told you what I want and what I'd be getting. Let's talk about what you want and what you'd be getting."

"I want my career and I'd lose it!" She had the feeling she was hanging on the edge of a cliff and slowly slipping into a bottomless chasm. She could feel ground crumbling beneath her grasping fingertips. At the same time, deep inside, she thrummed with an excitement that she tried to ignore.

"I don't think that's what you want at all." He reached behind his head, unfastened the leather thong and shook his head. Black hair swirled around his face, emphasizing his wildness, and the differences in their life-styles. "You've got your career. You've moved up to a lot of responsibility and you like your work, but it's not enough all by itself, is it?"

She didn't like to admit he was right. Those devastating dark eyes could see to her soul.

He placed his hands on her shoulders, the fingers of his right hand twiddling locks of her hair. "You'd get a family. You would have a baby, Faith."

"I can fall in love, marry and have babies, and you know it."

"But you'll be thirty soon, you're not dating anyone, and marriage is not looming on your horizon."

"That doesn't mean it won't be."

"Of course not, but do you really want to keep waiting?

The scenario you mapped out to me means you'll be about thirty-six before any babies of your own come into your life. And life has a way of handing us a lot of surprises. You can't put life in a daily planner.''

"Marriage is forever. I want to be sure. I want to be in love. You said you had several fathers. You don't have a stable background. I do. I want what I grew up having.'' He was making her uncomfortable because he was voicing some of her own doubts. She felt as if she was arguing half with him, half with herself.

"And I want that, too,'' he said solemnly. "I want a home, a wife and my family. I don't want what I grew up experiencing.''

"Well, then propose to a woman you know really well and you love.''

"I need a wife now. And we can get to know each other and love each other later.''

"And if we don't? Wouldn't that be hellish for us and for Merry?''

"Yes, it would be. Faith, I'm offering you a marriage of convenience. It doesn't have to be physical at first. Then if it's really bad, it can be annulled. Let's see if we can live together—''

"Most of the time it's the other way around. Men want to move in together and then maybe marry.'' She noticed that she was the one whose voice was rising while he was calm, collected. The man was dangerous, a threat to her future and her well-being. "This is impossible,'' she said.

"No, it's not. You're ready for a baby. It shows every time you touch Merry.''

"I have nieces and nephews I can take care of nights on end.''

"That's not satisfying you,'' he said quietly, with a persistence that annoyed her because he was right. It wasn't satisfying her. And she longed for a family, for a baby of her own. She turned to look at Merry, who was sleeping blissfully, unaware of the storm swirling around her that might change her life forever.

"My family wouldn't approve of you."

"They sound warm and loving and reasonable. They can't be vastly different from you," he said.

"They want certain things for me. They expect me to marry someone like the guys I've always dated. We don't go to rodeos or farm or ranch. We're city people who go to the symphony and the opera and the ballet. They want someone with a background like mine—"

"Who is going to pick out this husband—you or your family?"

"You know what I'm talking about," she replied impatiently. It was a crazy argument. She'd never done anything impetuous, reckless or unpredictable. Magic kisses and a sexy cowboy weren't reasons to change.

"Is it my heritage?"

"No, but don't you see, that's simply one more difference upon a sea of differences. It's your hair and your boots and your hat and your life-style and your background and your occupation. How many differences do I have to list? The biggest one is that we don't really know each other. How are you going to support a wife? Riding in rodeos?"

"Actually, that's not a bad way. And at some point, I want to buy some land and raise cattle. I know ranching from the years I spent with my granddad."

"I can't live on a ranch or marry someone who doesn't have a nine-to-five job. We're too different. Thanks for dinner and the proposal...and an interesting evening."

He moved closer and her pulse jumped. His arm went around her waist. "What about this? We seem to agree on this in a most delectable way."

Jared's mouth covered hers in a demanding, passionate kiss that she resisted for one-tenth of a second. As his tongue stroked hers, her insides felt as if they'd been turned wrong side out. A wave of heat washed through her, and her knees went weak. She wrapped her arms around his neck, thrust her hips against him and kissed him back. He was risk and danger, as tempting and breathtaking as a roller coaster. When his arms closed around her, why couldn't she remember that she liked safe, predictable men, the sure and the tame?

The kiss ended abruptly, and she wanted to tighten her arms and pull his head back down. Jared watched her as she opened her eyes.

"Lady, you need kissing. You're primed and ready for some real living after missing out for so long. Maybe we've both been waiting for each other." His words were soft-spoken, but they carried a note of conviction that shook her.

"I'll take Merry home." He released Faith, then strolled across the kitchen to retrieve his hat and to pick up Merry in her carrier. At the door he turned to look at Faith. "I'll pick you up tomorrow night about half past six. I'll show you around the barns, introduce you to some of my friends and get you and Merry settled in your box seats. Afterward, we'll eat some of the Southwest's best barbecue. In the meantime, you think over what I asked." He opened the door and left.

A whirlwind had just swept through her life, leaving silence and devastation in its wake. Or more accurately, she'd encountered a tall, lean cowboy who could see too much and was hell-bent on making her take a long look at herself, and her life.

The rumble of the pickup broke the quiet, then faded into the night. She switched off lights and went to her bedroom, her thoughts swirling with images and questions. She thought about Jared's kisses and her body burned, longing tugging at her. The memory was as clear as if Jared was with her now. Why had his kisses been so spectacular? She remembered watching him give Merry her bottle, the look on his face as he watched the tiny baby. His proposal taunted her. *Marry* Jared Whitewolf? It was impossible, absurd, out of the question. So why was she in knots over it?

Maybe she was suffering burnout at work. She looked at her hands, her bare fingers. Why was she so vulnerable to Jared Whitewolf? The whole day held a dreamlike quality, but his kisses were flaming reality, so much she wouldn't have been surprised to see her hair slightly singed. She would never know kisses like that from anyone else.

''That's no reason to marry someone,'' she said aloud. But suppose the kisses had been as devastating to him? Suppose this was a volatile attraction they'd never found with anyone else? Shaken by the thought, she moved around the room, getting ready for bed while her thoughts raged over his proposal.

And the sweet little baby. A pang of longing so intense it was painful tore at Faith. Jared Whitewolf had discerned her feelings more than any other guy she had ever dated. He knew she was worried about her thirtieth birthday, and he knew she loved babies and wanted her own. His little girl was precious. Maybe the experience of losing his friend and becoming a daddy really had settled him down.

She could not marry a cowboy! Her parents would have apoplexy. A drifter who ran away from home and never finished high school? He was all wrong for her, and she couldn't believe he'd coerced her into another date tomorrow night at the rodeo.

She looked around her bedroom, with its white furniture and pale blue carpeting. The room looked virginal—probably because it was. No man had ever spent the night in it. She had thought she was in love once in college, but the relationship never developed into anything lasting. Other than that, her dating had never become very intimate. She was cautious, and the men she dated were cautious.

So what had happened to all that great prudence with Jared Whitewolf?

Long after she'd gone to bed, Faith lay wide-eyed, staring into the darkness, remembering holding Merry in her arms, giving her a bottle. If she married Jared, she would have a little baby. Not a year from now, but as soon as they married. And yet, what would her folks think of Jared?

That question brought her back to reality, and she closed her eyes, but in minutes, memories of holding Merry in her arms danced in her head. And then her memories shifted to Jared. His dark eyes and strong arms were as clear as if he was in the room with her. A long, tall cowboy who was all she wasn't. And she had to admit, he excited her as no other man ever had.

Less than twenty-four hours later, Faith had met a dozen friendly people and seen more horses and bulls than ever before in her life. She wondered whether she was the only person in the large metal barn who was not wearing Western boots and jeans. Her pulse hummed with excitement and anticipation, and she was acutely aware of the man at her side. Merry was strapped snugly to his chest and seemed to enjoy her surroundings.

"Come on. I'll get you two settled," Jared said, taking her arm to steer her through the barn. As he reached out to open a door, she looked at his blue-and-white Western shirt, which pulled across his broad shoulders. He looked very much the cowboy tonight with his Western attire.

He led her to an empty box, where he sat with her while he buckled Merry into her carrier in the seat between them. Merry played with a bright red plastic car. Absorbed in her own little world, she raised the car to her mouth to chew on it.

"Here's her bag with bottles if she gets fussy. I'd wait out here with you, but I need to get ready."

"That's fine. We'll be all right. Uh, Jared, I couldn't help but notice you're wearing spurs," she said, a fact that had been worrying her.

He stepped over her and sat down in the seat beside her, propping his long leg on his knee. "The rowels are dull—feel them. I'm not going to hurt the animals. The spurs help me to hang on. And my spurs are supposed to be in contact with the horse's shoulders each time the bronc's front hooves hit the ground.''

She touched a rowel lightly and looked up at him as he reached into a hip pocket.

"Here's a program. When this is over, I'll take you to dinner.'' Stretching his arm across her, he took folders from Merry's bag. He leaned close, and she noticed the scent of him, felt his arm rest lightly on her knee. "Here are some things you can take home to look over," he said. "Here's my last physical, so you'll know I'm as healthy as that horse I'll ride," he said, thrusting papers into her hand. "Blood test, complete physical. Here's a list of my assets and net worth. At the moment I don't owe any money to anyone. Here are my brothers' addresses and phone numbers.''

Astounded, Faith looked at the papers he'd placed in her hand. "You don't need to do this!"

"Sure, I do," he answered easily. "If we're marrying, you should know what you're getting into.''

"We're not marrying," she said, wondering whether he was listening to her. His dark eyes drifted over her, and she became aware of herself, of her pale yellow silk blouse, her tan slacks. She could see the approval in his warm gaze, feel that swift arc of tension that erased the world and narrowed existence down to just the two of them.

He leaned closer to brush a light kiss on Faith's lips, just the faintest touch, yet it made her want to close her eyes, slip her arm around his neck and deepen the kiss.

"We'll discuss it later. But before I go, let me pin your earring to my hat for good luck," he said, taking one of the stud diamond earrings from her ear, his knuckles brushing her cheek and ear lightly. "Okay?" he asked, hesitating only inches from her.

"Okay," she barely answered, looking at his mouth and remembering his kisses.

He pulled off his hat, punched the earring through the band and fastened it next to the feathers.

"Why the feathers? More good luck?"

"Something like that. They came from Granddad's farm. That's why they're battered. I've had those feathers a long time." He glanced over his shoulder. "See that gate? I'll come out there and hopefully ride here in front of you. And let's hope Demon Rum doesn't toss me right into your lap."

Amusement danced in his dark eyes, but she couldn't share it. "I'm not certain I can stand to watch you. I've never fainted in my life, but if you get stomped on by a ten-ton bull—I'll pass out."

"Why, darlin', you *do* care!" he teased, stroking her cheek lightly. The contact was slight, yet it kindled a desire that was ready to blaze. "See you later," he added, grinning as he rose to leave.

He settled his hat on his head and went down the steps, vaulting the wall before dropping into the arena to head toward the gate. She watched his long-legged stride, appraised his broad shoulders and the black hair secured behind his head. Her pulse drummed in a steady beat of excitement. Why did everything seem more vivid, more intense, since she had met him?

She glanced around the arena, with its dirt-covered floor and metal chutes, and she knew that if she closed her eyes a year from now, she would remember this night in fine clarity, as if everything that concerned Jared was etched in her memory. Never before had it been that way with any man she had dated. Maybe that came from having known them for years. But she knew that wasn't so. Never, at any point in time, had it been reckless and dazzling with any of them. And it never would. The realization startled her. She looked at Merry, who smiled at her.

"You little doll. No wonder he spoke all that silly baby talk to you," she said, leaning over Merry. The baby cooed

and laughed and kicked her feet, drooling while her blue
eyes sparkled.

Faith wiped Merry's chin with a cloth bib that was
tucked into the bag. "You are a sweetie, and I have to
admit, your daddy's pretty nice, too. Maybe a little headstrong."

Faith glanced down at the papers in her lap and picked
up his physical, glancing over statistics. The man had a
clean bill of health. She felt a flicker of relief, because she
suspected he was the kind of man who attracted women in
droves, and she imagined until Merry came along, he'd had
a relatively casual attitude toward sex.

His blood pressure was good, his cholesterol level fine.
Heart and lungs fine. Then came a staggering roster of
sprains, fractures and broken bones: broken thumb, broken
fingers, fractured shoulder, sprained ankle, broken collarbone, broken arm, broken wrist, broken leg, broken ribs.
The list was long, and she wondered if it was all from bronc
and bull riding.

Shifting to the page of assets, she glanced over figures
and was shocked. She knew her impression of him was
prejudiced by his lollygagging in the park. He seemed like
a drifter, and she hadn't thought of him as having so much
as a bank account, but the figures on the page were impressive. She straightened the papers on her knees and really studied the figures.

He had sizable savings, plus his house on Peoria, which
had been appraised and was worth about what Faith would
have guessed for a house in that area of town. A trust from
Dusty had been set up for Merry. Faith had suspected that
one reason for Jared's proposal might have been her steady
job and nice income, yet now she knew that wasn't the
case.

He hadn't proposed because of her income—he had
plenty of his own. Faith looked at the figures again, unable
to grasp that a man who did not work regular hours could
have such a net worth. How could he spend his days in the

park and still save money? She pulled out the page with
his brothers' addresses. A picture of three boys was tacked
to the page. It was a battered picture, taken years earlier,
and she held it closer.

Jared had written down their names and drawn arrows
pointing to each one. Jared looked the youngest, standing
between the other two. All three had the same black hair,
the broad firm jaw and prominent cheekbones. Faith had to
admit that she found Jared to be the most handsome of the
three rugged brothers.

Beneath the picture Jared had boldly scrawled vital statistics.

*Wyatt: thirty-three, father of Kelsey and twin baby girls,
Robin and Rachel. Wife is Alexa.*

*Matt: thirty-four, single—confirmed old bachelor. Wheat
farmer in western Oklahoma.*

*Mother: Costa Whitewolf, died of drug overdose in a
Wakulla hospital.*

*Grandfather: Loughlan Whitewolf. Grandmother: Cor-
nelia Whitewolf. Own farm in southwestern Oklahoma near
Lawton.*

Faith lowered the paper, put it in the folder and placed
the document in Merry's bag. The baby began to fuss and
Faith unbuckled her, then lifted her out of her carrier.

''I'll bet you're tired of sitting there. Let's stand and look
for your daddy, who will be riding a wild old bull. I may
have to hold your hand and hide my eyes. Actually, I'm
not sure either one of us should watch.''

Merry gurgled and Faith cuddled her as she moved
around the box. The seats began to fill up with people, and
when the rodeo commenced, Faith held Merry up so she
could watch the horses parade past in a grand procession
during the opening ceremonies.

The first event was bareback riding, and Merry began to
fuss, so Faith placed her on a seat, changed her and then
picked her up to give her a bottle.

As she fed the baby, she watched the first horse leap out

of the chute and buck, the rider flying off and landing hard.
She shut her eyes the next time a ride began. Her palms
were damp. How could Jared earn a living this way?

Calf roping followed, and she could bear to watch it.
Then the clowns performed, and after their act, saddle
bronc riding was scheduled. Faith's nervousness increased.
She hadn't been able to watch men she didn't know get
tossed around. How would she be able to watch one she
did care about? And she did care. Though his arrival in her
life had caused upheaval and stirred longings she should
probably ignore, she had to admit, she liked being with him.

At the sound of the buzzer, the first rider burst out of the
chute. Faith drew a deep breath, horrified as the horse
bucked and spun and the man was thrown, hitting the
ground hard, sending up puffs of dust. The man looked as
if he would be stomped beneath the hooves, but he rolled
and jumped to his feet, scooped up his hat and exited to
applause while pickup cowboys got the horse out of the
arena. Faith looked down at Merry, who was gazing back
with solemn blue eyes.

"Your daddy is going to ride third, but I suppose you'll
be more interested in staying where you are and drinking
your bottle."

Merry continued to suck, and Faith looked up as the
buzzer sounded again and another wild horse leaped out of
the chute. This time the man rode longer, getting tossed
just a second before the buzzer sounded. He landed on his
back and jumped up as easily as the first cowboy had, and
she wondered again about Jared. What kind of man was he
to enjoy this sort of sport and earn his living at it?

In the chute she could see his black hat, see him looking
down at his horse. The roan bucked, slamming hooves into
the chute and banging around while the announcer continued speaking, stating Jared's name and winnings. Then the
buzzer sounded and the gate swung open.

The roan shot into the air. Jared's feet swung forward,
stroking back and forth while he held one hand high in the

air. Watching as his hat flew off and he stayed in the saddle, she held her breath. The horse twisted and bucked, moving closer to her box. Faith could hear the hooves thud against the dirt, hear the animal's snorts until they were drowned out by applause and cheers. She squeezed her eyes closed, then opened an eye to watch.

The buzzer sounded and the applause was loud. Jared slid onto the back of a pickup rider's horse and then jumped down, leaving the roan to others as he strode to scoop up his hat, then thumped it against his leg, which was covered by his chaps. Turning her way, he waved and then headed for the fence, where he swung his long legs over and dropped down on the other side.

Her palms were damp, she had bitten her lip, and she gulped for air, trying to catch her breath after holding it during his ride. She didn't want to watch him ride a bull. A horse had been bad enough.

She looked down at Merry, whose eyes were closed as she busily sucked on the bottle.

"Your daddy is wild and tough and crazy and charming. As adorable as you are, I can't be part of his life. Not in the next million years," she whispered.

Five

Steer wrestling was the next event, and it seemed violent in its own way, though not as bad as the bronc riding. Next came team roping, followed by barrel racing, and for a moment Faith enjoyed the rodeo, watching the pretty women ride like the wind, the horses performing with grace and amazing speed.

The clowns gave an exhibition, and Faith was sorry Merry had fallen asleep, yet even the clowns' antics with the powerful bull gave her some tense moments.

The last event was bull riding. Jared was first and Faith didn't think she could watch. Merry slept peacefully in her arms, and Faith drew a deep breath, watching Jared prepare himself in the chute.

The buzzer sounded and the gate swung open.

The huge gray bull stormed out of the chute, flinging Jared around like a toy, yet he clung to the animal's back as it twisted and bucked and kicked. The animal looked like a monster with its wide horns and massive body. Faith felt faint and hot, terrified for Jared, knowing she would be equally petrified for every rider. Unable to watch, she closed her eyes. If Jared was hurt or stomped, she wouldn't be able to stand it.

The buzzer sounded. Applause and cheers and whistles filled the arena. She opened her eyes and saw the bull twist in the air. Jared flew off, landing on his side as the animal charged.

Faith cried out, clutching the rail with one hand, her other arm around Merry. Jared rolled out of the way and jumped up to run for the gate while the clowns waved hats at the bull, who charged after Jared for a few feet and then swerved to chase a clown.

Sinking back in the seat, Faith watched Jared climb over the fence and disappear from view. She wiped her damp palm on her slacks, tried to catch her breath and waited for her heart to stop pounding. The next rider came out of the chute, and not wanting to watch, she looked down at Merry. At a gasp from the crowd, Faith glanced up and saw the rider sprawled on the dirt. While men ran out to help him, the clowns distracted the bull, dodging when it charged them.

The next rider did better, but he didn't last until the buzzer sounded.

"How'd you like your first rodeo?" Jared asked as he dropped into a seat beside her.

"I was terrified. I don't know how you can do that!"

He grinned. Dirt was smudged on his face and he had a scrape on his cheek. "I may win a lot of money."

"Did you ever think of taking up accounting or something sane and sensible?"

He laughed and touched her nose. Pulling off his hat, he unfastened her earring. "This brought me great luck," he said, "just like I thought it would."

"I think you've had a lot of luck before without my earring," she answered dryly, her heart fluttering because he was so close.

Leaning forward, he replaced the diamond stud in her ear, his fingers brushing her ear and throat while his face hovered only inches from hers. He smelled faintly of dust and leather and sweat. She looked at his mouth, the slightly full lower lip, and she remembered how it had felt to have his mouth on hers. His dark gaze met hers and her pulse jumped.

"Let's go," he said. "I'll put Merry in her carrier."

He took the baby gently from Faith's arms, his hands brushing over Faith, and then he knelt down to buckle Merry in her baby seat. He picked up the carrier and bag and took Faith's arm to head for the door. As they climbed steps, she heard the announcer's loud voice state that Jared Whitewolf had won bull riding.

"You don't have to stick around?"

"Not tonight. I'm accumulating points. I'll be back to-morrow night. We're going now."

We. Excitement bubbled within Faith, but she sternly reminded herself she was going to say no to Jared's proposal. She had rehearsed it dozens of times, imagining his arguments, her firm refusal and their goodbye.

This time Jared drove to a crowded restaurant on the city's edge, where they sat in a corner booth. The tables were wooden, the floor terrazzo, and tantalizing smells of roasting meat and a wood-burning fire filled the room. Merry continued to sleep, her hands folded peacefully in her lap.

"She's an angel, Jared."

"That she is."

They ordered, and over juicy ribs covered in thick red barbecue sauce, Jared asked her once again about her work.

"So you could open your own office if you wanted to and do the same thing you're doing now?"

"Yes, I could. And maybe someday I will. At the moment, I'm happy where I am and don't want the responsibility of starting up my own company."

"Seems like you already know a lot of people who

would want you to continue to handle their accounts. You could work from a ranch just as well as from a downtown office.''

She met his satisfied gaze and felt both annoyed and amused. ''You think you'll figure everything out all by yourself?''

He shrugged. ''I'm looking at possibilities.''

''Well, then, look at the possibility of getting yourself a regular nine-to-five job, hiring a nanny, dating someone for months and then proposing.''

''That isn't what I want to do. Nor is it necessary. I'll be able to take care of Merry by riding in rodeos and ranching. You saw what I earn.''

''Yes, I did.''

''Surprised you, didn't I?'' he asked, and this time there was no mistaking the amusement that danced in his dark eyes. ''You have me pegged as a vagabond adventurer.''

''Income or no income, you're still a drifter in my eyes.''

''I'll work on my image,'' he said, and she wondered if she had handed him a challenge.

While they finished their ribs, the crowd thinned. Conversation turned to their families once again.

''Have your grandparents seen Merry?'' she asked.

''Yes, I stayed with them right after Dusty died. They had five other children besides Mom and three of the children live on farms in the area, so Grandmom has a lot of children and grandchildren underfoot. The rest of the family is pretty settled. Much more like your family. My brothers and I were the wild bunch.'' He leaned forward to trail his fingers lightly over her wrist and hand.

''I'm going to prove to you that I can settle down like a rock in the bottom of a pond. When Dusty died and I was given Merry, some of the married guys' wives helped me look after her for a few days while we buried Dusty. He didn't have any other family, so I planned the funeral and took care of the legal stuff. Then I packed up and took Merry home to Grandmom. She showed me how to take care of the baby. I had a rodeo already scheduled in Arizona, in the Turquoise Prorodeo Circuit, so Merry and I went west and now we're headed back. I want to see my brothers this time. I figured Grandmom had told them about Merry by now, but she must not have told Wyatt.''

''So there is some stability in your life.''

His dark eyes filled with amusement. ''Does that make your heart flutter with relief? Or give me just a tad more chance with you? Granddad and my grandmother are as stable as your family. They've been on their farm since it was handed to them by the U.S. Government when they doled out land to the Indians.'' He reached out to slip his hand behind her neck. ''And when I settle, I intend to settle for good.''

''You yourself said you can't plan out everything,'' she said, feeling consumed by his dark eyes, aware of his fingers lightly trailing back and forth across her nape. He was as dangerous to her world as a stalking tiger. What recklessness in her drew her to danger? She knew she should have said goodbye. Yet here she was, biding her time with a daredevil who mesmerized her.

''I plan to settle,'' he replied. ''I'll do the rodeo circuit, but I'm coming home to the same house and my family.''

''Jared, that sounds lovely, but you and me—well, it's absolutely impossible.''

''Let's go where we can talk with a little more privacy.'' He picked up Merry and slid out of the booth.

When they stepped outside, it was as nice a night as the previous one, with a bright full moon and a cool spring breeze. Jared draped his arm across her shoulders and walked silently beside her.

Once they'd settled themselves in the pickup, they drove through the city, and at the top of a hill they marveled at the view of the lights of downtown Tulsa. To the west was the dark ribbon of the Arkansas River; to the east, lights shone brightly in residential areas.

When they reached Faith's condo, Jared drove through

the iron gates and parked in her driveway. He picked up the sleeping baby in her carrier.

As soon as they were inside Faith's home, Merry woke suddenly, and by the time Jared unbuckled her from the baby carrier, she was crying loudly.

"I'll take her," Faith said, reaching for her, "while you get her bottle ready."

Faith was aware of her hands brushing his arms and chest as she took Merry from him. "Come here," she said to Merry, heading toward her bedroom, "and let's change you and put on your pj's and get you ready for sleepy land."

Merry bawled and kicked, clearly not interested in Faith's chatter.

Jared appeared at the door, bottle in hand. "Let me have my girl, and we'll stop all that ruckus." His gaze went over the room and Faith blushed, imagining how sterile and pristine it would look to him.

He crossed the room, and his utter masculinity seemed to invade the area. She knew she would remember him being in her bedroom forever.

"This is where you sleep." He looked into her eyes, and the fiery heat she saw in his made her insides quiver and her breath catch. And she wondered what had been dancing in his imagination. Whatever it had been, she was sure it involved her.

He took Merry from her, and little hands grabbed the bottle Jared held as Merry jammed it into her mouth.

"Miss Piggy," he remarked with amusement. "You'd think she hadn't eaten for days instead of hours." He turned and sat on the white rocker. "Is this okay?"

"Sure," Faith answered, sitting on the foot of the bed, kicking off her low-heeled shoes, amazed how he seemed perfectly at home in her bedroom. He looked completely relaxed while she felt edgy, too aware of him in these intimate surroundings that she had considered a very private part of her life. He had pulled free the snaps on the upper part of his shirt, leaving part of his chest bare. He dominated the room, looking as incongruous in her white-and-blue frilly bedroom as a tiger in a bubble bath.

"Have you ever ridden a horse, Faith?"

"Yes, I've ridden, but not in years. I had lessons and rode pretty regularly when I was about ten, but that's the last. Have you ever been to the symphony?"

He shook his head. "No, but I'm willing to try it."

She could imagine his taste in music, suspecting their tastes in everything from entertainment to vacations were vastly different. "Where are the family pictures?" he asked, glancing around the room.

"In the spare bedroom. There's a wall of them."

"When Merry finishes, you can show me."

"There are so many of us, it's confusing."

"We have lots of aunts and uncles and cousins, so I'm accustomed to the jumble of a big family."

"If you left home at sixteen, you can't really be accustomed to a family at all."

"Not so. By age sixteen you've been through the formative years. And I've gone back to the farm off and on."

"I couldn't help but notice your medical history in the files you gave me. Was it from riding in rodeos that you had all those broken bones?"

"Yeah. That and one broken arm from the sorry bastard who was my mother's common-law husband number four."

"How awful!"

"He didn't last long in our lives, thank the Lord. Our mother could really pick 'em. They were as wild as she was." Jared continued to rock, and he looked down at Merry as she played with his chin. He turned and playfully bit her fingers and growled. She laughed, little bubbles of milk curling out of the corners of her mouth. Then she returned to drinking her milk and running her fingers along his jaw.

"Did you like the rodeo?" he asked Merry. "Did you

watch your daddy ride the big bull? Someday you'll ride your own horse.''

Faith watched as Jared spoke softly to Merry while he fed her. His long legs were stretched out in front of him, his boots were dusty, and she remembered the feel of his long, lean body pressed against hers. Her gaze trailed back up, over his jeans, Merry in his arms, his broad shoulders— to meet his gaze.

Embarrassed to be caught so openly looking him over, she blushed.

Merry finished her bottle, and Jared lifted her to his shoulder, patting her back. ''Let's go meet the family,'' he said to Faith, standing.

Faith switched on the light in another bedroom that held a queen-size bed and had a maroon and deep hunter green decor. All the time she explained who each person was in the family pictures, she was acutely aware of Jared brushing against her, shoulder to shoulder, his hand lightly resting on her shoulder, then moving to her nape.

By the time they finished, Merry was asleep again and Faith was tied in knots from all his light touches. ''I'll get a blanket,'' she said. ''Can I put her on the bed? She won't roll off if I put pillows around her.''

They laid Merry down and then switched off the light before venturing for the kitchen. But as they crossed through the living room, Jared took Faith's arm and turned her to face him. ''I've been waiting since last night to be alone with you,'' he said quietly, drawing her to him.

Her pulse jumped and her heart thudded. Now was the time to say no, but any resistance vanished as she met his smoldering gaze. She wanted to be in his arms, wanted his kisses. It didn't mean she wanted to marry him, she told herself fleetingly, the thought swept away the moment his arm tightened around her waist and he bent his head.

His mouth covered hers, and she trembled. Desire, hot as a flame, burned in her, making an ache low in her body, a basic need that was as strong as the need to breathe.

Again, she caught the scent of his aftershave and a faint masculine smell of sweat and leather. Her senses reeled. His kisses were powerful, heady stuff.

He fitted her to his body, one hand holding her tightly while the other ran through her hair. She felt his arousal, knew he wanted her. And she was discovering she had never wanted a man before as much as she wanted this one. Touching each other was a marvel, each kiss intoxicating. She loved the excitement, the challenge of him. He was the wrong person for her, she knew, but his kisses felt so right.

His shoulders were hard beneath her hands. She slipped her fingers across the strong column of his neck. The leather thong that tied his hair came loose, and coarse, long strands fell over her wrists, reminding her what an unknown element he was, a man who was as headstrong as he was fearless.

His hand inched slowly along her throat, sliding lower, a prolonged torment until his hand reached her breast, stroking so lightly, making her gasp and moan. Her breasts tightened. The ache she felt increased, and she yearned for more. His hand slipped beneath the silk blouse, cupping her breast.

He pushed away the filmy lace bra and caressed her nipple, his thumb drawing circles that tantalized. She caught his hand, trying to inject sanity into the moment, feeling caught on a thundering roller coaster of passion that could wreck her quiet life.

"Jared, wait," she gasped, torn between wanting him desperately and knowing she had to stop.

He stopped the sensuous onslaught to look at her while she struggled for breath and pulled her clothes in place. They both were breathing hard. She had felt his heartbeat and knew it was as erratic as her own. This tall cowboy was riding roughshod over her defenses, smashing them with kisses that melted resistance and good sense. But his racing heart told her that he felt something, too.

He fumbled in his pocket and pulled out a small box. "Marry me, Faith," he said, opening the box.

A ring glittered in the dim light from the hall. The sparkling light from the purity of the stone dazzled, dancing before her eyes, a surprise and a temptation. The diamond's brilliance held promises of excitement, of life as she had never dared to experience it. And craziness.

How could she even consider marriage?

She stared at the ring while Jared removed it from the box. Then he took her hand, pausing to look at her quizzically.

"I can't," she whispered. Struggling to find her voice and speak firmly, her gaze stayed on the ring. "I've told you all the reasons," she said, mechanically following her lifelong habits, customary caution and sensible plans.

"My reasons why we should marry are better. You know we have something between us you've never known before," he said. "And neither have I. This is special for me, too, Faith." He tilted her face to look at him, and she could feel the force of his determination wrap around her heart.

"I want you. We can fall in love later."

"Let's fall in love first."

"I need you now. Merry needs a mother."

"Get a nanny!" she snapped, coming out of her daze.

"I want you for my wife. There doesn't have to be a physical union until you're ready."

"That's the least of the problems!" she said, knowing it took all her will to keep from pulling him toward the bedroom. "I don't know you! We're not in love!"

"Take a chance, Faith." His voice was deep and strong and maddeningly sure. "You know you're not happy with your life right now. You love little babies and you want one. I'm offering you what you want."

"I'm not ready for this," she whispered, feeling panicked.

But she was drawn to the wildness in him, that streak that let him do what he wanted. He lived a life she had never dared. She had always done what was expected, followed in the footsteps of the rest of her family. They lived in the same part of town, they went to the same church. She worked for her uncle. She dated men like her brothers and father. She lived an orderly, routine life that was completely predictable and secure.

But here was a whirlwind who promised no such stability. He was a great unknown, an adventurer, wild and dangerous. He was a wanderer who followed his whims. Staring at him, she was silent while her emotions warred like fierce combatants.

"If you say no, I'm gone," he informed her quietly. "I'm not hanging around like those guys you've known all your life. I'm not into long courtships."

"How do I know you're into marriage?"

His dark eyes blasted her with a fire that burned to her heart. "I know what I want," he said in a husky, forceful voice. "I always have. Marry me."

If she said no, she knew he would disappear out of her life forever. She had no doubts about it. She was certain this man didn't bluff or speak idly. And if he did leave tonight, would she forever feel she had thrown away a lifetime of happiness?

"I have to have a church wedding," she said, barely giving it a thought, merely stalling while her mind raced.

"Fine. Just don't drag it out. Merry needs a mother."

She should tell him goodbye. Let him go. He was proposing to her in order to gain a nanny. That was the basic reason, but she knew better than that. There was something spectacular between them. He felt it, too.

"Faith, you know what your heart is telling you. This is right. I can feel it to my soul."

"I can't do it. I just can't do it. It's so against everything in my life," she said, wanting to wring her hands and grind her teeth. "It's against my family, my upbringing, my good judgment. No, I can't."

He placed the ring in the box and closed it, then put it

in his pocket. He brushed a kiss on her lips and passed her as he went to the bedroom to get Merry.

This tall, exciting cowboy was going to walk out of her life forever, and she would go back to empty nights and empty weekends and long hours of work and nothing else.

He came back with Merry, who was still asleep. Faith followed him to the kitchen. He placed his hat on his head and paused with his hand on the doorknob while he gave Faith a long, enigmatic look. "I'll miss you," he said softly. He opened the door, stepped outside and was gone.

Six

She looked around the empty kitchen. Was this what she wanted? She thought about standing in Jared's arms. She remembered holding Merry.

He was walking out of her life forever. She had no idea how to find him.

Did she want to live her life the way she always had? Did she want the same routine all the rest of her life? The same job?

Did she want a baby?

Everything inside her screamed to go after him. *Take a risk for once!*

He adored Merry and took good care of her. He was solvent, had plans for his future. His kisses were magic, the chemistry between them impossible to ignore. What was she waiting for—a clone of her brothers and her father? And here was her chance for a baby.

She couldn't let him go. With a pounding heart, she dashed across the kitchen and out the back door. He was leaning over the back seat of the pickup, buckling Merry's carrier in.

"Jared!"

He straightened and turned to face her. She stopped only a few feet from him. The wind caught locks of her hair and blew them across her cheek. She brushed them away.

"Yes, I'll marry you," she said in a rush, her heart beating so loudly that her own voice sounded strange and dim. He didn't move, and she wondered whether he had changed his mind.

"Do you know what you're doing?" he asked.

She shook her head. "No. I just don't want you to go."

He closed the space between them and pulled her to him tightly while he leaned down to kiss her hard, a breathtaking kiss that made her forget the proposal, her acceptance, everything except him. His tongue stroked hers, went deep into her mouth and she trembled, clinging to him, returning his kiss. She felt as if she had let go of that cliff she had been slipping over and now was tumbling into a raging river.

She slid her hands across his broad shoulders, wound her arms around his neck, relishing the solid strength of him and praying that he would be as good a husband as he was a father. As she melted against him, she knew her life would never be the same as it had been before she charged through the spirea bushes. This tall cowboy was taking her with him on his wild ride through life. Shock, uncertainty, doubts—all burned to vapor and vanished. Bubbling excitement pumped through her veins, and she returned his kiss. Their tongues tangled, slick, hot, an intimate promise and bond. Her heart pounded violently. The cowboy and the baby—her husband, her child. This cowboy's seductive proposal was impossible to resist.

He raised his head and she felt a loss. She opened her eyes to find him watching her in that disturbing manner he had. Moonlight spilled over her face, but he was in shadow. He reached into his pocket and pulled out the small box, withdrawing the ring again. He put away the box and held her hand, pausing before he said, "Will you marry me, Faith?"

"Yes," she answered.

He slipped the ring on her finger, then pulled her to him to kiss her again, brushing her lips with his. His mouth was firm and warm, the slight stubble on his jaw tickling her tender skin.

"You won't regret it," he said softly. "I promise to do everything in my power to make you happy. We'll make a good family." His mouth covered hers again, another fiery kiss that shook her. His kisses trailed to her ear. "I could grow to love you, darlin'," he whispered.

He bent his head, his mouth taking and giving, tongues tangling and desire escalating. With each kiss she felt needed. Each one carried her to a more dizzying height than the ones before and made her want so much more. At the same time, she felt uncertain and knew they had to have some clear understandings. She pushed lightly against his chest and he raised his head.

"Jared, we should talk about this." He ran his hand along her throat and she inhaled, feeling as if she was gasping to breathe. "I know we're attracted to each other, but you said it could be a marriage of convenience. I like your kisses," she admitted, blushing hotly, "but you have to give me some time. You don't want to wait to marry. I want to wait for the physical part so we can get to know each other. So there's a chance we'll really fall in love and not mistake lust for the real thing."

"Whatever you want," he said quietly. "We'll wait as long as you want to."

She drew a deep breath, wondering what kind of bargain she was making. This was not the marriage she had always imagined. "You still want to marry right away under those conditions?"

"I told you, I know what I want." He brushed a light kiss across her lips, lingering, making her want to step back into his arms. "Besides, darlin'," he whispered, stroking her ear with his tongue and sending little streaks of fire through her, "I don't think this waiting is going to be as long as you imagine."

She couldn't resist and turned her mouth to his for another long kiss. When he released her, she gazed up at him.

"Want to come back inside?" she asked.

He shook his head. "I'll put Merry to bed. Give you time to think about your wedding plans. Let's marry soon, Faith. Here's my hotel phone number," he said, pulling out a slip of paper.

"*Hotel?* I thought you said you own a home on Peoria." She stared at him while doubts hit her like a wave of ice water.

"I do. Dusty left the house to me, and we can go look at it tomorrow and see what you want to do to it. Right now, Merry and I are staying at a hotel."

She closed her eyes. "What else don't I know? How many other surprises are there?"

He caught her chin, brushed a kiss across her lips. "You'll adapt real well, darlin'. You efficient types always do. You'll move in and straighten up my life and get everything to suit yourself. We'll go to the rodeo tomorrow night, and sometime soon, I better meet your folks."

"I'll make arrangements. They're going to faint, Jared. Right in front of your eyes. Worse, my brothers may punch you out."

His white teeth flashed in a grin. "I'd bet my pickup that your brothers aren't the punching type. I'm not worried."

"You're right, I think. They can get a little worked up sometimes. And my grandfather—oh, my! Grandpa Kolanko says exactly what he thinks."

"I'll go with you to break the news, especially to Grandpa. I'll call you when I get to the hotel."

"What have I done?"

He pulled her to him again for one more devastating kiss

that left her wanting more. His mouth was fire and heady wine, every kiss bubbling worries away.

"See, you're ready for marriage," he said in a husky voice while his hand slid from her shoulder blade, down her spine, slowly and surely moving to her hip.

"Don't rush me."

"I wouldn't think of it," he drawled, and went around the pickup to climb behind the wheel. He waved, and she watched him drive away before she went inside and locked the door. Holding up her hand, she looked at her ring. It sparkled in the light and was big enough to impress her family.

At the thought of her family, her stomach knotted. Had she lost her mind? Jared Whitewolf had come into her life like a whirlwind. She touched the ring. She was going to be a wife and a mother. Something warm and joyous blossomed inside her and melted her fears.

In a daze, she moved through her condo and headed for her bedroom. Pulling on a blue cotton nightie, she got ready for bed and went over the events of the night. Long after dark she lay in bed, staring into the darkness, remembering their conversation. And she knew one thing—she wanted a baby of her own.

If this crazy marriage worked, it would be wonderful. If it didn't, this was her chance to have her own precious baby. Merry would be his. But *their* baby would be hers. At the thought of having her own baby, of being a mother to Merry and another baby, Faith let out her breath while joy filled her.

Scrambling out of bed, she switched on a light, got a pen and paper and began making a list, studying it thoughtfully. Then she retrieved the paper with Jared's phone number. She punched numbers, waited and asked for his room number.

"Hello." His deep greeting came out in a slow drawl.

"Were you asleep?"

"No, darlin'," he answered easily. "Just lying here thinking about you."

His words and sexy tone feathered a fuzzy warmth inside her. "Jared, I've been thinking about our—" She paused. It was difficult to get out the words. It still was dreamlike, impossible. She was marrying this cowboy she barely knew. "Our marriage," she said firmly, trying to view it as she would an ad campaign. "I think I should make clear what I want. *You* want a mother for Merry, and I'm happy with that. But I want—"

Again, words failed her. She was thankful she didn't have to look into his probing brown eyes. She was across town from him, yet she couldn't get out the words. She felt hot with embarrassment and then annoyed with herself for acting so foolish. "I want a baby," she blurted.

"I know that," he answered softly. "And we'll do our best. Whenever you're ready."

She wiped her damp palms and sighed. "Also," she said, running her finger down her list, "you'll agree to live in town for a couple of years before we try ranching?"

"We'll move when the time is right," he answered, and his amusement was clear. "Checking your list?"

She felt another wave of embarrassment. "As a matter of fact, yes. I'll call Mom, and we'll make arrangements to get together with my parents this weekend."

"Fine. I'm riding in a rodeo in Oklahoma City next weekend. I promised my brothers I would see them, and then I'm going to visit my grandparents. So get out your calendar, Faith, and let's pick the wedding date."

She picked up her calendar and looked into the next month. "How about the thirtieth of May?"

"How about the twenty-seventh of April or the second of May?"

"I can't possibly!"

"Sure, you can. Let's not postpone it. That was part of the deal. I have a rodeo the first weekend in May. We can marry and go to Colorado Springs for the rodeo."

"I'll call tomorrow to see about the church and let you know. Jared, you'll still have to get a nanny so I can continue working."

"Maybe. With my rodeo schedule, you and Merry will be with me weekends and you'll watch her while I ride. During the week, I can be home with her or take her with me to look at land. I have to buy land before I can start working as a rancher."

He waited, listening to silence, wondering if she was crossing nanny off her list.

"I don't know if it'll work out that way."

"If it doesn't, we'll make the right adjustments. If you get pregnant, are you going to keep right on working? You know you could work from home."

"I don't know. Jared, a lot of my friends who've married don't get pregnant real easily."

"I can't think of anything more pleasant to try to accomplish," he drawled, and listened to another silence. "Are you there, Faith?"

"Yes. And I guess that covers everything for now. You have this worked out in your head as much as I do in my list."

"Mine's a little looser. I adapt real easily."

"I hope you can adapt real easily to my family."

"Tell me all the family names and kids' ages again."

She set aside the tablet, calendar and pen and settled against the pillows to talk to him. After a time, she switched off the light and slid down in bed, listening to the rumble of his voice while he told her about his granddad's farm and the horse he liked best. And she realized when he talked about his grandparents, his tone of voice softened. That part of his childhood, at least, held good memories, and she was reassured to know there was a degree of security in his past.

Talk went from family to movies to sports. He explained bronc riding and bull riding to her, telling her how each event was scored, talking about the animals on the rodeo circuit.

She grew sleepy, wondering how much her life would change.

"Darlin'?"

"Hmm?"

"Are you falling asleep?"

"I suppose."

"I wish you were in my arms. Do you remember our kisses?"

"Too well," she answered, feeling her body tighten and desire flare.

"Good. You keep remembering, because I sure do. What we have is good, darlin'. It's very special. 'Night, Faith."

"Good night," she whispered softly, and switched off the phone. She glanced at the clock and received a stab of surprise. Almost half past four in the morning. How could she have talked so late? She rubbed her head on the pillow and closed her eyes, dreaming of being in his arms.

Jared lay in the darkness with his hands behind his head, thinking about his conversation with Faith. The woman was efficient, a planner. She wanted a baby—that had been plain the first few minutes he'd known her. She was restless, no longer satisfied with only a career. With his proposal, she now saw a chance to get the baby she had been dreaming about.

He could imagine Faith sitting in bed with her list in front of her, planning out her future. *Get pregnant, have baby, go back to regular life and wonderful career—and tell the cowboy goodbye.* She would have baby and career, and her life would be complete. Had he rushed her too much? Should he have opted for courting and winning her love first instead of pushing for marriage?

He rubbed his jaw. No reason the courting and winning couldn't come after the ceremony. Faith had asked for time before they consummated the marriage. Well, he would give the lady time. He had never planned much beyond the next rodeo, but he was going to plan now. After their wedding ceremony, he would try to win his lady's love.

Restless, he shoved aside the sheet and crossed the room to the window, looking down at the street below. A car moved along the empty street, lights throwing yellow circles on the dark pavement. He could see downtown Tulsa, but he wasn't facing the south part of the city where Faith lived. He could imagine her soundly asleep, satisfied with her plans.

He rubbed his jaw with the back of his hand. Could he make her happy? He was only a cowboy, pure country, and she was used to city suits. *I'm not good enough for the lady,* he thought, knowing that was exactly how her family would feel.

And what did he know about a happy marriage? Almost nothing—only what he had experienced at his grandparents' farm. He hadn't grown up with loving parents. Far from it. Three people's happiness was at stake here—had he moved too fast?

He recalled holding Faith in his arms, but doubts mingled with memories. There was a lot more to love and marriage than fiery kisses and rapturous loving.

He moved to Merry's small portable bed and brushed his knuckles over her soft cheek. A year ago, he would have packed and run from the prospect of marriage, but now, although scary, it seemed right.

Unsettled and unable to shake his doubts, he moved back to the window. He stood with his hands on his bare hips, his thoughts on the future while he gazed out over the city. He wanted a ranch and he thought he could manage one. He had good savings, and his granddad said he would help him get started.

Mulling over his future, Jared stared into the darkness. Could he pry Faith loose from her cushy job? She could do the same job from a ranch, and for a time she could drive back and forth into town if he could find land not too far out of the city. That didn't worry him. What was important was winning his lady's love.

On Sunday, the sense of being wrapped in a dream deepened. Faith spent the afternoon looking at the house on Peoria, a two-story frame with oak floors and a large porch with Doric columns. It was hers to decorate, and she made lists and measured and was aware of Jared's dark eyes constantly on her. He didn't care what she did with the place, and during the afternoon as he stood in the backyard, looking up at one of the large oaks, she wondered about him. He was so easygoing, with no particular roots except for his grandparents. He had been deeply hurt by the loss of his friend, but other than that, he seemed to take life as it came. Would he ever fall deeply in love? Would she? Her gaze ran across his broad shoulders and down to trim hips, and she remembered their first meeting and the sight of his bare, muscled chest. She was going to be his wife in less than a month.

By four o'clock, the dream was beginning to transform into a nightmare. Her nerves felt raw, her stomach knotted, and she rehearsed a dozen scenarios of how to break the news of her engagement to her parents.

She had called her mother, told her she had someone important she wanted them to meet and that she had some big news.

Jared had taken her home to change, and he came back to pick her up at six o'clock. One of Jared's friends, Will MacGiver, was keeping Merry at his farm near Tulsa. Jared had taken Merry to Will's before picking up Faith.

Through the window, she watched Jared climb out of his pickup. Looking every inch a cowboy, he wore a turquoise-and-black Western shirt, one of his fancy belt buckles, his jeans, boots and hat. Her parents would go into shock.

Nervous and unable to feel comfortable in anything, Faith had dressed four times, finally deciding on red slacks and a red blouse.

As they drove along the winding drive beneath stately oaks to her parents' two-story Tudor house, she wanted to flee. Her panic deepened when she saw a black car and a green utility vehicle parked in front of the garage.

"Oh, my word. My sisters are here! Did I tell you that all of us live within a two-mile radius of my parents?"

"Whoops. I'm afraid I can't promise that."

"We don't have to live that close. Jared, I should have told my folks first and then brought you to meet them."

"This will be all right," he said.

"How can you be so calm?" she snapped, wondering if anything ruffled his feathers.

He wound his fingers through hers, picked up her hand to brush a kiss across her knuckles and looked at her with dark eyes that momentarily banished her fears.

The minute she stepped out of the pickup, her worries returned. Faith took a deep breath as Jared retrieved a folder from the back seat and turned to drape his arm across her shoulders.

"What's that?"

"I think your father is entitled to the same information about me that I gave you."

"You don't have to do that!" she said between clenched teeth. "Jared, we can't go through with this."

"We surely can. Want me to kiss you right here and now and help you remember part of why this is so right?"

"No! Mercy, mercy, no! Don't you dare kiss me while we're here."

"Your family doesn't approve of affection?"

"Stop teasing me! How can you be calm? We'll go in through the kitchen."

"Tell me their names once more."

"Andy is the oldest, and I'm the next oldest. Meg, who's married to Stan, follows, and then Keith and Alice. Andy has two boys—Brian is eight and Joshua is seven. Meg's Caleb is seven, Geoff is six, Nina is five and Mattie is four. Keith's Ben is three, and Alyssa is two. Alice's boys are

Derek, five, and Graham, three. Mom and Dad are Tom and Evelyn.''

"I doubt if your folks and I will be on a first-name basis for a time," Jared drawled.

"You don't have even one little butterfly in your stomach, do you?" she asked, getting annoyed by his calm.

"No, darlin', I really don't. Want to feel my stomach and see?" he asked, lowering her hand.

"No!" She yanked her hand away and heard his chuckle.

"They're part of you, so they have to be good," Jared added cheerfully.

She paused with her hand on the back doorknob. "Jared, how can you be so sure about me?"

He gazed at her solemnly, his dark eyes making her heart skip a beat, her family worries forgotten. "I know what I want. And I know what happens when we kiss. I'll never get enough of that."

His certainty bolstered her, and she took a deep breath before opening the door. They entered a hallway that opened to various rooms, including a large kitchen with a terrazzo floor and skylights that spilled light over the appliances and ash cabinets.

"Mom, Dad!"

A slender, attractive blonde appeared, smiling at Faith, curiosity in her eyes when she looked at Jared. A tall man with sandy hair, slightly graying at the temples, entered the room.

"Mom, Dad, this is Jared Whitewolf. Jared, meet my parents, Evelyn and Tom Kolanko."

"Glad to meet you," Jared said easily to her mom while he shook hands with her dad.

"Come in," her mom said. "Meg and Alice are here. I think Andy will be here in a few minutes."

The back door opened and two little boys spilled inside. They took one look at Jared and screeched to a halt to study him. A couple followed the children inside. Dressed in slacks and a golf shirt, Andy Kolanko stared at Faith with curious green eyes.

"Jared, this is my brother Andy, my sister-in-law Glenna, and my nephews Brian and Joshua."

Jared shook hands with Andy, who studied him with a cold stare.

"Are you a real cowboy?" Joshua asked in a child's high voice.

"Yes, I am."

"Are you an Indian?"

"Joshua!"

"It's all right. Yes, I'm Native American and I ride horses. Do you like to ride horses?"

Joshua nodded solemnly.

"Let's go in the other room," Faith's father said. "Otherwise, Joshua will ask you questions until sunup tomorrow."

The boys trailed after Jared, and Faith knew they were enthralled by his boots, belt buckle and hat. He removed his hat and placed it on a kitchen chair. Joshua reached for it and Andy picked it up out of his reach.

"That's all right," Jared remarked easily. "He can't hurt my hat. Let him wear it if he wants to."

Andy placed it high on a shelf, shaking his head at Joshua.

"Jared was in the rodeo last night and Friday night. He won bull riding and was second place in saddle bronc riding," Faith said, aware she was babbling, wiping her damp palms together as the group moved to the living room.

In the large family room, her sisters were picking up a puzzle spread on a game table. "Jared, I'd like you to meet my sisters, Meg and Alice. This is Jared Whitewolf."

Short, dimpled and brunette, Meg smiled broadly. Almost as tall as Faith and with sandy hair, Alice offered her hand. As everyone sat down, Jared glanced at her father. "If you folks will excuse us, I think it would be a good idea if I talked to you right away, Mr. Kolanko."

A startled look passed over her sisters' faces. Andy frowned. Faith saw her mother's chin drop, and her father nodded without batting an eye.

"We'll go to the guest room." He motioned to Jared, and the two men left the room with Faith's two little tow-headed nephews trailing behind Jared. All the adults turned to stare at Faith.

She felt as if she were plunging into an icy pond. She took a deep breath and braced for the storm. "I'm engaged," she said, holding out her hand to show them her ring.

Her mother shrieked and fell back against the chair while Meg's mouth dropped open and Alice jumped up to run to their mother.

"You're what?" Andy asked.

"Engaged."

"To Hopalong Cassidy? When did you meet him? What in the hell do you two have in common? What about Earl?"

"I haven't dated Earl in five months and never will again," she said, answering the last question. "Mom, are you all right?"

"Who is this man?" her mother asked.

"He's a cowboy and I'm going to marry him."

"Oh, my word! Saints help us. Have you lost your senses?"

"Is this really my sister Faith?" Meg asked, staring at her. "Practical, her-future-mapped-out Faith?" Meg crossed the room to take Faith's hand and look at her ring. "My, that's nice. I'm impressed!"

"I'm not. How long have you known him?" Andy asked sharply.

"Long enough," Faith answered, suddenly feeling more sure in her decision.

"Does he have a farm?"

"No, he doesn't. But he has a bank account. That's what he's talking to Dad about."

"Well, damnation, you've lost your mind," Andy said.

"Andy! It's Faith's decision," Glenna said. "Stop being such a big brother."

The back door slammed shut, and Faith looked over her shoulder to see her younger brother Keith enter the room. Stocky, brunette like Meg, his green eyes held curiosity. "What's happening?"

"Faith's getting married!" Meg exclaimed. "To a cowboy."

Questions and protests swirled around Faith while she wondered what Jared and her father were doing. How would her father handle Jared?

"Does he have a ranch around here?" Andy persisted, and she knew her brother wouldn't stop until he found out all he could about Jared.

"He's a bull rider and a bronc rider. He owns a house on Peoria and he wants to buy a ranch."

"He's a bum," Andy snapped. "Hell's bells!"

"No, he's not!"

"The man doesn't have a job?" her mother asked, looking aghast.

"Where did you meet him?" Meg wanted to know.

"He was with his little girl at the park."

"My word, he's divorced and has children."

"One little baby and he's not divorced. He's never been married."

"Oh, my word. He has a baby and didn't marry the mother—"

"Mom, let me tell you about him," Faith said quietly, while Andy swore and moved restlessly around the room. Faith told them about Merry and how Jared came to adopt her while her brothers glared and her mother wrung her hands.

"Faith, make it a long engagement so you'll be sure," her mother urged quietly.

"Mom, we're getting married as soon as I can arrange it with the church."

"You can't do that!" Andy snapped.

"Andy, I'm grown. I'll be thirty soon."

"He isn't like us. Is his horse tied outside? Are you going to milk cows every morning?"

"If I need to," she answered quietly, looking at her tall, blond brother whose green eyes sparked with anger. They had always been close, and she knew his intentions were good even if he was annoying her.

"Andy, cool it," Meg said.

More questions came from all of them, and Faith answered them while everyone quieted. Her mother left to phone her sister. Meg and Alice had to step outside to see about the children.

"Let's go where we can talk undisturbed," Andy said, motioning to her and to Keith. Faith went to a back bedroom with them and Andy closed the door, turning to face her. "Have you lost your mind?"

"No. I know what I'm doing. Jared's nice."

"Nice isn't what's important. You can't possibly begin to know him. And he doesn't have a job."

"Let me run a credit check on him," Keith said. "I'll see what—"

"Stop that. He's showing Dad his credit background and his physical."

"Who are his parents and where do they live?"

Someone rapped lightly on the door. It opened and Jared stepped inside. "I've talked to your dad," he said easily, crossing the room to her. "Why don't you join your mother and sisters. We'll be along in a minute," he said. She looked at her brothers, who were glaring at Jared, and she wasn't certain that they would resist punching him. Particularly Andy.

She saw all three men were waiting for her to leave, so she closed the door behind her. Their voices were low, indistinguishable, as she stood listening a moment before she moved away.

When Jared returned, her brothers were tight-lipped and

quiet. Faith heard the back door open and braced for the next onslaught. It could be only one person.

Grandpa Morgan Kolanko strode into the room. Stocky, with white strands running through his sandy hair, he had a full, bushy white beard. Freckles covered his face, hands and arms. His curious gaze rested on Jared as he greeted the others.

She took a deep breath while everyone greeted him in return, and then they all looked at her.

"Grandpa, this is my fiancé, Jared Whitewolf."

"Good golly, girl! You're marrying mighty suddenly. And a cowboy at that," he said, extending his hand to Jared, who shook with him.

"Grandpa!"

"That's all right," Jared said easily. "I am a cowboy. Glad to meet you, Mr. Kolanko."

"That's a big belt buckle. Looks like one of those prize buckles."

"It is, sir. Bull riding."

Grandpa leaned down to study Jared's buckle as if he was looking at his navel, and Faith shook her head. "Grandpa."

"World champion," he said, straightening to study Jared. "Have you won more than once?"

"Yes, sir."

"Do you love my granddaughter?"

"I asked her to be my wife."

"And you want to marry him?" Grandpa Morgan's green eyes bore into her.

"Yes, I do," she said firmly, feeling Jared's fingers tighten around hers.

"Are you pregnant, missy?"

A chorus of protests rose as she shook her head. "No."

"Then that sounds good enough. Means we'll get some tickets to a rodeo, doesn't it?" he asked Jared with a twinkle in his eye.

"Yes, sir. You could have gone last night if I had known

you might like to. There'll be another one in Tulsa about five months from now. You'll have tickets.''

''Good. Now, why all the sour faces around here?'' he asked.

''Dad, there are no sour faces,'' her father answered. ''Faith's news is a surprise, that's all. Let's sit down.''

Jared sat in a chair near Faith and draped his arm across her shoulders, lightly playing with her shoulder while they talked, and she prayed her grandfather would not start asking questions about his mother and father.

In an hour they all went to the kitchen, where they ate sandwiches. Finally Faith felt they could escape. Before they finished their goodbyes, Faith had agreed to lunch with Meg on Monday and lunch with Andy on Tuesday. She could just imagine what the conversation would be both times.

When the pickup door closed and Jared started the motor, she fell back against the seat, doubts plaguing her. She looked at the house she had grown up in. Was she throwing away all stability and security and a happy future? She was marrying a cowboy who hadn't called any one place home in the past ten years. A drifter whose ambitions were centered on Merry and a family. Was she making a mistake?

''It'll be good,'' Jared said quietly, his fingers winding through hers.

''You're leaving town tomorrow,'' she remarked, still worrying about her decision.

''You're brave enough to deal with them without me. They love you and they want what's best for you. And at the moment it's difficult for them to think it's me.''

At the moment it was difficult for *her* to think it was him.

They rode in silence while her thoughts stormed. Her phone would be ringing when she got home and she would spend the next week trying to calm her family. And plan a wedding.

Will MacGiver's farm was east of Tulsa. As they reached

the fringe of the city and began to pass open fields, Jared abruptly pulled off on a dirt road.

"What's wrong?" she asked, suddenly afraid that her life was going to take yet another turn.

Seven

Jared didn't answer as he cut the engine, stepped outside, then walked around the pickup, a tall, lanky figure with moonlight spilling over his shoulders. His hat tilted to the back of his head, he opened her door and reached up to take her arm.

"Come here, Faith."

Her pulse jumped at the husky, determined tone of his voice, and she climbed down.

"I can feel your doubts like gale winds battering me," he said, sliding his arms around her waist. He leaned against the pickup and spread his legs, pulling her against him.

Her heart raced while indecision tore at her. Half of her wanted the engagement; half of her still resisted until she looked into his dark eyes and felt his arms around her. Tension flared, an almost tangible sizzle, as they looked into each other's eyes. The magic chemistry was there, urging her to tilt her mouth up to his.

His mouth brushed hers, warm, fleeting. Her heart thudded and heat flared low within her.

A new worry knocked on her door. He wasn't marrying her because he loved her. He *needed* her for Merry. Would he ever love her?

His tongue touched her lips and she quivered. His mouth was sure, seeking, seducing her senses. His arm tightened while his hand slid down her back over her bottom, pulling her closer against him. His thick manhood pressed against her, and her worries went up in smoke. She felt desired, womanly, needed. She was taking chances, running risks, and yet, this dangerous, wondrous man was as solid as a rock. She had seen the way he looked at Merry, the tenderness he poured out to her.

Faith Whitewolf. As she wound her arms tighter around him, she thought about his bloodlines, his ancestors who had roamed the land and lived by their strength and their wits. Maybe her family needed some of his risk-taking blood.

Jared ended the kiss abruptly and she opened her eyes. "That's better," he whispered. His hand slid from her shoulder down across her breasts. Her nipples tightened and she gasped with pleasure.

Jared wanted to pick her up, put her across the hood of the pickup and possess her, but he knew he had to go slow. They had to have a wedding first, and Faith had to be ready, to want him as much as he wanted her.

He slipped free the buttons of her blouse, his hands brushing aside the flimsy bra. He cupped her breasts and felt her quiver. Her hips thrust against him and her fingers threaded through his hair.

She was as soft as warm butter, her skin silken, and he wanted to feel her softness consume him. He wanted her beneath him, wanted to discover what would drive her to the height of passion, what would make her lose all her cool control.

Now wasn't the time or place, yet he had needed the

momentary intimacy as much as she had. The family gathering had been hell, but he could understand. Disapproval had steamed from her father and brothers. All evening Andy had looked on the brink of slugging him, and Jared didn't expect the man's anger to slack off until after the wedding. Someday he would be just as protective of Merry. He would probably be worse.

He bent, taking her nipple in his mouth, hearing a moan that threatened his iron control. It had been too damned long since he had been with a woman, and he was rapidly falling under the spell of this one. He was determined not to rush her, but it was straining every ounce of his restraint. He wanted her arms around him, wanted to hear her cry out his name. She was special, and every hour with her he wanted her more.

A motor registered in his mind and he realized a car was approaching. He straightened, pulled her blouse in place and held her close, turning her head against him so she couldn't be seen as twin headlights pierced the darkness and a car roared toward them.

While it swept past, he stroked her back, trying to let his body cool, but he was still pressed against her softness, still rock-hard with need.

"We better get Merry," she whispered, and moved away. He ached with wanting her as he walked around the pickup and climbed inside.

On Monday morning Faith reserved the church for the second of May, the first Saturday in the month. She had less than four weeks to plan the wedding. Jared had left town, but he called every night and they talked for hours. She was busy at work, busy with wedding plans and busy with getting the house ready. The time while Jared was away was taken up by her siblings, who were a divided camp, the males trying to talk her out of the marriage, Alice and Meg thinking it was wonderful.

But finally her wedding day dawned bright and sunny,

and as she got out of bed, she knew her life would change forever.

Faith stood in the dressing room of the church with Alice, Meg, and two of her best friends, Katie and Leah. Butterflies danced in her stomach while she thought of Jared. They had had so little time alone, but from this moment forward that would all change. She would be with him sometimes day and night.

Night.

Her pulse fluttered, and her thoughts skittered back to the wedding. Her bridesmaids were dressed in deep blue sleeveless dresses with straight skirts. She looked down at her white silk-and-satin dress without really seeing it.

She was going to marry Jared Whitewolf within the hour.

Doubts assailed her, and she wondered whether he was having last-minute jitters as well. She knew him well enough by now to suspect he had none. From their first meeting, he'd seemed determined to get to this destination.

"Faith, it's time," Meg announced. She crossed the room to straighten Faith's veil and brushed Faith's cheek with a kiss. "You're a beautiful bride."

"I think this is wonderful. I know you're going to be happy," Alice said, smiling.

When they left the dressing room, they found Andy standing in the hall. He strode to her, his walk purposeful, a scowl on his face. "Faith," he called to her, and she waved the others on, turning to her tall, blond brother, who looked handsome in his dark tuxedo.

"I thought you were ushering."

"There are other ushers," he said, pausing a few feet from her. "You can still get out of this."

"I don't want out, Andy."

"You don't love him."

"I'm doing what I want to do," she answered stiffly, knowing she couldn't put into words her motivations, or her feelings.

"I don't think he's in love with you. I can't figure it—why are the two of you doing this?"

"You've asked me before and I've told you before. We want to."

"Does he have some hold on you? Is there anything I can do?"

"No. I want to marry him," she replied firmly. "He wants to marry me. And we're not going to get married if I don't get out there."

"I think you're making a terrible mistake. He's not your type. He's all the things you don't know anything about. You're not into ranches and cowboys and cattle. And I know you're not one hundred percent sure of what you're doing. It shows, Faith. If you were falling all over him with stars in your eyes, I'd shut up, but you're not. I don't know why you're doing it, but it isn't about love."

"It's what I want."

"It can't be just to get a family, because Earl could have given you that. And would have. You were the one who broke it off. Dammit, you and Earl had far more in common than you and Hopalong."

"You have to stop referring to Jared as Hopalong," she said, losing her patience while Andy's scowl deepened.

"Hell, right now the guy's out there in boots and a tux."

"That's all right," she said through clenched teeth, clutching the bouquet of white roses and gardenias. "Andy, get out of my way."

They glared at each other. Her brother knew her too damned well. He probably could sense the qualms making her shake.

Reluctantly, he shook his head and stepped to one side. She swept past him. "Faith—"

She turned to look over her shoulder at him.

"I'll be there when you need me."

"Thanks, Andy. I know you will," she replied somberly, feeling a chilling foreboding.

"Faith," Meg called. "Andy, leave her alone! You're holding up the wedding."

"I'm going," he said.

"Our brother," Meg mumbled. "He can't understand how someone can fall in love with a person so entirely different. You're the only Kolanko to commit the sin, and it's beyond his comprehension. When a man loves a woman, it doesn't always matter about jobs and backgrounds."

Faith was quiet as she moved along the hall while Meg carried her train. Meg touched her arm. "Don't let Andy worry you. You're doing what you want. And you're marrying a man in love with you."

Faith wanted to cry out that he wasn't, but somehow Jared had Meg fooled.

Faith hurried to the foyer where her father studied her carefully. "Sure you want to do this?" he asked.

She nodded. "I'm sure," she said, feeling no such conviction, yet she was committed and she intended to marry.

They moved to the door as an organ flourish pealed in the air. And then they started down the aisle, and she looked at Jared who stood waiting at the altar.

Jared watched as Faith walked down the aisle toward him, and his certainty deepened a notch. This was *his* woman. Regal, poised, blond and beautiful. She was absolutely gorgeous, but the reason he had chosen her went far deeper than her looks. The woman was warm, caring, nurturing. She was efficient and intelligent, and he felt overwhelmed with his fortune in getting her to agree to marry him. He wanted this marriage to work.

When her green gaze met his, he could see her qualms. She looked pale, too solemn. He wanted to put his arms around her and reassure her that their life together would be good.

He wondered what she would think if she knew her father had offered him a sizable sum of money if he would pack up and disappear. He suspected her mother knew nothing about it. Nor did the others in the family. He was sure Andy wanted to beat him to a pulp, but in true Kolanko fashion, the man controlled himself. Keith probably felt the same. Only Meg and Alice were truly warm and friendly. Particularly Meg. He suspected she was glad to see her sister marry. And then there was Grandpa Kolanko. Jared thought he had the old man's approval.

He heard a soft coo and looked at Merry, who was in his grandmother's arms where they sat across from Faith's parents. Granddad caught Jared's eye and smiled.

Jared suspected Faith's parents were having difficulty adjusting to his Native American heritage, which showed so strongly in his grandparents. Wyatt and his family were seated in the row behind his grandparents, and Matt, looking as solemn as a judge, was seated next to Wyatt.

As Faith drew closer, Jared forgot about families. His bride was beautiful, and whether or not she loved him, he was going to relish the next moments. He hoped and expected that love would come to fill their lives.

When her father placed Faith's hand in his, Jared closed his hand gently around her icy fingers. Guilt stabbed him again that he had rushed her into this when she wasn't walking down the aisle starry-eyed and in love, but he would try to make it up to her. She raised her chin, and when they repeated their vows, her voice was strong and clear.

"I now pronounce you husband and wife."

The words were magical to Jared. He was married to this beautiful, wonderful woman, and he was going to do his best to make her fall in love with him.

Faith gazed up at her new husband. She had been dazed by him since that afternoon she met him and she still felt that way.

Husband and wife. She was *Mrs.* Jared Whitewolf. How had this happened so fast?

Jared lifted her veil, gently folding it behind her head. His actions were deliberate, his dark eyes holding her gaze.

He leaned down and brushed his warm lips across hers and then laced his fingers through hers as they turned to walk down the aisle to their future.

After the receiving line, the wedding party and family went back to the front of the church for pictures. Faith's mother and father hugged her. Meg gave her another hug. Even Andy wished her well.

Her uncle approached. "I wish you happiness, Faith. The whole office is still surprised."

"They'll adjust," she said, smiling as Blake kissed her cheek.

She turned to face Cornelia Whitewolf, who held out her arms. "Welcome to the Whitewolf family." She hugged Faith and stepped back. "Jared's our youngest grandchild—my baby. I'm so happy to see him married and settled. You'll be good for him, and both of you will be good for the little girl."

"Thank you, Cornelia," Faith said, turning to see Loughlan hand Merry to his wife and open his arms to hug Faith.

"Welcome to the family. Jared is blessed with you and Merry."

"I feel blessed, too," she answered.

"Faith, turn around and let's get your picture," Trey Holiday, the photographer, said. "Jared, get in the picture."

Much later, Jared's brothers wished her well. They were strangers to her, reminding her how little she knew her new husband.

The reception was held at her father's club, and guests spilled out onto the terrace and lawn until it was time for the first dance. When the moment arrived, Jared took her hand and led her to the dance floor.

"We've never even danced before," she said, realizing they should have practiced at least once. She had removed her train from her straight skirt. Jared placed his hand on her waist and held her other hand in his. She gazed into dark eyes filled with satisfaction, and they moved together as if they had danced a thousand times with each other. She forgot the reception, her family and guests. For the first time since she walked down the aisle, her nerves calmed and she felt sure.

When the dance ended, Jared asked her mother to dance and Faith danced with her father.

"I hope you're happy," he said quietly.

"Thank you. We plan to be."

"Just don't give up your job too fast. You've rushed into this marriage. Don't rush to change your entire life."

"You know I love my work," she answered, glancing past him at Jared. His hair was fastened behind his head and he looked handsome, this wild new husband of hers. Her mother was laughing at something he was telling her. His white teeth flashed, a contrast to his dark skin, and she longed to be dancing with him.

After they had cut the cake, Jared moved through the crowd that was largely Faith's guests. The few relatives he had had attended, but most of his friends were scattered across the country and few lived in Tulsa.

He turned to face Andy, who gazed at him solemnly. "Be good to her," the man said.

"I will be," Jared answered steadily. "She's very special."

Andy nodded, then moved away. Jared saw that his fists were clenched, and he wondered whether her brothers would ever approve of him.

Jared looked around the room, meeting Faith's gaze across the crowd. She was talking to friends, but watching him. They might as well have been alone as he stared back at her. He wanted to get the veil off her head and get her hair down.

"How's the groom?" Someone slapped him on the back and he turned to see Will MacGiver. His stocky, redheaded friend smiled at him.

"Glad to see a friend. Her family isn't falling over themselves with joy to see her marry a cowboy."

Will laughed. "She's the one who counts."

"Amen to that. That limo isn't due for another two hours, but I'm ready to get her and go."

"Patience, buddy. These shindigs are for the women. She's probably having the time of her life."

"I think I'll go see," Jared said, moving away.

The music changed to a fast number and Jared caught Faith's hand to lead her to the dance floor. In minutes he shed his coat and loosened his tie as he danced around her.

Faith couldn't take her gaze from the tall, sexy man she had married. He made her pulse race without doing anything more than looking at her. Sometimes just the sight of him set her heart fluttering.

It was late in the afternoon when they finally said their goodbyes to the family. Jared's grandparents were keeping Merry, allowing Faith and Jared to spend their week-long honeymoon alone.

They rushed to a waiting limousine. No sooner had they been seated, than they were whisked away. As they sped along the street, Faith felt a stab of panic. What had she done?

Jared slipped his arm around her, and she turned to look into his dark eyes.

He pulled her into his arms, his mouth covering hers in a long, possessive kiss that made her forget her surroundings, even the wedding. He shifted her to his lap, settling in the seat with his arms tightly around her while he kissed her. Wanting to be alone with him, she returned his kisses. They were husband and wife now. She wondered if it would ever cease to amaze her.

When his hand strayed lower, slipping down over her collarbone, she caught his wrist. "We're not alone."

Jared glanced beyond her at the driver and drew a deep breath, settling his hands on her waist while he looked at her. "Whatever you say, Mrs. Whitewolf."

The name sounded as if it should belong to someone else. She slid off his lap and straightened her dress as the limousine headed for the house on Peoria. They planned to change clothes and drive to the airport to fly to Colorado Springs, where Jared would compete in a rodeo that evening.

When they arrived at the house, Jared carried her over the threshold, closing the front door with its oval of etched beveled glass with a kick of his foot. He locked the door and set her on her feet, tightening his arm around her waist as he leaned down to kiss her.

His kisses tempted her to toss aside her request for him to wait to consummate their hasty wedding. Excitement strummed across her nerves like a bow across fiddle strings. Mrs. Whitewolf. She was married. Falling in love.

The last thought brought her up short and she opened her eyes, looking up at him as she pushed away. Was she falling in love with this man?

"If you really want to ride in that rodeo, we better change clothes."

His dark eyes were filled with desire. He studied her solemnly, and she wondered whether he was going to forget the rodeo. He brushed his hand along her throat, a faint caress that made her ache for more.

"I'm signed up so I need to appear." He swung her into his arms and headed up the stairs.

"You don't need to carry me all the way upstairs," she said, her arms wrapped around his neck.

"You're a feather, darlin'. It's good exercise for me and I like carrying you," he answered easily as if holding her was an effortless feat.

At the top of the stairs, he crossed the hall into a bedroom. A four-poster mahogany bed was placed opposite a matching chest and mirror. He set her on her feet. A thick beige rug covered the middle of the room. Around its edges, the polished oak floor gleamed. Jared reached up to pull out pins and remove her veil.

"We have a few minutes, and I've been wanting to do this since you walked down the aisle."

"I'm glad you waited," she said, watching him, his dark eyes on her while he pulled pins out of her hair. "You're ruining a very expensive hairdo."

"Do you care?"

"No," she whispered, finding his steady gaze as tormenting as his caresses. His eyes smoldered with longing. She felt fluttery inside, wanting him, and yet all her caution urged her to wait because they were strangers in so many ways.

Locks tumbled over her shoulders, and Jared could feel his desire escalating. Her lips parted, red from his kisses already. Her eyes were languorous, sexy. He wanted to peel her out of the wedding dress and make love to her and forget the rodeo, but he wasn't going to do it. They had made an agreement about this marriage. As far back as he could remember, he had satisfied his body's yearnings when he wanted. This time, he was going to practice control. He wanted a lot more than her body. He wanted her love.

He stepped back. "I'll change. We have to leave as soon as we can for the airport or we'll miss that plane."

Faith watched him go, closing the door behind him. She hadn't wanted him to stop kissing her, but she knew it was best that he did. All along she had told herself that she wanted to know him better before they fully became man and wife, but she was changing her mind swiftly.

She kicked off her satin pumps and began to unfasten the tiny row of buttons down her back. When she couldn't reach the buttons in the middle, she started from the bottom and worked her way up.

She still couldn't reach the middle buttons, and a glance at the clock indicated that in a few more minutes Jared would be ready and waiting. Biting her lip, she rushed down the hallway. Even though his door stood open, she knocked.

"Come in," he called.

She stepped inside the bedroom she had decorated in

bright maroon, hunter's green and white with a king-size four-poster mahogany bed, a chintz-covered love seat and a thick carpet in the center of the room. Jared straightened from rummaging in the closet. He gave a jerk to his head, shaking his shaggy black hair away from his face. It swirled across his shoulders, giving him that wild look she remembered from their first meeting. He was in his stocking feet, a pair of boots in hand. He was bare-chested, in jeans that were only partially buttoned.

"I can't get this dress unbuttoned," she said, staring at his chest. Smooth, brown skin was taut over powerful muscles. A few thin, pale scars slashed across his ribs and chest and shoulder. His stomach was flat, a washboard of muscles, and just above the vee of his jeans she saw a white band of what must be low-cut briefs.

He dropped the boots, and when her gaze flew up to meet his she realized how she had been studying him. His eyes filled with dark secrets she couldn't fathom, he crossed the room.

Jared drew a deep breath. "Turn around," he said in a husky voice. Her blatant perusal had sent his temperature soaring, and as he looked at her slender back, he felt on fire. She wasn't wearing a bra, and he could see her white lacy bikinis, the luscious curve of her bottom. He wanted to trail his tongue over her bare back, slide his hands around beneath the dress and haul her up against him.

Instead, he knew he better hold to his rodeo agenda. But it wasn't going to hurt to get in a few kisses. He leaned down to brush his mouth across her nape and heard her swift intake of breath. He took his own sweet time with the four remaining buttons, trailing his fingers across her back and down to the first button.

"Jared," she whispered.

His tongue flicked over her ear and he untwisted another button. He trailed his tongue across her shoulder, down over her back. She tilted her head back, and he leaned forward enough to see that her eyes were closed.

He twisted free another button and then the last. Before he released her, he slid his hands beneath the dress, letting one hand go around her waist and the other slide down, following the curve of her bottom.

She moaned and turned as his hand cupped her breast and his thumb flicked over her nipple. She reached out to trail her hands over his chest.

Faith hurt with a need that came to life forcefully. She raised her face and his mouth came down over hers. As their tongues tangled, she could feel his manhood hard against her stomach. His hand caressed her bottom as he pulled her up tighter against him.

How long did they kiss? Minutes or seconds? She twisted away. "You'll miss your rodeo."

Jared didn't give a damn, but he was going to wait. He had to try to win her affections. Otherwise, he felt certain the lady would be gone from his life.

Reluctantly, he released her, watching as she pulled her dress up. Her gaze raked over him, and he knew she could see the effect she had on him. She turned swiftly and left the room.

Jared wondered how long he could take this. Each time he held her in his arms, it pushed him closer to an edge where control vanished. He wanted her desperately, and he knew he was going to have sleepless nights and an aching body.

With a pounding heart, Faith rushed down the hall to dress. She wanted to be in Jared's arms, in his bed. She also wanted his love.

But words of love had never crossed his lips. And once she gave herself to him, she might be hopelessly lost— unable to love anyone else. Don't rush into it, she warned herself.

She drew a deep breath, thinking about the bargain she had gotten herself into. Would they ever fall in love? And if they didn't—should she rush to his bed? She wanted a baby of her own. And she felt Jared was holding back because he had promised her he would. Yet, like her, she sensed he was vulnerable to hurt. Was he trying to be cautious, too?

Knowing that time was precious, she dressed in new jeans that fit like a second skin, a red Western shirt, and she pulled on snakeskin boots that Jared had given her. She brushed her hair, knowing he liked it down over her shoulders. The reflection in the mirror seemed to be that of a stranger. Was it really her wearing tight jeans and boots?

"Ready?" Jared called.

Her body still ached for him and she was more than ready to start their life together. She picked up her purse and hurried into the hall.

He stood at the foot of the stairs. His hair was fastened behind his head again and he was picking up the carry-ons and his hat.

"Here I come," she said, rushing down the stairs. He glanced up, then dropped everything he was holding. He straightened and placed his hands on his hips as his gaze drifted over her.

"What?" she asked, stopping on the third step.

He came forward, fire dancing in his dark eyes. His hands went to her waist, then slid down to her thighs. "You are one good-looking woman."

"I feel half-naked in these tight jeans."

"I'll admit I'd rather keep you at home where no one can see you except me."

"That's ridiculous," she said, her cheeks turning pink as she descended the last steps.

Jared clenched his fists and jammed his hat on his head. Then he picked up the bags and carry-ons to avoid reaching for her. She rushed past him and he watched the switch of her hips, remembering when he had run his hand over her soft, round bottom.

His body was reacting to her as if he was fifteen years old and had never seen a woman. "Dammit," he muttered, and followed her out to the pickup. As she climbed in, he couldn't resist. He reached out, his hand following the curve of her jeans across her bottom. She glanced over her shoulder at him, a seductive, flirtatious look on her face, and then she sat in the pickup.

He grinned as she leaned in the open window. "You're irresistible, Mrs. Whitewolf."

Faith's pulse jumped. He acted as if he wanted her, yet he always stopped. But wasn't she the one who had asked him to stop? And wasn't he the one who had given her his promise that he would wait? So what did she really want him to do?

Hours later, they arrived at Colorado Springs and stood outside in a cool, crisp late afternoon waiting for the shuttle to take them to the rental car. Shuttles, taxis, buses and cars drove past while a crowd milled on the walk and people crossed the busy lanes of traffic.

Faith saw a mother turn to fix a broken strap on her suitcase. Her towheaded toddler, green ball in hand, wiggled free and climbed out of her stroller. The ball rolled away from the child and she toddled after it. The little girl could only be about eighteen months old, Faith guessed, thinking of how Merry would look at that age.

People moved in front of Faith, and she lost sight of the mother and toddler, but then she glimpsed the child's red sunsuit...and she saw the green ball roll into the street. Frozen with horror, Faith stared as the child toddled after her ball, oblivious of oncoming vehicles.

"Jared—" Faith started to run.

Someone yelled and a horn blared.

But Jared was already gone, dashing headlong into the lanes after the toddler.

Eight

Faith felt as if her heart stopped beating when Jared dodged a bus and snatched up the child as a shuttle slammed on its brakes and skidded toward her.

As the shuttle rocked to a stop, Jared rushed back to the sidewalk. The mother took her child, holding her and crying while a man asked Jared if he was all right.

Faith stared at him, knowing that she had married a man of action. He would always rush into things. And he was a man who didn't stop to think about the danger involved. Was she going to be able to cope with a daredevil who threw caution to the winds?

Jared returned to her side. "There's our shuttle," he said, pointing past her. She glanced around to see the blue-and-gold shuttle waiting at the curb.

As soon as they boarded, Jared flung their bags on a shelf and sat down beside her. He glanced her way, but said nothing.

At the car rental agency, she stood outside in the hot

sunshine and waited while he made arrangements for the car. She watched him through the glass as he leaned against the counter. He looked relaxed, as if the incident and any effects from it were over.

He didn't speak until much later, when they were settled in the rental car.

"Why so quiet?" he asked.

"My nerves are still vibrating." She twisted in the seat to look at him. "Do have any nerves in your body? Are you afraid of anything?"

Afraid of losing you ran through his mind. Jared kept his eyes on the road. "You're angry because I dashed out into traffic."

"I'm not angry. I just don't know whether I can live with someone who is constantly throwing himself into danger."

"You do every day when you drive to work. The freeway isn't the safest place to be. Besides that, you had already started running toward her. If I hadn't been there, darlin', I know who would have been out in front of traffic."

"I don't know whether I would have or not. But I'm not just reacting to what happened today. Bull riding, the broncs. When a crisis happens, you're right in the middle of things."

"Someone needs to be," he answered solemnly. "And you were already on your way. I recall you charging through the bushes at the park to rescue Merry, so it's the pot calling the kettle black."

"Maybe," she replied, still thinking how close he had come to being struck by the shuttle bus. "I'm thankful you saved the little girl."

"Then don't worry. That's the first time in my life anything like that has ever happened and let's hope it's the last."

"But I'll bet you've waded into fights. I'll bet you'll do dangerous things when you own your ranch."

"Our ranch. Are we fighting?" he asked, picking up her hand to brush his lips across her knuckles. His breath was warm, his fingers locked through hers were firm. She gazed into his dark eyes and shook her head.

"No, because I might have run out there if you hadn't. The little girl would have been hit by the shuttle if you hadn't scooped her up. It just made me wonder again whether I can cope with your way of living."

"Believe me, darlin', you can."

His words came back later to haunt her as she watched a large Brahman bull bound out of the chute with Jared clinging to it. She closed her eyes, listening to the crowd, unable to look again until the buzzer sounded. She watched Jared jump on the fence out of the way of the charging bull. Would she ever grow accustomed to the wild side of him?

Early in the last ride the bull rider was tossed, but his hand was caught in the rope and the bull flung him around like a rag doll. She'd closed her eyes, feeling a knot in her stomach. The crowd had become quiet, and then a collective sigh went up from the audience. Only then had she opened her eyes. The clowns had chased the bull from the arena while men knelt over the rider, who lay motionless in the dirt. Time passed, and more men went out to look at the inert cowboy. Over the loudspeaker the master of ceremonies announced they were clearing the way for an ambulance. Watching the terrifying scene unfold, she had thought how devastated she would feel if it was Jared on the ground.

Had she made a mistake? Tying her life to a man who was accustomed to violence and action? Every time doubts rose, all she had to do was think of the quiet moments with him, times he had been with Merry, and then she felt confident she had done the right thing.

When Jared made his way to the box, she could see his

concern for her on his face as his dark eyes searched hers.
"Okay?"

"I need to ask you that." She couldn't keep from reaching for him. She saw the startled flicker in his eyes, and then his arms went around her and he hugged her.

"I'm fine. Actually, I won the bull riding."

His shirt smelled like leather and cotton, a fragrance she suspected she would associate with him forever. He released her to look at her again and she smiled, relieved the rodeo was over for the night.

"C'mon," he said. "It's time to eat and see that you have some fun."

They went to a rustic restaurant with a group of his friends. The music was loud, and when Jared took her hand to dance, she shook her head. "I don't know the two-step."

"It's just like it sounds, and incredibly easy. Here, look." He showed her the steps and she watched his dusty black boots move through the basic dance. Then he took her hand to lead her to the dance floor. After the first few steps, she realized it was easy and she moved with him, her gaze locked with his as she remembered the dance they'd shared during their wedding, which had only been hours before—not the lifetime ago that it seemed.

After the slow number for the two-step, the band broke into a foot-stomping fast number and Jared whirled her about the dance floor. His hat was pushed to the back of his head, and his hair was untied and hanging loose. He grinned as he spun her around until he was in such a sweat that he popped the snaps on the front of his shirt down to his waist.

As they danced, Faith couldn't help but look at his bare chest that was damp with sweat. Virile, sexy—he lived life with a zest that she had never experienced. Was he going to be *too* wild for her? Would she be too tame for him?

She'd noticed how women flirted with him all evening, but he'd been casually cool and kept his arm around Faith's shoulders, carefully introducing her to everyone as his bride.

It was in the early hours of the morning that they returned to their hotel. Jared had gotten adjoining rooms. He unlocked her door, stepped inside and pulled her into his arms to kiss her. The minute his mouth met hers, she melted. Always, in his arms, her doubts went up in smoke, burned away by kisses that made her ache for more.

When he released her, she was breathless. She wanted to pull him closer, yet she was uncertain about his feelings. Gazing up at him, she tried to decide what he really felt for her.

"This is our wedding night, but we made an agreement and I'll stick by it," he said quietly, caressing her throat, his fingers lingering, moving to trail across her nape. Tingles radiated from his touch and she was already on fire from his kisses. She wanted to tell him she was ready to toss aside her request to wait before they consummated the marriage, yet she felt uncertain.

He brushed a light kiss across her lips, then turned and left, closing the door to his room behind him. She stared at the closed door, half tempted to go after him.

She lay in bed that night and felt alone, too aware Jared was only feet away. Was he soundly asleep? She suspected he was, suffering none of the desire he had ignited in her. All she had to do was get up and go into his room and she could end this waiting period that was of her own making. At the same time, the caution that she had practiced her entire life warned her to take her time and be sure what she wanted. They were married, but it was in name only, something she needed to remember.

Restless, she got up and went to sit by the window, gazing outside at city lights, remembering Jared's kisses, his eyes on her all during their wedding ceremony, the moments in his bedroom later.

It was over an hour before she climbed back into bed

and lay staring into the darkness, still too aware he was asleep only yards away from her.

The next couple of days were uneventful, and on Tuesday they arrived home to a quiet house. Faith looked at the new furniture, the few things she had brought from her apartment. The big living area was rustic, comfortable. She had decorated it in a way that she hoped he would like. The polished floor gleamed and furniture was large and comfortable with a deep-green-and-beige color scheme. The walls were bare, the mantel bare—they would add things after they had lived here awhile. Although she'd placed some of her books on the bookshelves, she realized Jared had very few possessions other than his pickup and saddle and clothing. The house was silent except for the scrape of Jared's boots on the floor.

"I'll grill steaks and we can sit outside. It'll cool when the sun goes down."

She went upstairs to shower, changing to cutoffs and a red T-shirt. When she stepped outside, Jared was standing at the grill. He had a beer in one hand, a long fork in the other. He had shed his shirt and was bare-chested.

He turned and looked at her, his gaze drifting over her legs and then back up to her face. His dark brow arched. "Wow. I haven't seen you in shorts before," he said, looking at her legs again.

"The feeling is mutual," she answered, and his dark eyes flicked to hers as he gave her a probing stare. They had been married four days now, and in those four days the tension between them had built. He constantly touched her, brushed against her, kissed her often. Her nerves were raw, her awareness of him continuing to heighten while she debated whether to toss caution aside and tell him she was ready to be man and wife in every way.

Her gaze slid over his muscled back as he turned meat on the grill. In spite of his daredevil life-style and his strong will, she knew Jared had a vulnerable side. Growing up, he had been hurt, and she didn't want to add another hurt.

Nor did *she* want to get hurt. Once she took their relationship to the next step, she feared the consequences. She might never be able to accept anything less than his love. And he might never fall in love with her.

She moved farther away from him, touching the flatware he had set on the table. This night, she would cling to caution; it was too soon to consummate their shaky marriage.

They spent the rest of the week looking at land since Faith was still on vacation. On Sunday morning, they drove to Anadarko and out to the farm to get Merry, spending a day with Jared's grandparents and then starting back to Tulsa in the evening. They got home long after midnight and tucked Merry into her tiny bed in the small nursery that adjoined the master bedroom.

During the middle of the night, Faith awakened to hear Merry screaming. She shoved away the sheet and rushed to Merry's room. As she stepped inside, Jared was already picking her up. He wore low-cut white briefs and nothing else. The faint glow of the night-light highlighted the curve of solid muscles. She became aware of herself, of the T-shirt that was all she was wearing.

He jiggled Merry and then turned, looking at Faith. "You take her and try to calm her. I don't know what's wrong."

She took Merry from him and paced, speaking softly. In seconds, when Merry quieted, Faith looked around. Jared had gone, but he returned wearing his jeans.

"You have a magic touch. What do you think is wrong?"

"Your grandmother thinks she might be getting a new tooth. Maybe that's all it was."

He leaned against the doorjamb and she was aware of his dark eyes studying her. "Want me to take her?"

"I don't mind. Besides, I think she's gone back to sleep," she said, holding Merry away to look at her. Smoky lashes sparkling with unshed tears fanned over her full, rosy cheeks. "She's asleep." Faith carried her to the bed and leaned over to put her down.

Jared stood watching Faith, the T-shirt pulling across her bottom with each step. When she leaned over the baby crib, her shirt hiked up. He drew a deep breath at the view of her long legs. The shirt covered her bottom. Barely. But his imagination whisked it away.

She straightened and crossed the room. The shirt was loose and her breasts bounced slightly as she walked. She looked disheveled from bed, feminine, alluring. Together, they walked into the darkened hall that had only a faint light from the bedroom and a shaft of light from her open door.

"Faith," he said, his voice husky. His pulse pounded, and he couldn't resist reaching for her, his arm sliding around her waist. He pulled her close. The shirt was the only thing she was wearing and he could feel her warm, soft body.

Sweat popped out as if he was in a sauna. He leaned down to kiss her. The moment his mouth covered hers, their tongues touching, his roaring pulse drowned out all other sounds. The world shifted beneath him, desire sweeping him on a rushing current. With a hunger that threatened to consume him, he kissed her and molded her body to his.

Each time they held each other and kissed, he knew they were moving closer to consummation. His bride was sexy, adorable and so good with Merry. Faith was all he wanted, and he ached to take her to his bed and discover her secret pleasures. He wanted to make wild, passionate love with her, but he had to remember the stakes. While he was becoming desperate for her body, he wanted so much more. He wanted the lady's love and rushing her to bed might cause him to lose her.

Faith clung to him, knowing the first buttons of his jeans

were unfastened. She remembered him standing in his briefs, his firm buttocks outlined clearly. He leaned away from her now, his hands sliding slowly up over her rib cage, moving beneath the T-shirt to cup her breasts. She gasped with pleasure, forgetting theirs was a marriage of convenience, forgetting everything except his hands and the strong man caressing her.

She hadn't known it could be this way between a man and a woman. She had never been turned to a quivering mass of boneless jelly before, never wanted a man with a craving that blocked out rational thought. She trailed her fingers over his chest, down across his stomach.

Jared shoved the T-shirt higher and paused to look at her body, bared to his view. He inhaled deeply, trying to hang on to his control. Rosy skin, pink nipples, golden hair, lush curves and a slender body. He palmed a breast, its softness having the opposite result on him. Rock hard, he wanted her. He bent to flick his tongue over her nipple.

Faith's fingers bit into his arms, feeling firm muscles while pleasure raked her. The ache low in her body intensified. She wanted his loving, was more than ready for him. Her hands trailed across his smooth, powerful chest while her heart thudded.

He took a nipple in his mouth, biting so lightly, then curling his tongue around the taut peak. She gasped and twisted, her hips thrusting toward him, but he shifted, his hand sliding to the juncture of her thighs, spreading her legs slightly, searching in the soft curls.

"Jared, please—" she whispered, knowing there was a huge void in her life that only he could fill. This strong man was exciting, virile, sexy enough to turn her to quaking mush. Why was she waiting?

His hand moved, finding her hot, honeyed center, stroking her. Jared watched her through hooded eyes as she tensed. Her hips moved frantically, and while he caressed and rubbed her, her fingers dug into him. Her lower lip was caught in her white teeth, her eyes were closed and her head was thrown back, the golden mane of hair hanging over her back. She was lost in a frenzy of passion and he was going to lose his control. He couldn't get his breath and his heart thudded violently against his rib cage.

"Jared, your bed." Even though she whispered, he heard her words.

He felt as if he might explode. His body throbbed, hammering for release, wanting her beyond anything he had dreamed possible. Faith was going up in flames, hips wildly moving while she clung to him as if for life, whispering what she wanted.

"Jared, please—" She was wet, hot, ready for him, but he wanted her heart ready and aching with a need that would begin to match his.

A spasm rocked her and Faith gasped for breath as she arched against him. "Jared," she whispered again, tugging on his arms. His arms wrapped around her, crushing breath from her lungs as he kissed her deeply. She could feel him trembling. He was covered in sweat, and she knew he was having as strong a response as she was, yet he was sticking to their bargain. He picked her up and carried her to her room, setting her on her feet.

Her body pulsed with need for him, need for completion. She no longer cared about marriage agreements. She wanted him, and he had to know it. She clutched his upper arms.

"I want to stay. God knows, I want to stay with you, Faith. But we made a bargain and I made a promise that I intend to keep." His voice was a husky rasp, while his midnight eyes devoured her.

He turned swiftly and left her room, closing the door. Fighting the urge to run after him, to throw herself at him, she sat down. Her body throbbed. She was ready; she did not want to wait any longer. She stood and crossed the room, her hand on the knob, and then she paused. *He doesn't love me* ran through her mind. Yet she knew how he'd trembled when he held her and kissed her. He felt *something*.

Sitting on the bed, she wrapped her arms around her drawn-up knees. She ached for his loving, and for his love. It would come with time, she told herself, but that was little consolation now. She closed her eyes and could see him standing holding Merry, wearing only his briefs. She groaned, knowing sleep would be long in coming tonight.

The next morning, she woke, dressed and found Jared with breakfast waiting and Merry happily in her baby carrier while he spoon-fed her baby food.

"My goodness, this is service I'm not accustomed to before going to work. I usually just drink juice and eat toast," she said, looking at the bowl of fresh fruit, the orange juice that was poured and the toast he had buttered. "How's our little girl?" she asked, brushing a kiss on Merry's head.

"She's none the worse for the night. She fared better than I did. I'm taking her with me to look at some property today. We'll go to the gym—"

"You take this baby to a gym?"

"Sure. They have a sitter for little ones. I have to stay in shape for the circuit. Use it or lose it."

"I don't think you're in any danger of losing it," she remarked dryly, and he grinned. "I should be home by six."

Faith leaned against the counter to drink her juice, watching Jared feed Merry. There was a cozy intimacy to sharing the morning with him. She relished it, thinking of her lonely nights and rushed mornings before their marriage. Merry looked adorable, diligently taking each offered bite, her blue eyes on Jared. And Faith didn't blame her. He was worth watching. One long leg was propped on a knee as he leaned across the table to feed her. He wore jeans and a T-shirt and his hair hung loose around his face. He shook it away and glanced at her, arching his brows as he caught her studying him. "Remembering last night, I hope?" he asked quietly.

She inhaled. "Maybe, but I better get my thoughts on work."

His gaze flicked over her, and she became aware of her appearance, the straight red skirt and her white blouse.

"You look great. If you're not afraid of mashed bananas getting spit on you, come here."

"I think I better give the little lady plenty of room," she said, worrying more about what would happen if she let him hug and kiss her.

He set down the small jar of mashed bananas and stood, his gaze locked with Faith's as he crossed the room to her. He slid his hand behind her head.

"Am I going to have to change because of wrinkles?"

"I wouldn't think of causing you to wrinkle," he answered, leaning forward to kiss her. The only contact was his hand on her nape, but every inch of her body came alive, quivering with awareness of the last time he had touched her. As his tongue slowly stroked hers, delving into her mouth, stirring her response, she slid her arms around his neck.

"I can't resist you," she whispered, her mouth moving against his. Dimly she heard Merry babbling and beginning to fuss.

He pulled away to study her. "That's a good start to the day." He turned back to feed Merry, and Faith felt her nerves quivering and little fires building inside her. She drew a deep breath and forgot about breakfast, rushing past him to collect her things and get out of the house before she threw herself at him.

She hadn't been at work an hour when her uncle called her into his office. As soon as she was seated across the desk from Blake, he smiled at her.

"You look like the beautiful new bride. How's married life?"

"Very nice."

"Good. Now, let's talk about life here in the office. Faith, we're so pleased with the work you've been doing. I think you're a real asset to this office."

"Thank you," she said, feeling a twinge of guilt because she hadn't given a thought to her job for well over a week now.

"And because of the accounts you have helped us to get this year and the way our clients like your work, I think it's time we promoted you. Porter also deserves to move up. He will become vice president of accounts. You will take his place as vice president of design."

"My word! This is really a surprise," she said honestly, not expecting a promotion like the one she was receiving for another few years. "I'm thrilled! I didn't expect anything like this."

He smiled and talked about her new position while her mind wandered to the thought of telling Jared. And she realized that her new husband was going to be less than thrilled. Shoving aside the worries that had cropped up, she tried to concentrate on what Blake was saying.

By noon everyone in the office was congratulating her. As soon as she had left Blake's office, she called Jared, but no one answered and she remembered he was going to look at property. She dreaded telling him the news. She knew he wouldn't be impressed with her raise, and the promotion would tie her more closely than ever to her work.

Just before she left for lunch with her close friend, Katie, she paused at a window. She looked out over the treetops and grassy area beyond and the wide blue-gray ribbon of the Arkansas River, the tall smokestacks of the refineries and the industrial area beyond it. Where was Jared and when would he be home? Was he going to hate her new promotion? She remembered how nothing ever seemed to bother him, but she suspected this might.

And she had to give thought to her own reaction. Her

priorities were changing. And, she realized, Jared's feelings about her work were becoming important.

Beneath bright sunshine, Jared walked beside the Realtor. High grass swished against his legs. He looked out over the expanse of land stretching away from the house and drew a deep breath. The land was rolling, covered in high green grass. An occasional tall cottonwood stood against the horizon and trees lined the creek that meandered three hundred yards from the house.

He glanced at the house. Weeds grew to the door. Shingles had peeled away from the roof. Screens were missing from broken windows and weathered boards needed painting, but the basic structure would be sound if it had a new roof. Made of brick and wood, the long ranch-style house had an overhang above a porch that ran the length of the house. The agent, Jim Creighton, unlocked the door and motioned to Jared to enter.

"The house needs work, but the buyer will get the land at a bargain rate because the estate wants to sell and they don't want to wait. The house can be torn down and another one built, for that matter. You'll save enough on the land. Everything around here costs more than this place."

Merry played with a rattle, and Jared carried her easily as he walked into the living room and looked at the large stone fireplace, the wide-plank floor and the empty built-in oak bookshelves that flanked the fireplace. He wandered from room to room, and he could imagine the place repaired and he could see Faith, Merry and himself living in it. The rooms were large, with four big bedrooms and three baths. Along the living area was a window that gave a panoramic view of the sloping land to the south.

"I'd like to bring my wife out to look at it," he said, relishing talking about Faith. The word *wife* was still new and unique to him, something he had never before applied to himself, but now every time he said it, he smiled.

"Sure. What time is convenient?" Creighton asked, getting out a small black notebook and opening it to write down the time.

"Tonight should be fine. It'll stay light until late. How about eight o'clock?"

Creighton gave Jared a key and told him to look when he wanted and get back with him. They locked up and Jared told the agent goodbye, saying he was going to stay to look around. As soon as the agent had driven away, Jared got into his pickup with Merry and drove across the land behind the house. He found tracks and followed them, driving over the property until he had satisfied himself that he had found the ranch he wanted.

He couldn't wait to show it to Faith.

The minute Faith walked through the door that night, Jared caught her up in his arms and swung her around. She laughed, and as he let her slide down the length of him, her smile vanished. She tilted her head and closed her eyes when he kissed her. Her heart raced and thoughts of work vanished. Finally she leaned away to look up at him. "You look happy."

"I am. I found us a ranch today."

"No! You bought land?"

"'Course not. I want you to see it and see what you think," he said, nuzzling her neck.

"I won't know one thing about buying a ranch. Where's Merry?"

"Sound asleep. She likes the place."

"Oh, I'm sure. Merry always loves the things her daddy does."

"That she does, darlin'."

"Where is this ranch?"

"That's one of the good things. Only a stone's throw out of town. I can get back and forth easily, and we can live right here for a long time."

Faith remembered her promotion, but she knew she should hear him out about the ranch first. He sounded pleased, and she wondered if it was as close as he said. And every time he talked about how easy it would be for him to get from Tulsa to a nearby ranch, she wondered if what was really on his mind was her working on a ranch and coming into town a couple of times a week to an office.

"I have the key, and I thought we'd go look at the place, then I'll take you to dinner."

"That sounds like a bribe."

"Nope. I can do better than that if I want to bribe you," he drawled, his tongue following the curve of her ear. Faith inhaled, trying to concentrate on their conversation, feeling she had been away from him for days instead of hours. "If you don't like the place, I'll keep looking. The house is a shambles, but it looks as if it can be fixed up to be real livable. And I promise to put in a new kitchen."

"That sounds ominous. A new kitchen means very bad shape."

"Maybe so, but it has great possibilities. I can always see the great possibilities," he said, raining warm kisses down to the vee of her blouse. She could smell the woodsy after-shave he wore, feel his warm breath on her, and it was difficult to keep her thoughts on the concerns of the day.

"Jared, I was promoted today to vice president," she said breathlessly, barely thinking about the consequences as she felt his fingers twist the top button of her blouse free.

He straightened to look down at her. "You should have told me when you came in. Congratulations! That's fantastic."

"I was afraid you wouldn't be happy about it."

"If that pleases you, then it suits me just fine, darlin'. I'm not surprised. You have to be the best talent they have."

She felt as if a weight had been lifted from her shoulders. He seemed genuinely happy for her, and for the first time since she had learned about the promotion, she felt really thrilled about it. "You mean it?"

"I mean it," he said with warmth in his dark eyes. "And we'll take Merry and go celebrate your promotion. We can look at the ranch site tomorrow night."

"Oh, no, we can't. Uncle Blake told Dad about my promotion, and Dad's having a celebration for me tomorrow night. It'll be dinner at his club with the whole family, close friends and some of the office people. So we can go look at the ranch tonight when Merry wakes up."

"Congratulations again, Faith. That is really great."

"Thank you," she said, looking up at him, feeling drawn into the depths of his dark eyes where magic wrapped around her and shut out the cares of the day. She stood on tiptoe and wound her arms around his neck and he leaned down to kiss her.

Merry's cries caused them to move away and Jared turned, striding across the room. "I'll get her. You change and we'll go out."

The phone rang and Faith picked it up to hear Meg's voice.

"Congratulations! I've heard from Dad about your promotion! That's fantastic."

"Thanks, Meg."

"Bet Jared thinks it's great, too."

"Yes, he does."

"I thought you two might want to celebrate before the family shindig tomorrow night. Would you like to bring Merry over here so you two can be alone?"

"That sounds great, but Merry doesn't know any of you."

"She knows us a little from the wedding, and she's going to get to know us plenty."

"Umm, let me ask Jared."

"Ask Jared what?" he asked, strolling back into the room with a teary-eyed, tousled baby in his arms. He got her bottle from the refrigerator and Merry reached for it as he uncapped it and placed it in the microwave briefly.

"Meg offered to keep Merry tonight while we celebrate."

"If that pleases you, then it suits me just fine, darlin'," he drawled, capping the bottle after the timer sounded while balancing Merry on one hip. The baby grabbed the bottle and jammed it into her mouth. "You know she likes to be with other children, so if Meg is up to it, okay."

"Fine. You have a deal, Meg. We'll keep yours in return."

"I had a method to my madness. Bring her any time."

Jared took the phone from Faith. "Thanks, sister-in-law."

"Any time."

He handed the phone to Faith, then pulled out the pins in her hair so it fell over her shoulders while she talked. His fingers brushed her neck lightly, then touched her cheek while he stood close enough that she could feel the warmth of his body.

"And Merry can stay tomorrow night, too," Meg said. "Stan's mom will be here, and she'll look after the kids while we're at the party. How's that?"

Faith inhaled deeply as Jared's finger slipped beneath her collar, gliding lightly over the curve of her breast.

"Faith?"

Startled, she realized Meg was still talking. "Right. I better go. Thanks a million, Meg." She replaced the phone and turned to catch his hand in hers. "I can't talk when you do things like that." She leaned closer to Merry. "Hello, sweetie. I missed you today."

Glancing up at Jared, she held out her hands. "You've had her all day. Can I have her now?"

He handed Merry over. The baby stopped drinking to smile at Faith, squealing in delight, and Faith felt something squeeze her heart.

Warmth and love enveloped her for the small baby in her arms. "Oh, Jared, I love her so!"

He smiled and rubbed his knuckles on Faith's cheek. "She probably fell in love with you that afternoon you came to her rescue."

"I love you, sweet thing. You're my little girl now," she said, heading toward the family room and the new rocking chair.

Jared watched her, feeling a deep yearning. Would she ever look at him with the same tenderness in her eyes that she bestowed on Merry?

An hour later, Faith had showered and changed to jeans and a T-shirt. They left Merry at Meg's and Jared drove southeast out of the city. While he drove, he told her details about the ranch. "It just came on the market, Faith."

"Why are they selling at such a reduced price?"

"The couple who owned it left it to their only daughter, who has ignored it for about a year. She lives in England, cares nothing about the ranch and simply wants to be rid of it."

The pickup ran over a rickety bridge above a dry creek bed. "We'll have to replace this bridge."

"I don't know why. There's no water in the creek."

"There will be when the next big rains come. I know how these creeks can fill up to become raging torrents where before there'd been nothing but dirt." He drove up to the house that was bathed in the early evening rays of the setting sun.

Faith gazed at a rambling ranch house of weathered wood with a porch along the front. Shingles were missing from the roof, and the porch rail had fallen to the ground and was half-hidden by weeds.

"Jared, it looks like it needs a lot of work," she said, appalled by the run-down condition of the place.

"We can get it done," he said cheerfully. "It's structurally sound except for the roof. Come look at it."

Faith walked beside him, trying to concentrate on the house and land, far more aware of the man at her side. His arm was across her shoulders, and he kept her close against him until they had finished their tour.

It was almost dark when he leaned back against the pickup and pulled her around to face him. "Want to buy it?"

"Just like that?" She laughed. "Shouldn't we look around at other places? You rush into everything."

"Only things I want to rush into. Only very special deals," he said, his dark eyes working their magic on her senses.

"I don't know anything about ranches. The house is all right. But I think you should look around some more. This is a big decision." She rubbed her forehead. "I might as well save my breath. You rushed into marriage. You're going to plunge into this."

"I'm not rushing anywhere. I think I'm showing impressive restraint," he said, and Faith wondered whether he was talking about the ranch or about making love to her. His fingers stroked her nape while his other hand slid down over her bottom in a casual, feathery stroke.

"Jared, do what you want," she said, knowing he would, anyway.

"It involves you, too. This will wipe out that net worth of mine. I'll have to take out a loan."

She looked up at him, touching his jaw, feeling the faint stubble. "I have savings you can have."

"Thank you, darlin'," he replied warmly. "You keep your savings. You might need it sometime. I'll manage. And Granddad is going to get me started with some stock."

A breeze blew over them and he looked beyond her. "It's going to be good out here. I just know it is. Let's go call Creighton before someone else gets to look at the place."

"I think you should take more time, but okay."

No one in her family would buy something the size of

this ranch within hours of looking at it. And she suspected if Jared could have taken her with him on the first viewing, he would have bid on it right then. It amazed her the man asked her opinion.

She rubbed her forehead again. How well would this news be received at the party tomorrow night?

Nine

The next day Jared said he would take Merry to Meg's and come later to the celebration because he would be delayed looking at records at the courthouse.

Faith dressed in a sleeveless deep blue dress with a straight skirt. An undercurrent of excitement ran through her, and she knew it wasn't the promotion or the party. She was looking forward to being with Jared tonight. Humming, she fastened her hair on her head and wore her diamond stud earrings.

When she arrived at the club, they were serving cocktails on the terrace and in the glassed sunroom. She accepted congratulations from her parents, her father beaming when he hugged her.

"I'm proud of you," he said.

"Thank you, Dad. Jared is going to be a little late. He had an appointment."

"Sure. Blake told me about the clients and accounts you've helped them acquire this year. That's good."

"Thank you."

"There's Blake now." When her father moved away, she saw Andy standing a few yards away watching her. He raised his glass of wine in a toast. "Congratulations," he said.

"Thank you."

"Where's the cowboy?"

"Jared had an appointment. He'll be along soon."

"Still the happy bride?"

"Yes, I am," she answered evenly, wondering how long her brother would feel antagonistic toward Jared.

She sensed someone watching her, and she turned and spotted Jared's dark head above the crowd. People moved and his gaze met hers.

"Here's Jared now. Excuse me, Andy." She walked away without looking back.

As Jared came into the room, surprise rippled in her. He was wearing a dark suit, dressed like other men in the room, yet he was far more handsome than any other man there. With his long hair, he still had that wild aura, and his Western boots that showed beneath the hem of his trousers set him apart from the others.

When she approached him, Jared's gaze slowly drifted down over her and back up to meet hers again, and she could see the approval in his dark eyes.

"You look great," he said when he reached her. "Good enough to haul out into the bushes and have my way with you."

"I'm about ready for you to do just that," she said, giving him a steady look. His dark brows arched, and she could see curiosity light his eyes.

"If that pleases you, then it more than suits me just fine, darlin'," he drawled in a husky voice. "It suits me a hell of a lot." He had always had that way of responding to her that made her feel sexy, all woman. "Let's stroll down the hall and look at the artwork."

Tempted, but remembering the party, she smiled and

shook her head. "You're not going to muss me up before the party starts. The only artwork to look at in the hall are pictures of past presidents of the club."

"Maybe they hung one of those Monets you like. Let's go see."

Unable to resist a few moments alone with him, she let him take her arm and lead her into the hall where they were alone, music growing soft in the background as glass doors closed behind them. She looked up at him, feeling her pulse skip at the desire she saw mirrored in his eyes.

"You're getting your way again," she remarked.

"You just told me what you wanted. We need some privacy."

"You're not going to make love to me here at the club!"

"We can always try the garden. In this heat we'd have it to ourselves."

She laughed, knowing he was teasing her, but the smoldering look in his eyes wasn't a tease, and her heart fluttered with anticipation. Clearly—and not in the throes of passion—she had told him what she wanted, and she couldn't imagine he would let her remark pass without acting on it.

He tightened his fingers on her arm, pulled her into an empty salon and closed the door.

"They might have plans for this room."

"So do I," he said, pulling her into his arms.

"You're wearing a suit I haven't seen."

"It's new. I got it so I would come a tad closer to fitting in with your family."

"Did you really?" she asked, wondering if her family made him feel like an outcast. "Well, I can tell you," she said in a throaty voice while she ran her hands over the lapels and then down to his thighs, "it is very sexy."

"I'll remember to wear it more often."

"Well, maybe not as sexy as those briefs you wear."

"So you noticed."

"I don't think I missed a thing. And I'm sure you didn't."

"I can remember everything you've worn in exact detail," he drawled, brushing light kisses along her temple and cheek and ear while his arm tightened around her waist.

"Remember, don't muss me. Dad will probably make some kind of toast and everyone will look at me and I don't want to look as if we've been—"

His open mouth covered hers, and she no longer cared about her hair or her dress. One touch was all it took and she was lost. When she felt his hand skim over her bottom and then pull her dress up to caress her thigh, she caught his wrist and stepped away. She twisted a lock of hair back in place on top of her head.

"We have to go back to the party. This is one night we'll be missed."

His eyes were the color of midnight and held flames that kept her pulse racing. "You go, darlin'. I'm in no shape to join everyone right now," he said in a husky voice. "I'll look at those club presidents' pictures and maybe cool down."

She left and in a few minutes he joined her. He took her arm and she walked around the room with him while he greeted her family and their guests until they separated, talking to different people. Later, she looked across the room to see him talking to a group that included two of her female friends from work, both sisters and her brother Keith. The women laughed at something he said, and even Keith seemed relaxed and was smiling. She tried to focus her attention on the cluster of people around her and listen to Blake talk about his day at the races.

Jared shifted, glancing across the room to meet his wife's gaze. Someone spoke to her and she looked away. His eyes ran over her again. She was a beautiful woman, and he wasn't going to keep waiting to make her his wife. She said she was ready, and the mere thought of her remark made him hot.

Wisdom said he should wait until their life together was more firmly established, but he was beginning to get lost in traffic and forget to do things he should because his thoughts were constantly on her. His nerves were stretched raw, and he couldn't remember having a good night's sleep since he had met her. He corrected himself wryly. He hadn't had a good night's sleep since he met Miss Merry. Between the two females in his life, his sleep was almost nil.

He excused himself from the group around him and moved to the bar, knowing he was the only person in the room drinking beer. But he had never acquired a taste for wine or champagne.

He saw the people in her group raise their glasses in a toast to her, and he was certain they were congratulating her on her promotion. He was glad for her and felt no threat from her job or her family, because the lady had been ready for a change from the first moment he met her. He wondered if she was beginning to like this new world he had pulled her into. A world of rodeos and travel and ranching and babies. And sex. He knew she liked that. And he knew that once they came together as man and wife, he would take her places she'd never dreamed possible. And if she should become pregnant, he hoped someday she would just flat leave her job and come home to be with their children.

"How's the cowboy?" a man asked behind him.

Jared turned to face Faith's stocky grandfather, who was the only man in the room without a suit and tie. He wore a blue sport shirt and slacks and shook hands amicably with him.

"Fine. Enjoying my wife's moment of glory."

"She ought to be home with the babies, but that will come in time." He tilted his head to study Jared. "It will, won't it? More than little Merry?"

"God willing."

"Where'd you get the beer?"

"Right here." Jared turned and asked the bartender for another beer.

"Thanks. This fizzy stuff has as much taste as creek water. Think you can keep riding those bulls when you get to be half my age?"

Jared smiled. "I hadn't really thought that far ahead, but I doubt it. I'm not sure I'll ride them more than another four or five years. It's good money, though."

"Yep, so I've read. Unless the bull gores you or something like that."

"I try to avoid getting in their way. By the way, I just bid on some land. I intend to start raising cattle as soon as the deal closes."

"Did Faith agree to this?"

"Yes, sir. The place is close to town so I can get back and forth."

"Or she can get back and forth. Well, good for you." He raised his beer. "Congratulations on your new ranch. I'm glad you came along. We need new blood in this family. I saw your finances. You're right good at that rodeoing, but that's hard work."

"So are a lot of other things," Jared remarked dryly.

"I haven't ridden a horse in forty years."

"Soon as we have our place, you come out and you can ride."

"Will you have anything tame enough? These old bones can't take much."

"Sir, I expect those old bones can take a hell of a lot, but, yes, I'll have something tame enough for you."

Grandpa Kolanko chuckled. "You're not scared of me, are you?"

"Why should I be?"

"I don't know, but I scared the wits out of the last fellow she dated. I think it was my money."

"Well, I don't want your money. They've announced dinner, sir. I'll go get my pretty wife."

"You do that."

Jared moved through the crowd and took Faith's arm.

"Was Grandpa bothering you?"

"Hell, no. He's enjoyable."

She glanced up at Jared as if doubting what he said. "You're the first one to think so. He makes Andy and Keith nervous. He just irritates Dad because he'll say whatever comes to mind."

"That's plain old honesty and that's okay."

"I think my family is accustomed to a little finesse and subtlety."

"How's this for a little finesse and subtlety?" Jared asked softly, moving behind her in the crowd as they entered the dining room. Between them, hidden from the view of others, his hand drifted down over her bottom.

She turned her head slightly. "Someone is going to see you."

"Never. I have nimble fingers filled with finesse." His hand caressed her lightly across the bottom again, drifting down over her thigh.

"Congratulations, Faith," a tall, brown-haired man said.

"Thank you, Dan. Dan, this is my husband, Jared White-wolf. Jared, Dan Haworth. Dan is Uncle Blake's and Dad's accountant."

"Glad to meet you," Jared said, shaking hands and then resting his hand on her shoulder.

"You almost got caught," she said when Haworth turned away.

"Like hell. Wait until we're seated and see what I can do beneath the table."

"You keep your hands to yourself until we get home!" she said, smiling and nodding at someone who called congratulations to her.

She went through dinner barely aware of anything except her handsome husband. His light caresses heaped more kindling on the fires already burning steadily in her.

As she cut into a thick, juicy steak, Jared leaned close to her.

"I've made an appointment to see Andy tomorrow."

Shocked, she lowered her fork. "Excuse me. I couldn't have heard correctly."

"Yes, you did. I want a will—"

"Why?" she asked, placing her fork on her plate and feeling chilled.

"I want him to look at the contract for the ranch and I need a will because of you and Merry. I want you listed as my beneficiary, and you and I should appoint a guardian for Merry if something happens to us. It's routine, Faith. Something I feel I should do as a father."

She thought of the dangers of bull riding and reached beneath the table to place her hand on his knee. "You think you can deal with Andy?"

"He has your interests at heart, so there shouldn't be a problem," he answered, his hand covering hers and lacing with her fingers to give her hand a squeeze. He released her and turned away as Meg said something to him.

Faith picked up her water to sip, realizing Jared was probably winning over her family, one by one. She wondered who would be the last one to lose his animosity toward her new husband—Andy or her dad.

During dessert she felt Jared's hand caress her knee. She was engaged in conversation with Porter, who sat on her left and she couldn't turn away. Slow, long, feathery strokes from Jared's fingers journeyed between her legs. She dabbed at her mouth with her napkin, placed it carefully over her lap and closed her fingers around his wrist. His arm stilled, but his fingers kept moving, just a slight rub, a faint pressure that made her body tense and desire ignite. She tried to focus on Porter, knowing she was losing the train of what he was saying.

Finally they stopped talking, and she turned to Jared.

"You're mighty free with your hands."

"Not as free as I'm going to be," he said softly.

The clinking of a spoon against a glass brought silence to the group, and her father stood up to propose a toast.

"To our new vice president. Best wishes in the coming year!"

Everyone murmured congratulations again while Faith stood. "I want to thank you, Mom and Dad, for the dinner tonight and thank Blake and my co-workers for all they've done." Faith turned to Porter and raised her glass.

"I would like to propose a toast to my co-worker and supervisor, Porter Gaston, Graphic Design's new Vice President of Accounts."

Everyone lifted their glasses in another toast and Porter acknowledged his thanks. Faith glanced at Jared who gazed at her with a sexy promise and faint hint of amusement in his dark eyes.

She sat down and conversation resumed while she turned to her husband. "Will you stop fondling me, because someone is going to notice."

"Notice what? That I like flirting with my wife? That isn't scandalous."

"What you're thinking is! And your hand is all over my legs."

"You think you know what's running through my mind?"

"I know how you're looking at me and what your hand is doing right now. Behave!" She had her knees pressed tightly together, but his fingers moved indolently back and forth where her legs touched together. Flames darted from each stroke of his hand.

"I'm barely touching you. What's the harm in a little playing around?"

"You make me want to slide right under the table and pull you down there with me, dinner or no dinner," she whispered, leaning close to his ear.

"Oh, darlin'. I had no idea—"

"The devil you didn't! Now I'm going to talk to Porter and you put your hand in your own lap."

"That's no fun!"

"Try a little circumspection until we get out of here."

"If that's what you want," he said with a sigh. "I'll bottle up all my natural inclinations brought about by that sexy little dress and the best-looking pair of legs I've ever seen."

"Thank you," she said, her pulse racing. He had stirred her to a white-hot flame of need. She wondered whether he realized the full effect he had on her. And how much did his flirting mean to him? She suspected it came as naturally to him as breathing.

She turned to Porter and didn't know whether she was really relieved or not that Jared kept his hands to himself.

Shortly after dinner, when they started to leave the party, Jared draped his arm across her shoulders as they headed toward the door. "We should tell Meg we're leaving and call Stan's mom to tell her we'll be there soon. We're the first to leave, you know," Faith said.

"I've already taken care of all that. I talked to Meg." He held the door open to the hallway and she went through, Jared falling into step beside her. "I asked Meg if she would mind keeping Merry all night."

"Why did you do that?"

"We've bid on the ranch. Even though it is night, I want to look at it one more time with you. By the time we drive there and back to town, it'll be late picking up Merry."

"Meg doesn't mind?"

"Not at all. You know your sister. She's like you. She could have a dozen kids and be happy as a clam."

"You don't know that about me," Faith replied, knowing he was right. She had missed Merry during their honeymoon, missed her when she went to work each day.

"Oh, yes, darlin'. On this point, I damn sure do. Tell me I'm wrong," he said, pausing at the front door to wait for her reply, blocking her path until she answered.

"You think you're so smart," she said primly, and he grinned, pushing open the door.

"Tell me about your new position—will you change

your office?'' he asked as they moved across the brightly lit parking lot.

''I move day after tomorrow, and you'll have to come see it.'' She talked while they drove out of the lot and headed southeast out of town. It was a perfect spring night with a full moon, cool breezes and twinkling stars overhead. She sat twisted in the seat where she could watch her husband. *Husband.* The word was still new and amazing to her. Mrs. Whitewolf. She didn't think of herself yet as Faith Whitewolf. Jared had fit in with her family tonight far better than she would have ever guessed. And he had found an ally in her maverick grandfather, who was too blunt and outspoken for the rest of the family.

They turned onto the dusty driveway, crossed the rickety bridge and soon passed the darkened ranch house. She looked at the moonlight splashing over it.

''Jared, in the moonlight the house looks lovely,'' she said, imagining how it would look remodeled.

''I know it does. It looks great in my imagination. It's a nice big house, and we can get it looking even better than the one on Peoria. And it has all that glass on the south side. It'll be filled with sunshine day and night.''

''Not night,'' she said, smiling.

He picked up her hand to brush a kiss across her knuckles. ''You're the sunshine at night,'' he said softly.

Longing for him spilled through her. It had been a wonderful night with everyone showering her with good wishes, but it was the tall man beside her who had made the evening special.

''Jared, suppose Meg needs to get us for any reason?''

''Here's my cell phone. We'll hear it ring. Don't worry about Merry. Meg will have everything under control.''

As the pickup bounced over ruts and bumps, grass swishing against the vehicle, she looked at the rolling land. ''How do you know where you're going? You're not even on a road.''

"I drove around when I was out here with Merry yesterday."

She wondered about his knack for the outdoors and animals. She would be hopelessly lost and never know where she had driven before, particularly if she hadn't stayed on a path.

They drove up a hill, and he parked near a tall oak with limbs spread like open arms. Jared climbed down, and when she stepped out of the pickup, silence enveloped her. He removed a blanket from the back and took her arm.

"You carry a blanket?" she asked, wondering about her husband's past.

"This is the blanket I took to the park for a picnic with Merry. Faith, there have been few women in my life since Merry's arrival."

"It wasn't any of my business, anyway," she replied, but she was glad of his answer.

"There are only two females in my life now, and one isn't even a year old yet," he said, spreading the blanket.

"Jared, what are you doing?"

"Enjoying you and our new home-to-be," he said, shedding his coat and tie. He unfastened the first buttons on his shirt, leaving a small vee of his chest showing. He strode back to her side. "Look around you."

He draped his arm across her shoulders, and she stood close enough beside him to feel the faint pressure of his hip against hers, the warmth of his body. Lush green land spread away from them in all directions, rolling, grassy and bright in the silvery moonlight, dark and shadowed where groves of trees stood. As breezes moved over the grass, it waved like a sea beneath the wind. In the distance, in a dip in the land, she could see the ranch house nestled near tall oaks. Near the house, moonlight shimmered on a stretch of the running stream.

"This is beautiful," she said, hearing only the sigh of the wind, wondering what her life would be like in the future.

"More beautiful than anything else in the world," he whispered in a husky voice, and turned her to him. It was then she realized he wasn't talking about the land, but about her. "You really are."

"No, I'm not," she whispered in return, "but I'm glad you think so." Her pulse raced, and when she saw the small bit of his chest revealed by his open shirt, she couldn't drag her attention away from it, remembering vividly how he looked bare chested.

"I want to go back and pick up a thread of conversation we had earlier tonight," he said.

"Do you really?" she asked while anticipation shook her. She was unable to stop staring at the small bit of his chest exposed by his unbuttoned shirt. In the moonlight his burnished skin looked darker than ever. She could detect his woodsy after-shave, a faint clean, soapy smell on his skin. She leaned forward, her tongue stroking that smooth bit of flesh, feeling his chest expand as he inhaled. "Because the last thing I want to do is talk."

Ten

Jared growled low in his throat, a deep masculine sound that made her feel wanted, sexy. She wanted him to love her. She wanted to love him, to please and touch and kiss him. This tough, wild man who was so strong and fearless had some voids in his life and she suspected he could stand some loving. And she was certain he was vulnerable where his heart was concerned.

He had kept his part of their marriage bargain. He had done everything he could to please her, including waiting as agreed to consummate the marriage, and allowing her to decorate the house on Peoria. He had bought a new suit to fit in with her family, consulted her on buying his ranch. Now she wanted to please him and she desperately wanted his loving.

It was time they tried to make the marriage real. Even though she had Merry, Faith was ready for another baby—Jared's baby.

He placed his hands on either side of her head and tilted

her face up to his while she carefully tried to work free the remaining buttons on his shirt.

Dark eyes bore into her as if searching for her feelings. "I want to make you mine in every way," he said in a husky voice that was tight with emotion. Was she really as vital to him as he said?

His fingers slid over her head, shaking free the pins, causing her hair to tumble down over her shoulders. "We took a vow to have and to hold. I want you to want that with all your being. Including everything it implies."

Her breathing jammed, her heart raced and her body trembled from the searching of his dark eyes. He lowered his head, laying siege to her mouth, giving to her, stirring up a storm that roared around them.

Caught in the vortex of emotion he created, she stood on tiptoe, winding her arms around his neck. Her fingers tangled with the leather tied around his hair and it fell free. She felt the coarse strands slide over her bare arms, knew she held and kissed a man so different from herself. A cowboy whose wild streak she loved and needed even though it took her breath and scared her senseless.

She shoved his shirt off his shoulders, letting her fingers travel over the bulge of powerful muscles, feeling the strength in the arm tightly banded around her waist. His kisses had unleashed a tidal wave of desire that rushed over her.

She ached low in her body, a hollow craving that only he could fill. She was not a virgin, yet no man really existed before Jared. No man had ever driven her to the depths of need like he did. No man had ever stirred such a storm of passion or treated her as if she was the sexiest woman on earth.

"I need you," Jared said, his mouth covering hers, his tongue stroking hers, moving in a rhythm that created a gush of heat that centered between her legs.

"Jared, I don't have much experience—"

"Darlin', that's one thing we don't have to worry about.

The yesterdays are gone. It's us and now," he whispered, and she accepted what he said as passion overwhelmed her.

His hands slid slowly over her, down her sides, over her hips and thighs and then around, moving languorously to the top of her dress. He tugged down the zipper, and the air was cool across her back and shoulders when he pushed the dress away. As it fell to the grass in a heap, he leaned back. His hands stilled while he took in the sight of her.

"You're beautiful," he said in a voice that sounded full of awe. Watching her, he slid his fingers slowly up her rib cage, moving to her breastbone. He flicked the catch to her bra and pushed it away. He palmed her breasts, and her body tensed, hot and eager. While he held her lightly, he leaned down. His tongue stroked around the nipple, making her groan and cling to him, her need heightening to a frenzy. Her breasts tightened, ached for his mouth, and then he took her nipple in his mouth, his tongue stroking in a sweet torment, his teeth biting just enough to send little shocks streaking in her.

Jared shook, fighting for control. Since that first afternoon he had wanted her in his arms, bare, open to him. He wanted her softness surrounding him, her body beneath his, and he felt he had waited aeons for this night.

"I want you, Faith. I want us to love out here on our land where we'll have our family. Our home and our hearts will be here," he said, the words a husky rasp, and he had no idea whether she heard him or not. Then she turned her head, trailing kisses on his throat.

"Who's planning now?" she whispered. Her tongue flicked over his ear and tension wound tighter in him. "I thought you never planned ahead," she whispered with her eyes closed, her hands stroking him. She opened her eyes to look at him. "You're planning your life. And mine."

"Life's a gamble," he said, "but love is something you can plan on. It's rock solid."

His answer was sharp, but the part about love shook her.

How could he feel so sure about something he didn't know? "You can't know yet what we'll have together."

"I know what I feel and what I want," he answered in a husky rasp.

She drew a deep breath, and he wondered whether she believed him or not. He bent to kiss her breast, caressing the other breast, his thumb rolling over her nipple while his tongue stroked a taut peak. Her hands fluttered over his chest and back, sliding lower and caressing him, exploring each plane and angle as if she was as desperate to know his body as he was to know hers. Her fingers were a raging torment that threatened his control.

He wanted a place and a moment in time she wouldn't forget. *He* would never forget, but he was head over heels, heart and soul in love with the woman and she couldn't see it and wouldn't believe him if he told her.

He picked her up, set her on her feet on the blanket, and then he stepped back again to look at her while he yanked off first one of his boots and then the other.

As he straightened, her wide green eyes met his gaze. Moonlight splashed over her features, and while she might not think love was possible yet and might not be in love with him, she wanted him. Desire smoldered in her eyes like a burning fire. She still wore flimsy lace panties and her thigh-high hose. He ran his finger along the top of one of her stockings, feeling her firm satin-smooth skin.

"If I had known there was some bare leg up higher—"

"It's a good thing you didn't know," she interrupted, stroking his chest, her fingers drifting down to his waist. She reached out to unfasten his trousers. Her slender fingers were deft, sure. When his pants fell, he stepped out of them.

Faith inhaled, her body steaming. His manhood was thick, already thrusting out of the low-cut briefs. She hooked her fingers in the elastic band and pushed them away, drawing them down his strong legs and feeling the rough texture of short hairs on his legs scrape against her palms.

She stayed on her knees to curl her fingers around his hard shaft as she leaned forward to kiss him. He gasped, his fingers tangling roughly in her hair, and then he hauled her to her feet to kiss her. While he kissed her, the last flimsy bits of her clothing flew. Urgency made his hands shake and sent tremors of desire racing in her.

He picked her up, her body bare and warm against his naked body. Holding her close, he knelt on the blanket, still kissing her when he lowered her on it. Then he moved down her body to caress the slight arch of her foot. Her bones felt delicate, so special to him. "Every inch of you is beautiful to me."

Faith stared at him, his words spinning in her mind. This strong cowboy followed his impulses. What havoc would he wreak in her life? And what pleasure? Her need for him was crushing, all-consuming. She watched him steadily as he leaned down to trail his tongue from her foot to the inside of her knee while his dark eyes were on her. She rested on her elbows, watching him, wanting to reach for him, tingling from every stroke of his hands and mouth. As he looked at her, his dark eyes drew her into midnight depths where reason and plans vanished.

"I want you, Faith," he whispered.

She reached for him. Her hand cupped the back of his neck and she sat up, pulling him forward to kiss him, trailing her tongue across his lips and then sliding her tongue into his mouth. He leaned over her to kiss her long and hard. When he moved away, he trailed kisses down her throat, to her breast. He lowered her to the blanket as his foray dipped lower across her belly, his tongue a flash of hot fire. Then he spread her legs and trailed kisses between her thighs, his tongue stroking, circling, showering wet hot kisses on the center of her warmth.

She cried out, arching, her thighs spread, ready for him, her hands clutching his shoulders. He shifted, his hand going where his mouth had been on the sweet, hot bud. He stroked and rubbed, building a pressure in her while she clung to him, her hips moving. With each stroke he could feel the tightening in her body.

"Jared, please, I want you," she whispered.

He wasn't sure he could last another ten seconds, but he damned well was going to try to hold back. He was going to make her remember this night, and he wanted to forge a bond between them that would last through the days to come. He was claiming his woman with his hands and his mouth, taking possession of her body, hoping it ran deeper and he was uniting with her soul.

Faith cried out, tumbling over a brink only to want him more than ever. She gripped his arms, pulling him to her. "Jared, I need you and want you. I ache—"

He swooped down, his mouth capturing hers as if he could take her words and keep them forever. He straightened and moved between her legs and then reached for his pants to remove a packet. He was poised over her, virile, his manhood hard and ready.

She took his hand. "No. You know I want a baby."

"You're the one who always says not to rush into something."

"Maybe I'm learning from you," she answered breathlessly. "Are you going to talk all night?"

He tossed aside the packet and lowered his body. She felt the velvet tip of his manhood touch her and she arched her hips, a hot shimmer of excitement making her quiver. She slid her long legs around him, her hands running down over his lean body, down over his firm buttocks as she caressed him and tugged him closer.

He thrust into her. She was incredibly tight and he paused, sweat pouring off him while he tried to control his urges. "Darlin', I'm going to hurt you."

"Never!" she gasped, her legs tightening around him while her fingers dug into his buttocks and he was lost. He thrust into her, hearing her cry.

"Ahh, Jared, how I've wanted you!" she whispered, moving wildly beneath him, her head thrashing, and he knew he wasn't hurting her. Far from it. Then thought stopped as he moved with her, kissing her, trying to be joined with her as much as humanly possible.

Tension pounded him, building until he knew he wasn't going to last any longer. Dimly he heard her cry, felt her arch higher beneath him, felt wild spasms rock her. She was fire and passion, burning him to cinders.

"Faith, love!" he ground out the words, thrusting deep within her, wishing he could hold her forever. She clung to him, their bodies locked together. Rapture ripped him apart; his fire and substance spilled into her. She was his woman now and forever.

Faith felt as if she were settling back to earth from a ride across the sky on a shooting star. Only Jared had been no shooting star, but a flesh-and-blood man whose lovemaking was wild and passionate and breathtaking. She stroked his back, still wanting him, aware of the kisses he showered over her temple, cheek and throat.

Winding her fingers in his dark hair, she was amazed at the depth of her reaction to him, astounded at the abandon she had shown. How deep did her feelings for him run? Was she falling in love with this wild man she had married? She stroked him, feeling a breeze cool her damp shoulders, the rest of her body bearing his weight, their legs tangled together.

"I never, ever would have believed that one night I would make love to a man on a blanket out in the woods under a starry sky. You're a wild man, Jared Whitewolf."

"And you're a fine, wild woman. And it's pretty damned nice to make love under the stars, don't you think?"

"Yes, it is," she answered shyly, remembering how wantonly she had loved and responded to him. And it amazed her now to lie naked in his arms and feel the wind blow over their sated bodies. Never in her life had she dreamed of doing such a thing. He shifted beside her and pulled her close in the circle of his arms.

"Darlin', you finished me off." He propped his head on

his hand to look down at her and he smiled. "And it was a damned good finishing, too."

She traced the line of his jaw, surprised by the night, still astounded to be married to such a man.

"You're a rash, impulsive man." She grew silent while his hand trailed over her, gentle strokes that made her feel cherished. Her thoughts drifted to the part of his life that worried her. "But if I fall in love with you, I don't think I can take your bull riding. How long do you plan to keep on doing it?"

"Your grandfather just asked me that a few hours ago. I haven't planned what I'll do. Ride until I don't want to ride, I guess."

Moonlight splashed over her, and Jared looked at his bride's curvaceous, beautiful body that lay bare to his view. Soft, wondrous—she was all he had hoped for and much more. He felt boneless, unable to stand or move more than his hand as it slightly stroked her. Her skin was silky smooth. Her golden cascade of hair was disheveled, fanned behind her head and on her milky shoulders. Her skin was lovely, pale next to his. Pink and white and golden. His hand strayed to a full breast and he traced her aureole.

"Jared." Her voice was languid.

He lay down beside her and pulled her close as they lay on their sides, facing each other.

"This is perfect," he said, his bass voice a deep rumble.

"It's perfect tonight. I don't want to sleep out here on this hill every night."

"We'll sleep in our bed in the big bedroom in the house, but I wanted this tonight. I feel part of this place, and now a part of you."

Faith's pulse drummed at his words, but she found it difficult to believe him. He was rash, impetuous, impulsive—he had never settled in his life. Would he really settle now? Another inkling of worry intruded.

"Jared, have you ever done anything besides rodeo riding?"

He chuckled, a deep-throated sound that came up from the depths of his chest. "'Course I have, darlin'. I've hired on ranches, done bronc busting, worked for a vet once. I've worked for a blacksmith and I can shoe horses. I worked for an electrician for a time. I've cooked, washed dishes, driven race cars."

"What's the longest you've ever lived in any one place?"

"I didn't keep count, so I don't have any idea."

"Surely you would know if you'd spent years in a place," she said, aware he nudged her legs apart with his and twined his leg high between hers. His body was heated, slightly damp. His breathing had returned to normal as had hers, and he was still trailing his fingers over her. From her waist over the curve of her hip, then along her thigh. She drew a deep breath. How could he stir desire in her so easily?

"Darlin', I've never in my life spent years in any one place. Our mother moved all over the U.S., and after I ran away, I traveled across country and into Mexico and up into Canada. While you, luscious woman," he said, nuzzling her neck, "aside from college, have probably lived right here."

Faith felt his shaft, hard against her thigh, and knew he was aroused again. Her pulse jumped as his casual strokes changed to caresses that started a blaze. She shifted, feeling a wrench of desire. Her hands moved over his chest while he showered her with kisses.

Jared wanted her again. He suspected the next thousand years wouldn't be enough to satisfy him. She was lush, naked, too tempting. And he was remembering the past hour and their torrid lovemaking. Erotic images taunted him. He shifted, lying on his back, and pulled her on top of him to play with her breasts before raising his head to take a nipple in his mouth.

He wanted her more now than he had wanted her before. He knew he might have sealed his own fate. If she got pregnant from their lovemaking, she would have the baby she'd always wanted. But if their marriage didn't work out, where would that leave Merry and him? He knew his fear was premature—and perhaps even paranoid—but he couldn't imagine life without Faith in it.

And he didn't want to stop. The marriage was consummated and there was no turning back now. He stroked her back, his hand sliding around over her stomach, down to the tangle of soft curls, searching, finding the ready bud, teasing and hearing her cry out as her fingers tightened on his shoulders.

"Here's the best kind of ride, darlin'," he whispered. He lifted her hips, settling her on his hard shaft while a storm of passion broke over them.

Faith moved with abandon, shocks of pleasure raking her while his hands played with her and moonlight spilled over their bodies. She felt wild, free, amazed at her zest for lovemaking.

Rapture burst as she felt his deep thrust, his hands clenching her hips. And then she felt as if she melted into a boneless puddle on top of him. His arms, sure and strong, enveloped her, and he kissed her damp temple, murmuring endearments that she barely heard through her still-thundering pulse.

They slept in each other's arms. Then Faith woke to his caresses and loving again. And they slept and loved again, each time their need and passion seeming stronger than the time before. As the first faint pink tinged the sky and stars faded from sight in the eastern sky, she lay exhausted in his arms.

"Jared, it's morning. We're stark naked out here."

"So who's going to see us?" he drawled, amusement lacing his voice.

"I have to be at work in a couple of hours! I don't even know what time it is!"

He rolled over to look at her and smiled, brushing a kiss across her lips. "So I'll get you to work maybe just a little late, but they'll understand. Tell them we were making out all night—''

"I'll do no such thing!" she exclaimed, and saw the twinkle in his eyes. She slapped her palm against his shoulder. "Devil!"

"Sexy lady. I'll bet you haven't been late to work ever."

"Maybe once or twice—and the last time was on my lunch break when I met you. See what you do to my life?" she said, standing up. She blushed, waving her hands. "Where are my clothes?"

"You look damned good this way," he said in a husky voice, standing, his shaft hard and ready.

"I have to go to work."

"Do you really?" he asked, stepping close to kiss her throat. His hand stroked her breast, his thumb playing over her nipple and she moaned.

"Jared, I will be so *late*—"

"It'll be worth it," he whispered.

Within minutes, she decided it was.

Eleven

Faith leaned forward, her fists knotted as she stared through the glass down at the arena and then looked at the television screen in the private box. They were at a Texas rodeo, and she sat with Jared's friends and their wives in a plush box in a fancy arena. The television camera took her right down into the chute with Jared and she watched him secure his hand to the broad back of the Brahman bull.

The buzzer sounded, and she shifted her gaze from the television to the window. Everyone around her ceased to exist. Her entire focus was on Jared as the bull leaped in the air and twisted in a corkscrew turn. She closed her eyes, unable to watch, finding each rodeo more devastating than the last. It was late July now, and she had been watching him compete since that first week she had met him in April. And her fear had only grown worse with each competition.

Someone nearby gasped and fingers clamped on her arm. "Faith, he's all right," a deep voice said. "He'll be okay," Bud Tarkington, one of Jared's friends, repeated.

Faith opened her eyes and saw Jared dangling from the bull as it made another violent leap, kicking the air and twisting as if trying to shake free of the cowboy flopping against its broad side.

Jared fell, a hoof coming down on him. Then the clowns dashed in, waving bandannas at the bull. Jared got up and walked over to pick up his hat. He scooped it up stiffly, staggered a step and then righted himself.

She fled from the box. She didn't know whether she'd said anything to the others or not. She couldn't stand his riding and now he was hurt. If he hadn't walked out of the arena on his own, she would have fainted right there in the box.

She rushed through the cavernous halls and down concrete steps, holding the cold iron railing as she dashed back to where the pens and animals and riders were.

She found Jared sitting on a cask while a paramedic taped his ribs. He looked up, grinned, and then his smile faded. "Thanks, Gene."

"Sit still while I fasten this. You need to go to a hospital and get an X ray to make sure you don't have a punctured lung. Don't lift anything heavy. And stay off the bulls."

"Yeah, right. Thanks. This is my wife, Faith Whitewolf. Faith, this is Gene Cole."

She nodded, unable to say anything.

"Glad to meet you, ma'am. You can drive him to the hospital."

As she nodded, the paramedic snapped shut a bag and then moved away. Jared stood, going to her. "Look, I'm okay."

"I'm not," she said stiffly. "Jared, I couldn't stand seeing you hurt."

"I'll mend."

"This time! Suppose it had been your neck? I can't take your riding. You're a father now. Merry needs you. She's already lost her mother and a daddy who loved her."

"Faith, I just cracked some ribs."

She looked away as his hands settled on her shoulders. "I've never done anything very physical," she said. "I barely can swim. I don't ski. I'm not accustomed to that kind of life and I just can't cope with it." She looked into his eyes. "Will you stop bull riding?"

Jared gazed into green eyes filled with concern and fear and he knew he couldn't push aside her worries as nothing. "Darlin', at the rate I'm going, I'll qualify for the National Finals. That's a helluva lot of money that we need. I've never been badly hurt. A few broken bones is all."

"You could get killed and you know it."

"I told you, you run the same risk on the freeway."

"Don't be ridiculous! Jared, give it up, please," she said, feeling desperate. His determination to keep competing reminded her of the chasm between their feelings. She was deeply in love with this wild cowboy, while he didn't love her enough to give up his reckless ways.

He slid his arm around her and turned her to walk with him. "Let's go pick up Merry from your folks' house and go home."

"We're going straight to the hospital."

"If that pleases you, then it suits me just fine, darlin'," he drawled.

She walked with him through the arena and out into a warm night. "I'll drive," she said, climbing behind the wheel.

They rode in silence to the hospital, where he disappeared while she took care of the admitting details and then sat, waiting. She looked at the pale green walls, the fluorescent lights overhead, the tall vending machines that held snacks and drinks, but her thoughts were elsewhere, racing over the night. When she saw Jared get hurt, she hurt. And she could barely breathe. And she knew now that she was deeply in love with him.

The realization was startling. At the same time, it seemed as if she had loved him a long, long time. He was everything she needed. He filled the voids in her life. He was her soul mate. Because in many ways they were alike. They loved Merry with a deep intensity. And she loved the ranch and could see the beauty he saw. And maybe she needed his recklessness to balance her caution.

I love him. How long had she loved him without acknowledging it? How long was she going to wait before she told him?

She thought back to that first night when he had made love to her beneath the starry sky, and she knew she had loved him then. That was not just lust. It had gone far deeper with her and she knew it did with him. She had given him her body that night, and her heart.

She gazed down the empty hospital corridor, wanting Jared to come striding down it, wanting to throw herself into his arms and tell him.

She loved him, this tall, lean cowboy who was a continual surprise and delight in her life. This sexy lover, reliable father, true companion. And because she loved him, she couldn't live with his bull riding.

She couldn't help but notice the irony. Had she realized she loved him at the moment she was going to have to leave him?

She heard the jingle of spurs and the scrape of boots as Jared came back down the hall, and her pulse jumped. He held out his hands and grinned. "Lungs fine. Ribs will be okay soon. Let's go home."

They went through the doors and into the night. As they reached the pickup, she turned to him, taking his arm. "Jared."

He looked down at her and his brows arched quizzically.

"I know it's not the most romantic spot—we should be in a better place than a parking lot. But I want to tell you now. I love you."

Jared's heart thudded until he thought it would burst in his chest. He held her, trying not to crush her to him too tightly, ignoring the pain in his ribs from holding her so close. Tears stung his eyes and a lump filled his throat while joy consumed him. "Ah, my darlin'. I've waited since that first afternoon to hear those words. Ah, Faith, how I love you. My darlin' Faith."

His words thrilled her, and her pulse jumped. Yet wisdom nagged with the worry that plagued her—how deep did his love run? Enough to give up his bull riding? Would he put her and Merry first, before the wild thrills he also loved?

She clung to him, kissing him, knowing problems that might be insurmountable loomed, but for this moment, they loved each other. She loved him, and now he knew she did. And he loved her in return.

She had no idea how long they stood in the parking lot kissing, but someone drove past and honked and she realized where they were. She pushed against his chest. "We're creating a scene. We should go."

"Yes, ma'am. Let's go home."

She unlocked the pickup door and worries came tumbling back. As Jared gingerly climbed into the passenger seat, she thought about tomorrow night's rodeo.

When she drove out of the hospital parking lot, she glanced at him and saw him turned in the seat, studying her quietly.

"Faith, I stand to win too much to quit. And I'm not hurt that bad."

Hurt stabbed her heart. The reminder of the rodeo made vivid pictures of his being thrown from the bull dance in her mind. Her brief joy vanished and was replaced by concern. "You're going to ride again tomorrow night, aren't you? Even with your ribs taped."

"I haven't decided."

His words chilled her because he hadn't ruled out competing. And she knew he was going to. She couldn't stand watching him ride, risking everything, and she wasn't going to again.

"You have a baby to think about, if you're not going to worry about my feelings."

"Darlin', I worry about your feelings a hell of a lot. I just know the dangers better than you do, and you've blown them all out of proportion in your mind."

"I have money you can use for the ranch."

"You save your money. You might need it sometime," he answered.

"Jared, I can't take your bull riding. I can't sit by and watch you get hurt. I can't live with that. You have to decide—bull riding or our marriage."

He reached over to brush her cheek with his fingertips. "Darlin', you know what's most important to me. And tonight was a bad night. Give it a little time."

She wondered whether he realized how deep her feelings went—both her love for him and her dreadful worry for his safety.

"I meant what I said."

"I know you do right now, darlin', but my world is new to you," he answered gently.

She drove in silence, her thoughts whirring, while her jangled nerves tried to calm.

He'd been spending every day at the ranch and had a crew working on the house. They would soon be able to move into it, and she suspected that he wanted to—no matter their original agreement. His grandfather had delivered a truckload of cattle, and Jared had bought two cutting horses and a gentle mare for her.

And the time was fast approaching when he wouldn't be able to care for Merry during the day. Meg was keeping her now at least one day a week, and Faith's mother was also keeping her a day. Jared said he would write an ad for a nanny. The drive to the ranch was an hour—not an impossible commute—and she knew that the time would come when he would want her to be the one to commute because he would need to get up at dawn to go to work.

Now instead of a man of substance, he was a man deeply in debt. It was going to take long hours and hard work to make the ranch pay, and the first years would be critical.

And he could ease up his financial crunch with his rodeo winnings, but what good would that do if he were permanently injured or killed?

When they reached her parents' house, they picked up Merry, who was asleep, and drove to their house on Peoria.

Faith tucked Merry into bed, running her fingers over the child's silky curls. She bent down to kiss her soft cheek.

She went to the kitchen to open a can of pop. Moments later Jared came in with a towel wrapped around his waist. His hair was damp from his shower and she drew a swift breath, her pulse jumping at the sight of his smooth bronze skin and muscled chest above the stark white bandaging.

"Don't start sweet-talking me," she said forcefully. "Even with broken ribs and the doctor telling you not to, you're going to ride tomorrow night, aren't you?"

"If I don't hurt any worse than right now—yes. I want to ride. Faith, I can't give this up. And there's no reason to. You're scared because it's not familiar to you."

"I'm scared because I'm not a daredevil who doesn't show an ounce of caution."

He crossed the room to the refrigerator to get a can of beer and popped the top. He took a long drink, set the can on the table and crossed the room to face her.

Every step closer to her he took, her pulse revved up several notches. "Don't try to change the subject," she whispered as his arm slid around her waist.

"Darlin', all I can think about is that you said you love me." He leaned down, his mouth claiming her, destroying her arguments and burning her fear and anger to cinders.

Two hours later she lay in the curve of his arm, his long leg between her legs while he slept, and she stared into the darkness. She couldn't live in a constant state of fear, and she knew they were on a collision course about a lot of other things in their married life. It was time to get a nanny for Merry. She knew Jared wanted to move to the ranch. She thought about the long commute to work and dreaded it, yet that might be the only solution. She could see them working out everything except the real obstacle in their marriage: his bull riding. He wasn't going to give it up and she couldn't live with it.

Tears stung her eyes and she wiped at them, realizing she might have rushed into a terrible mistake. In the most basic way they weren't suited. They'd been married only three months, but compatibility wasn't coming with time.

She turned her head. Moonlight spilled across the big bed and she looked at her handsome husband, whose dark hair covered half his face and cheek. He looked as wild and masculine asleep as he did awake. Maybe more with his long hair falling across his face. And she loved him deeply and had been in love with him for a long time now.

She reached out, running her finger along his firm jaw, feeling tiny bristles. Her fingers moved lightly across his chest and desire stirred. Their lovemaking was fantastic, exciting. If only he wasn't so reckless about his rodeo riding!

She lay back in the darkness, knowing a few more caresses and he would wake and they would love again. She ran her hand across her forehead, wondering what she should do.

On Saturday night she kissed him goodbye at the door while she held Merry in her arms. In spite of taped ribs, he was going to ride in the rodeo. This time she wasn't going to watch.

"I'll be home by half past eleven. We can go out with the crowd if you want. We could take Merry along. She's no trouble."

Faith shook her head, feeling as if she was kissing him goodbye for longer than just tonight. "No. I want to stay home."

His dark eyes studied her, and she gazed back steadfastly, feeling a clash of wills between them. Then he slipped his hat on his head and brushed a fleeting kiss across her lips. "Take care." With a jingle of spurs and a scrape of his boot heels on the concrete, he strode across the drive and climbed into his pickup to drive away.

She closed and locked the door and hugged Merry, feeling tears sting her eyes as she prayed that he would be safe. He had a rodeo the next weekend in Phoenix and then another one in San Diego the following weekend. They had planned the trip together, and she'd intended to take Merry along, but that morning she'd canceled her flight. She and Merry would not go with him.

Merry wriggled and Faith carried her to the family room to set her on a blanket on the floor. She crossed her legs and sat down to play with Merry, but all the while her stormy thoughts were on Jared.

She was coming out of the shower after eleven when the phone rang. She heard Bud Tarkington's voice on the line and her heart lurched.

"Faith, Jared's okay, but he wanted me to call you to tell you he'll be late getting home."

She relaxed slightly, wondering if he had gone partying after the rodeo with the others, feeling a strange rift that he would go without her.

"Fine," she answered evenly.

"He had a little accident tonight."

"What happened? Where are you?" Her fears rushed back, and she gripped the receiver tightly.

"We're at the hospital and he's giving 'em hell now to let him go. A bull kicked him and he has a slight concussion. If he doesn't get out of here soon, he said to tell you he'll call you. They're trying to talk him into staying for observation."

"Bud, try to talk him into staying. I can be there in less than half an hour."

"No need," Bud answered casually. "He'll probably be released by then. He just wanted you to know where he was so you wouldn't worry."

"Thanks," she said, replacing the receiver when Bud said goodbye.

A *concussion*. The doctors wanted him in the hospital tonight, but she knew he would talk them into releasing him. She just couldn't cope with his reckless life-style. He was too wild, too willing to take huge risks.

Didn't he love his wife and child enough to take care of himself? Apparently his behavior spoke for itself where she was concerned.

She paced the floor until he came home, rehearsing a dozen speeches and ultimatums that all flew right out of her mind when she saw him. He had a bandage across his temple and he looked full of vitality, as if he hadn't received a scratch.

She flew into his arms to kiss him, all thoughts of discussion gone. His mouth met hers, and his strong arms reassured her that he was very much all right.

Jared held her and kissed her hard, wanting her and hating that she hadn't gone with him tonight even though he had been thankful she wasn't there to see him get hurt. From the moment he regained consciousness in the ambulance and his fuzzy thoughts cleared, he worried about facing her.

When he had stepped through the back door, his worries evaporated. Her pale face and green eyes showed only concern. Without a word of dissension, she had raced across the room into his arms.

Surprise and pleasure engulfed him and he bent his head to kiss her hungrily. He probably wouldn't have been thrown from the bull if he had been concentrating better. He was still intoxicated by her declaration of love.

Her hands fluttered over him as if she had to reassure herself that he was actually in her arms, and his heart pounded with joy. His arousal was swift and hard, a hungry need for her, his urgency matching hers. He tugged her T-shirt over her head, tossing aside the flimsy bra as he bent to take her nipple in his mouth. He wanted her and he wanted to give to her because she had bestowed the biggest gift of all on him when she said she loved him.

As he kissed her and flicked his tongue over the taut peak, his fingers deftly unfastened the buttons of her cutoffs and he shoved them away.

"I was so worried," she whispered. "I don't want to hurt your ribs—"

"You can't," he said, yanking off his own shirt. Driven to possess her, to feel her softness, he flung aside clothing. His pulse pounded, drowning out sounds. His hands roamed over her. He wanted to thrust himself into her dark warmth that bound them completely. He went down on his knees, his tongue tracing a fiery pattern as she parted her legs and moaned.

Urgency was as great in her as it was in him. Jared pulled her down, and as Faith stretched on the kitchen floor, he moved between her legs.

"Jared, your ribs—"

His mouth stopped conversation. Faith's heart drummed and her hands ran across his strong shoulders. He was home, safe, loving her, and at the moment that was all that mattered. His shaft slid into her warmth and Faith gasped with pleasure, wrapping her legs around him while they both moved in a frenzy of passion. Release burst in her, a white-hot, all-consuming pleasure. "I love you," she whispered.

"My darlin'," he gasped. "My love!"

Spasms of pleasure racked his body and she held him, still moving with him, lifted up and carried to another brink, feeling the pressure build and then burst in another release while she cried his name. His arms tightened around her and his weight settled on her as they slowed.

"Ah, love." He showered kisses on her. "I missed you being there tonight."

"You should be in the hospital."

"And miss this? Not on your nelly, darlin'!"

She closed her eyes and held him as he trailed kisses

over her temple and stroked her. He was here and safe in her arms and that was what was important for now. Tomorrow she would face the future, but this hour, she wasn't going to think about anything but his kisses and lovemaking.

Finally, after lying sated in each other's arms, he rolled over and then stood. When she rose beside him, she started to pick up her clothes. Instead, he lifted her into his arms.

"Jared, you'll hurt yourself."

"Stop worrying. I'm not going to do anything I shouldn't."

"Oh, not much, you aren't. You've been doing things you shouldn't since I met you," she accused, and he gave her a lopsided grin.

"Like making love on the kitchen floor," he said.

"We should get our clothes."

"No one is here to see them. Merry won't care or know." He felt a splash of tears on his chest. "Hey, darlin'."

In the bedroom he set her on her feet. He bent down to tilt her face up, his thumbs wiping away the tears as he brushed her face with his lips, trailing kisses to her ear. "I'm here and I'm just fine."

"They wanted you in the hospital for observation. Aren't you supposed to be awakened periodically through the night?"

"Yep. And we can do that right here at home."

"I'm setting your alarm and mine, so I'll be sure to wake up," she said firmly, moving to first one bedside table and then the other.

Jared caught her around the waist as she finished setting the second clock.

"I'll be sure to get you up."

"I know you will, darlin'. In the meantime, come here," he drawled.

He kissed her and she clung to his neck and kissed him

back until he stretched out on the bed and pulled her into his arms.

In minutes, as Jared stroked her, he felt her relax, and soon he could feel her deep, even breathing.

As she slept, he held her in his arms. He knew he should be in the hospital for observation, but he wanted to be home with Faith, and he was thankful they had released him. And he had heard her whisper of love in the throes of passion.

He stroked hair away from her nape. Her body had cooled and she drew steady breaths. He didn't know whether she was exhausted and slept because of their passion or because of the release of tension over her fears about his safety. Or a combination of both. Usually he was the one asleep first. Or so she told him. He stroked her throat, her bare shoulder, knowing he could push the sheet away and start the fires all over again.

He loved her more than ever. He had thought if they consummated their marriage, he would get his sanity back and stop thinking about her every waking minute. Instead, it was worse than ever. He was wildly, head-over-heels in love, and her feelings ran deeper than he'd realized. There was no mistaking the way she had thrown herself into his arms, showering kisses on him, tearing at his clothes with an urgency that went beyond any sheer physical need.

His thoughts shifted to bull riding. He couldn't give it up. He was piling up winnings, earning money that would relieve some of the debt he had taken them into. And he still didn't feel it was that dangerous. People ran risks every day. He did on the ranch; Faith did on her way to and from work.

He shifted, touching the bandage lightly. His head pounded as if someone were swinging a sledgehammer into it. But a month from now it wouldn't matter. He could not give up his riding, and he was banking on her growing love to get them through this.

Over the next four days, they argued over their future without coming to any conclusion. As he packed to leave for Phoenix, Faith watched him while Merry babbled and crawled on the floor, playing with plastic blocks.

"Jared." Faith took a deep breath, wondering whether she would regret what she was going to say. "We've discussed this before. If you go to Phoenix and San Diego and ride in the rodeos, I won't be here when you come back."

He halted, his eyes narrowing as he focused on her. He dropped his carry-on over a chair and crossed the room to place his hands on her hips. "Faith, that's absurd. We're going to have a lot of money from this. It's like my asking you to give up your job."

"I don't think it's the same at all," she replied, knowing that if he kept his distance, she would have the strength to speak from her heart. Tears stung her eyes. She was losing him. She was losing Merry. And she loved them both with all her heart. So much that she couldn't bear the risks that Jared took with his life—with his family's livelihood.

He gazed at her solemnly. "Darlin', we all gotta do what we gotta do," he said quietly, and her heart squeezed painfully. She had always wondered if he was easygoing about everything he encountered in life, but she saw now that when he felt strongly about something, he dug in his heels and wouldn't yield an inch.

"Just give up the bull riding, that's all I ask. Go ahead and continue the saddle bronc riding."

"Bull riding is what I do best. It's all I've ever been good at," he said quietly. "I'd like to please you. Damn well I'd like to, but this is income we need, and it's something I can do to support this family, and it doesn't scare me. I have to do this, Faith."

"You want the bull riding more than our marriage?"

"Hell, no. I'm hoping you'll come around to my side of it."

"I'm not going to. I can't. The risks you take are just too great. I haven't liked this from the start, and it's only gotten worse with each rodeo. Jared, I can't bear it when you get hurt.''

"For a woman ready to walk out, you care a damn lot about my welfare,'' he remarked. ''Did you mean what you said about love?''

"Yes,'' she answered in a forlorn whisper. ''But did you?''

"Damn right.'' He stepped forward, tightened his arm, and his mouth covered hers. His tongue slid deep into her mouth, stroking hers, hot, demanding, reminding her of every intimacy they had shared.

She could no more resist responding than she could resist breathing. Winding her arms around his neck, she kissed him passionately in return, trying to hold him with kisses, trying to make him see that they had something fine and special between them that he was destroying.

His hand tangled in her hair and his other hand slid down, his palm caressing her bottom as he pulled her tightly against him. His arousal pressed against her and she trembled, wanting him, wanting to change his mind, to hold him. Wanting him to love her enough to give up bull riding.

He broke away, stroking her cheek and throat. ''I have a plane to catch. I love you, Faith.''

A knot filled her throat and she was afraid if she spoke she would cry. She watched him pick up Merry. He paused and looked at her. ''If you leave, what will you do with Merry? You can't take her with you.''

"You know I'll take care of her until you're back, but then I'm gone.''

"I hope not,'' he said solemnly. He hugged and kissed Merry, then he handed the baby to Faith, picked up his carry-on and draped his arm across Faith's shoulders. ''I'll call you tonight.''

At the door, Jared leaned over Merry to kiss Faith again, a long, slow, lingering kiss that was heartbreaking.

He strode to his pickup, a long-legged, jeans-clad cowboy, and she felt as if he were tearing her heart out and taking it with him. She waved, telling Merry to wave bye-bye. Merry's small hand waved in the air.

"That's right, love. Daddy's gone bye-bye," Faith said, letting the tears fall now. "I love you," she added.

Jared would be gone nine days, and Faith knew she had some tough decisions to make.

On the fifth day she missed her period. Two days later, she called Meg and asked her sister if she could move in with her temporarily.

"Of course you can move in here," Meg said quietly. "I thought you said Jared is gone."

"He is. I told him if he left, I wouldn't be here when he came back."

"You're sure about what you're doing?"

"I think so," Faith said, wondering whether she was sure about anything any longer.

"What about Merry?"

"Can I bring her with me until he gets back and can take her?"

"You know you can."

"I can take her to Mom's when I'm at work. I've already talked to her about it."

"Don't be ridiculous. It's summer, and the kids are home. What's one more kid around here, and the girls adore playing with her. When are you coming?"

"I need to pack and then I'll be over."

"Does he know this?"

"Yes, he does," Faith said, thinking about the hours they had spent on the phone since he left.

"It seemed like you were pretty happy."

"I was, but there are problems."

"Okay. See you when we see you."

Faith replaced the receiver and hot tears gushed, falling over her hands. She didn't want to leave Jared, but she couldn't stay. And she might be taking a baby of her own away with her. She felt her flat stomach. She was only two days late, but she had never been late in her life.

She heard Merry cry and she turned around to hurry to her room.

The last thing she did before leaving was prop a note to him on the kitchen table. She looked around the room that was filled with memories that tore at her. She couldn't stay and she couldn't go. With tears in her eyes she turned and went out the back door, locking it behind her. She had already packed her car with their bags.

Merry began to cry, fussing again as if Faith's unhappiness was jarring her small system, too.

"Don't start crying, sweetie, or I'll cry right along with you," Faith said, jiggling Merry and then settling her into her car seat and buckling it.

She slid behind the wheel and started the motor, looking at the house once more and seeing only a tall, lean cowboy.

Two days later Jared unlocked the back door and entered the kitchen. The moment he saw the note propped on the kitchen table, his heart lurched.

A week later, Jared sat on horseback and surveyed his land. He'd known he was going to miss Faith dreadfully, but he couldn't have imagined the all-consuming pain that had eaten at him for the past week. How many times had he picked up a receiver to call her and tell her to come back, that he would never ride in a rodeo again. But he'd stopped because he needed this year's earnings for the ranch to survive. And he prayed constantly that she might change her mind, but the more time that passed, the more he gave up that idea. He had a nanny for Merry, Mrs. Slocum, a nice woman with high recommendations who had agreed to live on the ranch. He had bought a trailer house and had it brought near the main house.

"Dammit," he swore softly, turning the horse, trying to get his mind back on cattle when all he could see was Faith's big green eyes, remember her soft cries of passion, dream about loving her again. "I miss you so damned much," he said to no one, wishing the wind could sweep the words right to her heart. And he knew if he didn't get her out of his thoughts, he was going to get hurt riding because he was no longer concentrating as he should. "Faith, darlin', how I need you! And so does Merry." Merry had been fussy ever since Faith left. His little Merry who had always been smiles and sunshine. Maybe she was picking up on his unhappiness. Whatever it was, she had lost her constant sunny disposition. "Darlin' Faith," he whispered again, looking longingly over his shoulder at the hill in the distance where they had made love for the first time.

That same morning, Faith sped through traffic on the freeway, heading downtown to work, her thoughts on Jared and Merry. She slowed for a red light, then glanced at her watch. Jared would already be up and working. They had talked once since his return a week ago and it ended in a stalemate. And though their marriage was on shaky ground, Jared had made it clear she could see Merry whenever she wanted. She knew he had a nanny now, and that he had moved to the ranch.

She had never dreamed she could miss him so badly. And instead of the ache and longing fading, they intensified.

And the nights. Nights were horrible, lonely, unbearable.

She'd lived with Meg for four days and then found a furnished apartment that she had no interest in and hated to go home to. Her life had dulled to empty days and sleepless nights.

The green light flashed and Faith accelerated. Suddenly a car whipped through the intersection, running the red light, and Faith saw it only a second before it broadsided her car and spun her across the intersection. Her car struck another car, and she hit her head, darkness exploding as she lost consciousness.

Faith could hear someone calling to her. Sirens blared and as she tried to get out of the car, she felt disoriented, uncertain. Then she remembered the car and the crash. She climbed out on the passenger side, and someone thrust a handkerchief in her hand.

''Here, miss. Your head is bleeding.''

She had been unaware of the blood and pressed the clean white handkerchief against her temple. The tall, brown-haired man held out a card. ''If you need a witness, here's my number. I saw the guy run the red light. I have a cellular phone if you need to call your work.''

While she thanked him, a police car arrived and in minutes she was surrounded by police, a paramedic and witnesses. She called work to explain what had happened and then called her mother to tell her she was fine in case the accident came over the news. Then she called Alice, who said she would come pick her up.

It was over an hour later when she got back to her apartment, washed and changed. The cut on her temple was not as bad as she had first feared. Alice had driven to the crash to get her, and now Faith had Alice's car for the rest of the day, yet she wasn't going back to work. She stood at the window of her apartment, but saw nothing outside.

Instead, she was remembering Jared telling her she faced danger when she drove to work as much as he did with his bull riding. She was gripped with fear when she watched him ride, but that wildness in him was what had drawn her to him in the first place.

Jared was right. Life was filled with risk. And it was too precious to live wrapped up in fear. Tomorrow morning she had a doctor's appointment, and then she would know whether or not she was pregnant. Although she was certain what the answer would be.

She looked at the apartment that held no memories, no loving or laughter, no scrape of boots on the floor or babble of a baby. Was this what she wanted? Never!

Her pulse jumped at the thought of Merry and Jared. They were worth all sorts of risks. Since Jared had come into her life, it had been filled with joy and excitement.

"Jared," she whispered, glancing through the doorway at the phone in the kitchen. "Jared, you were right," she whispered.

Twelve

She was pregnant! Oblivious to the summer downpour, she walked out of her doctor's office. She wanted to leap in the air with joy. And she wanted to rush to find Jared and tell him. She stopped, forgetting she was standing in the rain beside a tall building on a busy thoroughfare. The city faded from her consciousness. All she could think of was Jared. They were going to have a baby!

Dazed, she walked to her car, closed her umbrella and slid behind the wheel, sitting, staring at the raindrops as they streamed down the windshield. She placed her hand on her stomach. They were going to have a baby. *She* was going to have a baby. This was what she'd wanted when she entered into their marriage. And in the back of her mind, all along, she had thought if she had a baby, she would be complete. When she married, she had felt if she didn't fall in love with Jared and things didn't work out, she could leave him and raise her baby by herself and be completely happy. But she knew she could never be happy without her husband, and the little girl they already had. She felt a wrenching ache to tell Jared the news.

Faith was supposed to return to work. Instead, she drove to the house on Peoria. She still had her key and she entered through the back door. The house was silent, empty, yet every room was filled with Jared's presence as memories stormed her. He had moved some of the furniture to the ranch, and there were bare places where there once had been tables and chairs.

She went upstairs and stood in the doorway of the bedroom. Their big bed was gone. Drawers were open, the closet doors stood open. He had moved everything to the ranch.

Memories swirled—moments in his arms, intimate moments of passion in bed. She crossed the room to the phone, which was on the floor. Wondering whether he had disconnected it, she picked it up and heard a hum.

She wondered whether she had made the most colossal mistake. She remembered how impetuous he was; how much women flirted with him. Suppose someone else was already moving into his life?

And the most crucial question of all: could she put up with his bull riding? She was going to have to. She just prayed it wasn't too late to try to get back what she had thrown away by leaving him.

Call him, an inner voice urged. *Go back to him.*

Her hand paused briefly over the phone, and then she knew with glaring certainty she didn't want to wait anymore. This was one time in her life she wasn't going to be cautious. She was going to act as swiftly and impulsively as Jared. She picked up the phone and called the ranch, listening to rings, her heart pounding with eagerness.

"I love you," she whispered. "Please pick up the phone so I can tell you."

Instead, she heard Jared's bass voice as the answering machine clicked on. She replaced the receiver. She didn't want to leave a message—she had to talk to him to tell him she was coming home.

Home. Merry. Jared. Faith placed her hand on her stomach. She ached to be in Jared's arms, to hold him and tell him that she loved him, absolutely, completely and without stipulations.

She called out of work. Rain still came down in a steady stream, and she stared at the shimmering sheets on the windowpanes as she called the ranch again. This time she left a message, then hung up the receiver. She drove to her apartment to pack.

She would stop by the office on the way out of town. It would take about an hour to wind up things there and to tell them she would not be in tomorrow, either.

Her pulse hummed with eager anticipation. Jared. She would see him soon. If he was out of town, she would wait. She loved the man, and she was going home to him. They were still married and she wanted it to work out. She was going to do her best to see that it did. And they had a baby on the way.

''Here I come, mister, whether you're ready or not!'' she said as she locked the door behind her.

Half an hour later, dressed in jeans and a long-sleeved Western shirt, she stopped at the office, but was delayed while Porter piled papers in front of her and her secretary gave her calls.

Jared climbed out of the muddy pickup and slammed the door. He had taken Merry to Mrs. Slocum's this morning because of the rain and mud. He could get Merry to the older woman's house easier than she could get out to his. Now the sun was trying to come out, the earth was steaming, and water dripped from every leaf and eave.

He was covered in mud and had spent the morning repairing a fence that went down in the night. He peeled off his boots on the back porch, dropped his coat and tossed his hat down on a chair before he unlocked the back door and went inside.

The silence of the house always reminded him of his loss. He missed Faith more than ever—something he intended to change this weekend.

He saw the blinking light on the answering machine and crossed the room to play back the messages.

The first was from the hardware store in Coweta, saying that the baling wire he had ordered was in and ready to be picked up. The second call was from Faith. His heart lurched at the sound of her voice, and he leaned closer to the machine as if he could get closer to her.

"Jared, sorry I missed you. This is Monday morning. I don't know where you and Merry are. I'm going by the office for an hour and around ten o'clock, I'll head to the ranch. We need to talk," she said, her voice filled with emotion, and he wondered whether or not she was crying.

"Ahh, darlin'." He glanced at the clock. It was one o'clock. If she'd gone to the office at ten, she should be at the ranch by—

His thoughts lurched. *The bridge.* The bridge leading to the ranch that was usually over a bone-dry creek bed was now unsafe to cross.

"Dammit!" He ran for the back door. Last week they had had a torrential rain and it had weakened the structure. He had started to repair it, but then the rain commenced again and he had to wait. He had placed a sign beside the road warning anybody that it wasn't safe, but the storms last night and this morning could have demolished his sign.

He hopped on one foot, pulling on a boot and then pulling on the other. Dashing across the yard, he jammed his hat on his head. He raced to his pickup, jumped in and turned on the engine. He started down the road, swearing each time the pickup skidded in muddy, slick ruts.

Leaning over the wheel, he drove as fast and recklessly as he dared. "Don't cross the bridge, Faith! Don't cross it!" He yanked up the cellular phone and punched her office number, praying she was still there and had been detained. Visions of the raging creek danced in his mind. It would now be up and roaring.

The sun was shining, but he knew it hadn't been long enough since the deluge for the water to have gone down.

"Graphic Design," a cheerful voice answered, and he tried to remember the receptionist's name, only able to see her bright blue eyes and red hair.

"Emily, is Faith in? This is her husband."

"Sorry, Mr. Whitewolf, she left a long time ago. She won't be back for a few days."

He swore, his heart and stomach knotting. "How long ago did she leave? It's important that I know exactly."

"Oh, gee. I think she's been gone since almost twelve o'clock."

"Thanks," he said tersely, and clicked off, tossing the phone down in the seat beside him. He glanced at his watch and his insides tightened another notch. By now she would have reached the bridge.

He prayed, slipping and slowing, knowing he would be no help to Faith if he slid and got stuck in the mud. Whenever he could, he accelerated, racing across the ranch. He was almost to the bridge, his palms were sweaty, his heart thudding. He topped a hill and his breathing stopped.

Faith's black car was already on the bridge.

Thirteen

Faith turned at a bend in the road. Her gaze swept the landscape for any sign of Jared. The day was crystal clear after the rain, the land still green and lush, wildflowers blooming with tall yellow sunflowers scattered across the fields. The sun was high, lifting her spirits even higher, if that was possible. She would see him soon. And she wasn't leaving him this time.

She followed another curve and drew her breath as she started downhill, braking to avoid getting stuck. Mud was deep and the car slipped, but she barely noticed. Her attention was riveted on the tumbling waters ahead. The creek bed had always been dry. Jared had said it could fill and now it had.

A gushing torrent of water rushed along only inches below the bridge. A board was nailed to a tree. Whatever writing had been on it was now runny, and she gave it little notice because all her attention was on the roaring creek that looked like a river. She had to cross it or go back to the city.

She debated only a minute. The water was still below the bridge, not over it. She slowed, and every foot nearer she felt greater trepidation about driving across the bridge. She remembered how it rattled and shook when there was no water. She reached it and started across. It shook and she could feel it sway, but she was on it now and there was no going back. The swaying increased. A loud crack sounded like a gunshot.

Faith watched in horror as the end of the bridge seemed to sway and then tumble away into the water.

The car was going down. She was going to wash away.

Her mind raced and she opened the window, unsnapping her seat belt and trying to get out of the car. She got her head and shoulders through, trying to fling herself out of the window. Cold water poured over her.

"Faith!"

The call sounded like Jared's voice, but she couldn't think about anything except survival. Cold water swamped her, taking her down, the current tumbling her along. She gagged and closed her mouth, struggling to reach the surface. Water flung her against something solid, and pain burst in her shoulder. She kept fighting to reach the top. Her lungs felt as if they would burst and then she broke through, gulping air.

"Faith!"

It was him. "Help!" She couldn't fight the current and was swept along. She struggled, trying to reach a bank. The water pulled her under again and then she broke the surface, gulping for air, fighting with all her strength to move to the bank.

Strong arms closed around her suddenly. "The baby!" she screamed over the roar of the water.

"She's okay!" Jared yelled back. They were both borne on the current, and she struggled along with him, but to no avail. Ahead, a large log bobbed and floated and a new terror gripped her. If they slammed into the log—

Her stomach instinctively tightened, and she renewed her effort to cross the rush of water bearing them downstream.

And she realized they were beginning to move out of the middle of the stream. The bank loomed closer, but they were nearing the log that disappeared below the surface. She wanted to double over and protect her stomach, protect their baby, but she couldn't and still stay afloat.

"The baby!" she cried again, terrified they would hit the submerged log.

"She's all right!" Jared yelled back, and turned them in the opposite direction.

"Jared, the bank—" She screamed above the constant roar of tumbling water. And then she saw why he was turning her. Ahead, a tree had fallen into the water. If they were swept into it, he would hit it first.

She prayed the log was nowhere near them, and then it bobbed to the surface only yards ahead of them. She looked at the tree rushing up to meet them.

"Hang on," he yelled. "Put your arms around me."

She wrapped her arms around his chest and then jammed against his body, her legs sucked in an undertow, but they were against the tree. She caught a branch and released him as they both worked their way toward the bank. Jared held her, his arm around her waist. She waded in deep mud that sucked her down and pulled on her legs and feet. And then they were out of the water and she fell into his arms.

"I love you!" she cried, sobbing and shaken now that the ordeal was over.

He picked her up and strode up the hill, carrying her back along the creek toward the road. She clung to him, gasping for breath. "I can walk."

"I'm not letting go of you," he said gruffly, and his arms tightened around her. She raised her mouth for his kiss. His pickup was standing in the road, door thrown open, motor still running.

He reached in, turned off the motor and set her on her feet. Faith looked up into his dark eyes and then he swept her to him, his arms crushing her against his chest as he leaned down to kiss her. She felt faint, her heart pounding and her insides in a free fall. When he raised his head, his dark eyes bore into her.

"I put a sign up, warning everyone not to get on the bridge."

She glanced across the roaring water and remembered the sign she had barely given a glance. "I was too busy looking at the creek."

"Let's go home," he said. He got the blanket out of the pickup and handed it to her, and she wrapped herself in it while he retrieved the boots that he had yanked off before going in the creek after her. He threw them on the floor of the pickup and pulled her close beside him. She wrapped her arms around his waist and clung to him.

"Merry is at Mrs. Slocum's house. I'll call her and ask her to keep Merry until I come get her tonight." Jared tightened his arm around her. He didn't know why she had come out to the ranch, but whatever the reason, he hoped he could keep her there. When he had watched her go into the creek, he felt as if he were being torn in two. He wanted to love and hold her all night long. And he was scared to hope she had come back for good.

As soon as he slowed and parked by the back door, he climbed out and reached for her. A rainbow arced across the sky over them, soft tints against a deep blue sky, but it was nothing compared to the rainbow of hope in his heart. He led her inside, closed and locked the door and looked down at her.

"Let me call Mrs. Slocum so we won't have any interruptions."

"All right, but sometime tonight, bring Merry home. I haven't seen her in a long time. I missed you both."

He gave Faith a quick hug and then he crossed the kitchen, tracking mud, and picked up the phone.

Faith had lost her sneakers in the muddy creek. She stood, still dripping slightly, and took in the sight of him. His jeans were muddy to his thighs, and his T-shirt was plastered to his body, every sculpted muscle clearly revealed. She loved him, bull riding and all. She dropped the blanket and began to unfasten her jeans.

He replaced the receiver, his midnight eyes filled with fires that sent flames soaring in her. He reached out to draw her to him.

"I don't care whether you ride bulls or not," she told him. "I need you."

"God, I missed you," he said softly, and pulled her to him to kiss her.

It was almost two hours later that she lay in his arms in bed, warm, dry, exhausted from loving and showering together and loving again. She sat up cross-legged, pulling a sheet up and tucking it under her arms.

He looked amused, one corner of his mouth curving slightly. "Why the sudden modesty?"

"I want your undivided attention."

"I can show you how to get my undivided attention," he said, tugging at the sheet and running his finger along the curve of a breast.

"Will you listen to me?" she said, tingling with excitement, wanting to tell him her news.

"Of course," he said attentively, but his fingers still strayed languidly over her.

"Jared," she said, catching his hand and holding it.

"I'm listening, darlin'. Say what you have to say."

"I don't care if you ride in rodeos."

"Thank you," he said solemnly. "But I *do* care how you feel...so I'm giving up the bulls after this season."

"Jared, I never meant for you to give up a dream. I just care about you so much. And I wanted you to know that I realize now life—and love—are gambles, and I don't want to waste a single, precious moment with you. I'm back to stay."

"That, darlin', is the best news I've heard since you agreed to marry me. Now, come here and let's seal it with a kiss."

"You stay right there," she said, pushing him back against the pillow as he started to sit up.

"There's more?" he asked.

"There's a lot more. Want me to tell you what you'll be doing next Memorial Day weekend?"

"Sure, darlin'." He lay back against the pillows with his hands behind his head. His skin was brown, smooth and warm, and his dark eyes were filled with satisfaction and love. "What will we be doing? You look like the dog that ate the Thanksgiving turkey."

"I'm waiting for it to dawn on you."

"Now I am curious. Next May…" Suddenly he sat up, sweeping her into his arms. "Tell me, woman, or I'll kiss you until I get the truth out of you."

She stroked his jaw. "We're going to have another baby!"

His smile vanished, and the look in his eyes made tears spring to her eyes. He pulled her to him to hug her and then he kissed her, finally moving back to look at her again. "That's why you came back," he said solemnly.

"I came back because I love you."

Jared's heart felt as if it would burst with joy as he heard her declaration. She was back and now they would truly have a home and a family. "Ah, darlin'! I adore you."

"And I've given notice at work, Jared," she said. "I know you're in a financial crunch now with starting the ranch. And I intend to work freelance from here sometimes, but right now, I feel like Merry needs a mommy and, of course, our baby will need me to stay fit and healthy. I told them I'd stay until they get someone, and that might take a little while, but not long."

"You're sure?" he asked quietly. "Because I don't want you to give up your dream."

She nodded, running her hands over his shoulder. "I'm very sure."

"I love you, Faith." He gazed into her eyes, and she felt encompassed in a velvet darkness that was filled with love. "I've always loved you from that first moment you came bustin' through the bushes and rescued us. Welcome home, darlin'," he whispered, and returned to kissing her.

Faith wound her arms around his neck, joyful to be back in his arms, knowing she had come home for good.

Epilogue

Faith rocked steadily as she looked at their six-month-old daughter sleeping in her arms. Her gaze swung from little Steffie to Jared who sat across the room reading to Merry.

As he finished the story about a family of rabbits, his gaze lifted and met Faith's. Warmth filled her at the love she saw in his eyes.

"Now, sweetie, it is bedtime," he said to Merry.

"Mommy," Merry said, sliding off her father's lap and hurrying across the family room to Faith. Merry was already bathed and ready for bed in her bunny-covered pink pajamas, her silky black hair curling over her shoulders.

She leaned against Faith's knee and touched Stephanie's cheek. "Sissy sleep?"

"Yes, she's asleep."

"Which you are going to be soon, my little one," Jared said, swinging her up into his arms. Merry giggled as she wrapped her arms around his neck. Faith looked up at them both and smiled. Her tall, lean cowboy husband was a very good father, and she knew she would never have the time for even the small bit of free-lance work she did from the ranch if he weren't so caring with the little girls.

Holding the sleeping baby close in her arms, Faith stood and walked beside them as they headed toward the nursery where Merry kissed her baby sister on the cheek before Faith placed the baby in her crib.

Then the three of them went to Merry's pink-and-white bedroom where Faith turned down the comforter on the four-poster bed, shoving stuffed bears aside. Merry rescued them, piling them around her as she settled against the white sheets. Merry pulled a battered stuffed horse into her arms, cuddling it and patting the bed beside her. "Story, Mommy."

Faith sat where her daughter indicated and Merry patted the space on her other side. "Daddy."

Jared stretched out beside their daughter, pulling her into his arms while Faith told the story of the three bears. Faith looked at Merry with her rosy cheeks and dark hair and lashes. She looked soft and sweet curled against Jared. He was rumpled, still in jeans and a chambray shirt from his day's work.

Before the end of the story, Merry's eyes were closed and Jared gently extracted himself and tucked the covers around her. He came around the bed to join Faith, draping his arms across her shoulders as they made to leave Merry's room.

"We're lucky," Faith said as she switched out the light. "We have beautiful little girls."

"All three of my girls are beautiful, and I'm the luckiest guy on earth," Jared said quietly. She turned to head back to the family room, but he tightened his arm around her shoulders. "Come here."

"*We're* lucky," she repeated softly, thinking how well he was doing with his saddle bronc riding and how the ranch was thriving. And he had seemed completely willing to give up the bull riding.

He led her into their big bedroom and closed the door quietly, leaning against it and pulling her into his arms to smile at her. "I love you, darlin'."

Filled with happiness, Faith brushed her fingers over his jaw, touching the rough stubble. "I love you, too, cowboy. Little did I know when I rushed through the spirea bushes at the park what I was getting myself into."

"You were an angel of mercy come to our rescue."

"I doubt if you needed much rescuing. You would have taken care of Merry if I hadn't been there."

"Not so. I needed you badly and I always will." He pulled her closer, and she wrapped her arms around his waist, smelling the familiar scents of horses and cotton.

"You were right about a lot of things," she said. "I was ready for more in my life. So much more," she said, thinking about their life together, the girls, the home she loved. "This house did fix up."

"Well, you were right yourself," he said, kissing her ear, pushing away her cotton blouse to nuzzle her neck. "I'm damned glad to be done with bull riding. In those eight seconds your whole life flashes before you sometimes."

"You never told me that before!" she said, and he chuckled softly, looking at her tenderly. And then the moment changed and she saw the fires burn in his dark eyes as he became solemn.

"I need you, darlin', more than the air I breathe," he said in a husky voice. He leaned down to trail kisses along her throat while his hand slid over her ribs.

"I couldn't resist you then, cowboy. I don't want to resist you now," she whispered as she turned her head, pulling his head down and placing her lips on his. Jared tightened his arms around her and Faith clung to him, knowing that day in the park had started her on a lifetime of love.

*   *   *   *   *

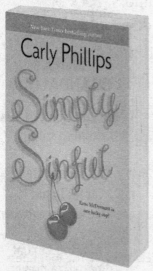

Carly Phillips is Simply irresistible!

Appearances can be deceptive in

SIMPLY SCANDALOUS

the 2nd book in this exciting trilogy.

"This is sexuality at its finest."
—*The Romance Reader*

"Alluring sexual, seductive power at its best."
—*Wordweaving*

On sale 18th February 2005

New York Times Bestselling Author

Vicki Lewis Thompson
Stephanie Bond
Judith Arnold

Three brand-new novellas!

Fool For Love

Available from 1st April 2005

*Available at most branches of WHSmith,
Tesco, ASDA, Martins, Borders, Eason, Sainsbury's
and most good paperback bookshops.*

SILHOUETTE®
Desire 2 in 1

is proud to introduce

DYNASTIES:
THE DANFORTHS

Meet the Danforths—a family of prominence...
tested by scandal, sustained by passion!

Coming Soon!
Twelve thrilling stories in six 2-in-1 volumes:

0105/SH/LC96

SILHOUETTE®

*Super***ROMANCE™**

proudly presents
a brand-new series from favourite author

Anna Adams

THE
CALVERT
COUSINS

A few Calverts may have flown the nest, but
somehow they always find their way home…

The Secret Father
January 2005

The Bride Ran Away
February 2005

The Prodigal Cousin
March 2005

0105/SH/LC100

SILHOUETTE®

Sensation™

proudly presents an exhilarating new series

Adventure, excitement and
supernatural love...

*Perfect for fans of Buffy, Anne Rice, Kelly
Armstrong and The Pirates of the Caribbean*

DARKNESS CALLS by Caridad Piñeiro
January 2005
A vampire helps an FBI agent find a psychotic killer,
and promises her eternal love.

ONE EYE OPEN by Karen Whiddon
April 2005
Can love blossom between a scarred man and
a female werewolf?

GHOST OF A CHANCE by Nina Bruhns
July 2005
A writer gets more than she bargains for when she
meets the man of her dreams—a sexy pirate ghost
under a 200 year old curse!

0105/SH/LC101

SILHOUETTE® Super ROMANCE™

proudly presents
a brand–new series from talented new author

LORI HANDELAND

The Luchetti Brothers

The Daddy Quest

March 2005

The Brother Quest

May 2005

The Husband Quest

July 2005

0305/SH/LC109